THE BURREN
a companion to the wild flowers of an
Irish limestone wilderness

THE BURREN

a companion to the wildflowers of an
Irish limestone wilderness

E. Charles Nelson
Illustrated by Wendy F. Walsh

Published by
Boethius Press and
The Conservancy of The Burren
1991

British Library Cataloguing in Publication Data

Nelson, E.C. (E Charles)
The Burren : a companion to the wildflowers of an
Irish limestone wilderness. - (Natural history)
I. Title II. Burren Conservancy III. Series
582.13094193

ISBN 0 86314 213 3 hbk
ISBN 0 86314 214 1 pbk

Colour separations and plan flats by Image Reproductions.

Designed, typeset in Adobe Garamond,
plated and printed throughout by the associate publisher,
Boethius Press, Aberystwyth, Wales and Kilkenny, Ireland.

Case and paperback bindings by Hunter & Foulis.

CONTENTS

At a distance, these bare rocky hills seem thoroughly
devoid of vegetation, and the desert-like aspect thus imparted to
the landscape has been compared to that of parts of Arabia Petraea.
But on a closer inspection, it will be found that all the chinks and
crevices caused by [systems of] joints, and the action of rain, are
the nurseries for plants innumerable, the disintegration of the
rock producing a soil, than which none is more productive.

Frederick Foot: 'On the distribution of plants in
Burren, County of Clare'

Though a quiet life offers various joys
None, I think, will compare with the time one employs
In the study of herbs, or in striving to gain
Some practical knowledge of Nature's domain

Walahfrid Strabo: *Hortulus*

FOREWORD

It was orchids that first drew me to The Burren, a pupil of Ireland's other great botanical artist, Raymond Piper. He led me on pilgrimages to most of the mysterious presences celebrated here in their own chapter, 'A Provocation of Orchids'. Other wonders have included spindle and blackthorn, cranesbill and madder growing together in the one gryke, the madder relying on its hooks and the blackthorn's stiffness for a lift into light; the translucent, scarlet berries of the guelder rose upstaging the stone-bramble's prostrate procession across the pavement; mudwort blooming in a puddle; the little clatter of aspen leaves; a pocket full of sloes; a palm full of juniper berries; quaking grass whose panicle seems to register your heartbeat as you clasp the stem.

This last might serve as an emblem for the intricacies and delicate balances that govern the mutual influence of each organism and its environment. One such organism is man, the re-arranger of stones; his roads following the lie of the land, inevitable as rivers; his livestock, with just the right amount of grazing, making space for wild flowers. Is such harmony a thing of the past? Will modern farming methods and mass tourism poison the limestone, 'a stone that responds'?

On my most recent visit to The Burren I wrote the names of the plants into my notebook as usual, a fresh page for each location. This time the names arranged themselves rhythmically, as though to release their power into prayers or spells. Campion, samphire, milkwort, lavender–these at Poll Salach. And on Black Head crowberry, juniper, saxifrage, willow. Prayers for what is irreplaceable. Spells muttered in the shadow of exploitation and destruction. At Corcomroe Abbey on my way home to Belfast this line came into my head: *Protect the Burren, Our Lady of the Fertile Rocks.*

More than any other part of the country, The Burren with its unique commingling of the fertile and the barren, the wild and the domestic, the visible and the invisible, the vast and the intimate, deserves to be thought of as the soul of Ireland. We owe the place respect, courtesy, reverence. This brilliant book reminds us that 'the beautiful things are difficult', as the Greeks used to say; that there can be no short cuts; that we shall die if we allow the wild flowers to die.

Michael Longley

Place names and plant names.

As far as possible, I have chosen to spell place names in accordance with modern Ordnance Survey maps and (within The Burren) in accord with Tim Robinson's map. In some instances the official spelling of English names differs from that familiar to most readers—for example, Ballyvaghan is correct (not Ballyvaughan). In some instances I have preferred to use the Irish name for a place or topographical feature.

Vernacular names of plants (in contrast to the Latin names) present even more problems than place names. As I refer frequently to Geoffrey Grigson's work and to older botanical sources, I have sometimes retained older vernacular names—thus for *Cirsium dissectum*, I use bog thistle, although the 'standard' English name, as published by M. J. P. Scannell and D. M. Synnott in *Census catalogue of the flora of Ireland* (2nd edition 1987), is marsh thistle. Irish names, in general, follow the *Census catalogue*.

Spectacle Bridge, Lisdoonvarna

IN THE STUDY OF HERBS

…and all about the hills
Are like a circle of Agate or of Jade.
Somewhere among the great rocks on the scarce grass
Birds cry, they cry their loneliness.

W. B. Yeats: 'The dreaming of the bones'

I love solitary places. Of all such places that are within my experience, the lonely limestone fastness of County Clare, that place known as The Burren, is to me one of the most winsome.

There are many who will disagree. Some friends are puzzled by my fondness for The Burren–for them the loneliness and bleakness are forbidding, and the melancholy rockscape is not welcoming. Yet even those who are intimidated by the barren, grey pavements have to confess to a fascination, over-riding their feelings of coldness, impelling continuing curiosity about the wild plants that inhabit The Burren.

1

The ability of this absurd landscape to beguile is not new. William Trevor explained the attraction thus:

> ...many nationalities are the botanists who become excited on the flat stone slabs of the Burren, which hasn't changed a bit in all its years. Rain has washed the goodness into fissured niches, laying out a desert for modest blooms of cheer. The very bones of Ireland's landscape break through its skin on the Burren, as they do on the mountains of Connacht and Donegal. The wild flowers seem like a compensation in so much harshness...[1]

I grew up in Northern Ireland, in Fermanagh, a county of loughs, woodlands and limestone hills. For as long as I can remember I have been fascinated by flowers and was determined to make my career botany. I remember well excursions with the local field club, led by well-known naturalists like Jack Moon, when we visited different localities and saw strange plants. We were shown blue-eyed grass and adder's tongue in the meadows below the old castle at Crom where an ancient yew grows; exotic water-soldiers were discovered in nearby ditches and I brought a plant home and proudly kept it in an old enamel basin for several months. At Derrygonnelly wild columbine lined a bohreen and we saw eyebrights in the heathy grassland on the slopes above Carrick Lough. On a warm spring afternoon there were galaxies of wide-open wood anemones among the bluebells on Inishmacsaint. I have vivid memories still of those excursions, and especially of my first encounter with an insect-eating plant, the slimy-leaved common butterwort, growing *en masse* in an oozy, abandoned quarry between Belcoo and Garrison. But there were disappointments too: mountain avens grow in Fermanagh at Knockmore and while we searched for them and found the tell-tale leaves, I cannot recall seeing any of its 'poached-egg' flowers on that hill. Thus many of the plants that I learned on day-trips into the byways and mountainy parts of Fermanagh, and among the water-meadows around Lough Erne, are familiar now as natives of The Burren in County Clare.

By the year I was ten I had acquired my own camera, a most sophisticated instrument in comparison with the ancient bakelite one that I had unearthed in a box in the attic; my Kodak box camera even had an additional sliding lens which could be engaged to take 'close-up' photographs. That summer we went on holiday to Lehinch, a great adventure for it was a long drive from Enniskillen along unfamiliar roads. I was armed with my new camera, and among the first photographs in my album are a few black-and-white ones taken that summer in The Burren, at the Cliffs of Moher and of the Spectacle Bridge at Lisdoonvarna.

I remember that visit but slightly. My mother had acquired a book about wild flowers (not one I would recommend nowadays!) and one afternoon we went looking for the 'Rare Plants', maidenhair ferns, Spring gentians, for anything marked with four stars and stated to grow in The Burren. I don't remember if we found any of them; perhaps we did. Like a legion of tourists before, and many since, we walked for a while on the limestone pavements, drove along the coast road, and went back to the beach having *seen* The Burren.

Limestone landscapes are to me 'bred in the bone'. From home we could see the table-tops of Belmore and Cuilcagh mountains that dominate Fermanagh, serving as marvellous weather-vanes, accurate to a fault. Favourite Sunday outings took in the Marble Arch and the Marlbank Loop, or the Correl Glen and Lough Navar, beauty-spots in Fermanagh's limestone wildernesses. Even while I was at university, limestone and its particular flora was not forgotten; I spent one summer working on a research project in a small area of limestone pavement on the lower slopes of Cuilcagh where I found maidenhair fern, and the next summer was occupied entirely with Cornish heath (*Erica vagans*) on the southern slopes of Belmore Mountain.

In 1971 the Australian National University, Canberra, accepted me as a research scholar in the Department of Biogeography and Geomorphology. Before long I was immersed in a stimulating new world inhabited by plants unlike anything that grows wild on Irish hillsides, belonging to uniquely Australian genera with strange names such as *Adenanthos, Banksia* and *Gompholobium*. The senior staff of the department included one of the world's leading experts on karst, Joe Jennings,[2] and I learnt much from him, at least by diffusion for I was not one of his students. Joe was a geomorphologist with a particular interest in the formation of landforms in limestone country; I was meant to be a plant geographer. Yet I had to learn from him because I had to understand the nature of one of the largest areas of limestone in the world, the bone-dry, tree-less Nullarbor Plain in southern Australia; it collides with the Southern Ocean on the Great Australian Bight at lonely, spectacular cliffs that stretch unbroken for hundreds of kilometres but which otherwise are reminiscent of the Cliffs of Moher.

I returned home in 1975 and eventually moved to the National Botanic Gardens at Glasnevin, on the northern outskirts of Dublin. There another new world opened; the wonderful flora of Irish gardens, a patchwork of plants from every continent, far more numerous than this island's truly native flora, enriched by the craft of gardeners. At Glasnevin I was enabled to return to my other infatuation–heathers–and spent much spare time stalking *Erica mackaiana* in Connemara, Donegal and Mayo. Peatlands were my haunts through the late 1970s and early 1980s; limestone was forsaken, temporarily. However one day during the spring of 1983 I received a telephone call from John Harrison, a producer with the BBC Wildlife Unit in Bristol, asking if I would participate with Dr David Streeter and Derek Jones in a natural history radio programme about The Burren. I hesitated only for a moment, and set off next day to reconnoitre. That was my second visit to The Burren. A few weeks later, John, David and Derek joined me and we hunted the pavements for interesting plants; we jumped on loose slabs of limestone producing musical sound effects to tantalize listeners, and watched ravens cavorting in the air above Lough Gealáin. We had two days of wonderful weather and enjoyed every moment.

I have been back to The Burren many times since that radio trail, learning some more about its habitats and their plants, and discovering some unexpected species. I have walked on the pavements in fine weather and in foul, trudged over the hills, rambled along deserted bohreens and explored secret woods. Nowadays I take colour photographs, and the Brownie box-camera is a boyhood memory. I have tried to comprehend the interactions between rocks, climate, plants and people, which are so intricate and so vital for the survival of The Burren. I have also stumbled upon the tantalizing host of enigmas that crowd around any description of The Burren's flora, but I have resolved none of them. In some ways I do not wish to solve the puzzles because they make the place all the more mysterious, more intriguing, and entirely enthralling.

During the past four years I have worked with Wendy Walsh as she has painted some of the plants that live among the stones of The Burren. Wendy worked directly from living plants to create a series of field-sketches, each one portraying the essential characters of flowers and foliage. One hundred flowers and ferns are illustrated here, and most of the paintings are unfinished, intentionally. The watercolours were not planned as templates for the identification of the native plants of The Burren; they were painted for pleasure as a personal record of a few years among the flora of a wonderful place. However we hope they will aid visitors to identify and name some of the plants encountered in the region.

This book is a distillation of my perambulations in The Burren, a singular, intoxicating wilderness on the western edge of Ireland. I have not attempted a comprehensive botanical treatise, nor a catalogue with descriptions and distribution data, nor a scientific exposition on the flora of The Burren. My intention, as the

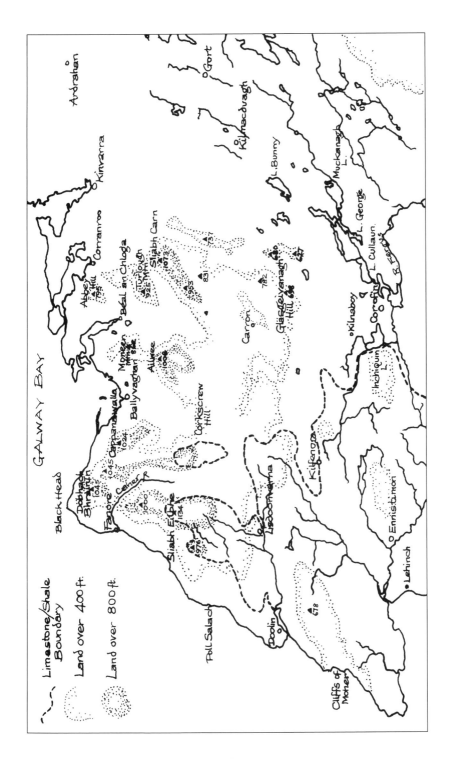

GALWAY BAY

Limestone/Shale
Boundary

Land over 400 ft.

Land over 800 ft.

Andrahan

Gort

Kinvarra

Kilmacduagh

Corranroo

L. Bunny

Abbey Hill
795

Béal an Chloga

Sliabh Carn

Muckanagh L.

Turlough
925

L. George

831

737

L. Cullaun

Moneen 862

1073

L. Fergus

953

782

Alluee
1000

Caron

Glasgeivnagh Hill 686

Blackhead

Dobhach
Bhrainin
1045

Carpanawalla
1024

Ballyvaghan

Corkscrew Hill

Kinaboy

Inchiquin L.

Corofin

Fanore

Caher R.

1000

Kilfenora

Sliabh Elva
1134

Lisdoomvarna

Ennistimon

976

Poll Salach

Doolin

678

Lehinch

Cliffs of Moher

5

subtitle indicates, is to narrate the marginalia of some of the plants, the stories about them, their folk-lore and history; botany interleaves with geology and archaeology.

When a westerly gale hurls stair-rods of rain horizontally across Cappanawalla and the best thing to do is sit snugly beside the fire, 'take down this book and slowly read…'. If you are one of those tormented souls marooned far from Clare, out of reach of its bright air and soft showers, someone who can only dream about its warm, gentian-spangled limestone, may these pages be your solace. Whatever your situation as you turn these pages, please dream on.

Erratic boulder at Poll Salach

A PATRIMONY OF STONES

There must be grazing overhead, hazel thickets,
Pavements the rain is dissolving, springs and graves,
Darkness above the darkness of the seepage of souls
And hedges where goosegrass spills its creamy stars.

Michael Longley: 'In Aillwee Cave'

The Burren is an enigma. At a casual or a distant glance there is nothing but a barren expanse of limestone, but this place harbours wonderful plants. It is a contradictory, obstinate land, rock from horizon to horizon.

What precisely is The Burren, and where are its boundaries? The English name Burren comes from *boireann*, a vivid word meaning a big rock or a rocky district and thus not an uncommon place-name in Ireland–villages and townlands in several other counties are called Burren or one of its variants because they are stony places.

In a strictly historical sense, Burren is the name of a barony, also known as East Corcomroe (Corcumruad), that occupies the north-western quarter of the modern county of Clare; it was the patrimony of the O'Loughlins, and one implication of the first written reference to the place in *Dindshenchas*[1] is that Burren was once part of a greater Corcumruad. While its roots may extend into prehistory, to one or more of the *tuatha* or petty kingdoms of the Gaelic clans or families, a barony is essentially a subdivision of a county comprising a cluster of townlands; present-day Irish baronies were delineated in the sixteenth and seventeenth centuries. Be that as it may, baronies are archaic territorial definitions that have been largely forgotten. This particular barony's name, prefaced in English by the definite article, has become a universal sobriquet for a more extensive region, the exact limits of which are not defined in minute detail anywhere, but whose substance, limestone, is taken for granted.

Situated on Ireland's western coast, almost two hundred kilometres due west of Dublin on the southern side of Galway Bay, The Burren's latitude is just above 53° North; in other words, it lies a little further north than Nottingham, Berlin and Warsaw, nearer the Arctic Circle than all the major cities in the United States and Canada, and as close to the North Pole as the Straits of Magellan, the Falkland Islands and Maquarie Island are to the South Pole.

There can be no doubts about The Burren's northern and western limits–the Atlantic coastline–Galway Bay and South Sound. But to the east and south there is scope for mistiness because its frontier can be drawn to correspond with the desires of the delineator. The southern boundary of the barony of Burren, as shown on modern maps, does not correspond with any striking natural boundaries, but meanders through the county following some ageless divide between townlands. From the coast north of Poll Salach the baronial border snakes eastwards and southwards around Lisdoonvarna, thence beyond Kilfenora to Leamaneh before curving north to Carron; after linking Mothair na Ceártán and Cathair Mhór (two prehistoric forts) with Knockanes, the frontier takes to the summits of Turloughmore Mountain and marches across the eastern flank of Sliabh Cairn towards Carcair na gCléireach (Corker Pass) and the sea at Corranroo.

But this is not *my* boundary. For me The Burren is the karst region, the limestone plateau of northwest Clare with a southern frontier corresponding *exactly* to the shale-limestone horizon (see map, p. 9), from Doolin around Sliabh Eilbhe to Noughaval and almost encircling Kilfenora, past Leamaneh to Lough Inchiquin. Much more disputatious is the eastern limit; I may occasionally stretch it into the lowlands of east Clare and south-western Galway, towards Kilmacduagh and Gort and Kinvarra, although for most of the time I think of New Line road, which skirts the plateau's eastern margin, Lough Bunny and Corrofin as the frontier. This is more or less that region mapped so finely by Tim Robinson;[2] indeed his multi-faceted map is my vade-mecum.

Boireann may be a rocky place but water, not rock, is the essence of The Burren: nothing else is so fundamental to this particular 'little lap of earth'. Water brought the rock into existence; aeons later frozen and running waters fashioned the karst landscape. Water, moreover, will be The Burren's ultimate destroyer. Meanwhile abundant water permits unique communities of plants and animals to flourish.

Ireland, the island that we know, did not exist three hundred and sixty million years ago. Plants with bright, colourful flowers–gentians and mountain avens, for example–had not yet evolved, nor had dinosaurs, birds and mammals. Mosses, ferns and gigantic horsetails, which are spore-bearing green plants that do not blossom, grew on land that was also the habitat of some amphibians and primitive insects. At that time, towards the beginning of the Carboniferous Period in the Palaeozoic Era, a tropical sea covered the Irish sector of the globe, the waters were rich in nutrients and therefore swarming with microscopic animals and plants. There was no outcrop of limestone where The Burren is situated, indeed the only dry land hereabouts was formed by high peaks of granite and schist; we call the remnants of that antique mountainous land 'Connemara' and 'Iar Connacht'. The mountains edged an isolated land which also incorporated some of the hills of 'Mayo'; if you could have stood on a summit and looked around, you would have gazed over an ocean towards other islands, including 'St George's Land' (modern Wicklow and western Wales). On a clear day, had that hill been high enough, you might have glimpsed

on the western horizon yet more mountains which today form part of Labrador
and Greenland because the Atlantic Ocean did not exist at that time.

In the sea there were many fish: sharks had evolved and so had bony fish; the
coelocanth which persists in small numbers deep in the Indian Ocean is the solitary,
surviving representative of one group of fish that thrived in Carboniferous oceans.
Multitudes of long-extinct insects, worms, molluscs, sea-lilies and starfish, jellyfish,
sponges and corals inhabited the warm ocean. Seaweeds (marine algae) also
flourished. Many of the microscopic marine organisms–both animals and
plants–that swarmed as plankton in the sea possessed minuscule skeletons of calcium
carbonate; when they died those skeletons fell to the ocean floor forming a mud
of almost pure calcium carbonate, the principal chemical component of limestone.[3]

As the Carboniferous Period advanced, sea-levels rose and fell, sometimes
exposing the very young limestones that had been deposited, and thereafter
returning so that further layers of calcareous mud were deposited upon the older
layers which slowly solidified and through millions of years turned into rock. The
encased remains of the sea lilies, corals, shellfish and other sea-creatures became
fossils. By the end of the Lower Carboniferous, there was a deposit of limestone
almost eight hundred metres thick fringing the shore of that island of granite and
schist mountains. During the Upper Carboniferous Period, beginning around
three hundred and twenty-five million years ago, the configuration of land and
sea changed and the ocean became considerably shallower; vast amounts of mud
and sand were washed into the ocean from the lands to the west of 'Ireland' and
so deposits of a different consistency, less rich in calcium carbonate, were laid
down in layers on top of the embryonic limestones–these younger layers solidified
into the sandstones and shales that nowadays outcrop through County Clare south
of Lisdoonvarna. These shales make the breath-taking Cliffs of Moher.

In general the Carboniferous limestone of The Burren is pure and fine-grained,
and contains fossils of many marine creatures, particularly crinoids (sea-lilies, stalked
relatives of starfish), molluscs of various genera including a bivalve named
Gigantoproductus (formerly *Productus*) *giganteus*, and corals (for example, species
of *Lithostrotion*).[4] Each layer has a different consistency and contains a distinctive
set of fossils because plants and animals were evolving and dying out throughout
the tens of millions of years that these eight hundred metres of limestone represent.
The layers of limestone are occasionally interleaved with thin bands of a darker,
much less soluble rock, sometimes of shale, more frequently of chert (a rock formed
from sand grains cemented with silica).

By the close of the Carboniferous Period, approximately two hundred and eighty million years before the present, a new land existed, its surface formed by layers of shale that capped the older, and deeper deposits of pure limestone. Seed-bearing land-plants including cycads, *Ginkgo* (maidenhair tree) and conifers colonized this portion of the earth, yet there were no plants with gaudy blossoms. Many new animals had appeared, insects had taken to the air, but there still were no dinosaurs.

The earth is not a stable, quiescent globe–earthquakes and volcanoes attest to its restlessness. In the last few decades, geologists have amassed evidence to support the theory of continental drift, and most earth scientists now accept that during the past two hundred million years the globe has expanded causing parts of all the continents to move about on remarkable pathways. As landmasses have altered their relative positions, oceans have disappeared and formed: the great southern continent called Gondwana fragmented, and in the northern hemisphere the North Atlantic Ocean expanded as Eurasia and North America were pushed apart. The Atlantic is less than one hundred million years old, so the rocks on the ocean bottom between Ireland, Greenland and Labrador are much younger than those of The Burren. The titanic forces that have shifted continents and forced such mountain chains as the Himalayas and Andes to rise, have in contrast scarcely affected western Ireland, except to separate it from America and Greenland. The layers of limestone deposited in the Carboniferous Period still lie almost horizontally, eloquent testimony to the stability of this region. No major geological faults have disrupted their bedding; only in the eastern part of The Burren is folding of the rocks evident–instead of the layers being flat and horizontal, they undulate so that the hills appear to be formed of a great swirls of limestone.

The Burren massif covered by shale and sandstone has not been entirely submerged under a sea since the close of the Carboniferous Period. The more resistant, younger rocks protected the limestone through the remainder of the Palaeozoic Era and for the entire Mesozoic, which culminated in the reign of the dinosaurs, that ended abruptly about sixty-six million years ago. The next major events to cause substantial changes in The Burren were the general cooling of the climate and the glacial advances–and retreats–of the last two million years, the Quaternary Period, during which water, as ice, moulded the hills of The Burren.

The earth's climate oscillates, cooling and warming and cooling again in cycles that range over many thousands of years. Through the Tertiary and Quaternary Periods–the last seventy million years–ice caps formed on Ireland's mountains many times causing glaciers to flow down the slopes towards the lowlands. When the climate warmed, the ice melted and plants recolonized the unfrozen soil. A glacier–a river of frozen water–has the same effect on hard rock as a piece of rough sandpaper on soft balsa wood: ice scours, gouges and smooths. In a human lifetime, a glacier may not appear to advance or retreat, but during many millennia ice is capable of moving boulders and transporting vast quantities of clay and gravel, and even of cutting valleys in solid rock. Throughout Ireland, beautiful corries perched on mountain sides, swarms of egg-shaped drumlins with loughs between, ribbons of eskers and dramatic u-shaped valleys proclaim the landscaping powers of ice. Glaciers have left thick deposits of clay in a few Burren localities, and everywhere massive boulders–erratics–sitting on the pavements, for having scoured rock from one region the glaciers had to deposit the debris somewhere else. The Burren's erratics can be limestone and sometimes they are granite from Connemara.[5]

The glaciers that invaded the Clare region removed the protective capping of shale and sandstone from northern parts of the county, thereby exposing the limestone core of The Burren. However, because The Burren's limestone summits are not greatly lowered compared with the base of the shales that once protected them from erosion, it is reasoned that the sloughing away of the shale took place during the most recent glaciation; had the limestone been exposed for a very long time, for the duration of several 'ice ages', the hills would have been worn away progressively by glacier after glacier and the whole region levelled to form just another part of that flat, continuous plain which stretches eastwards from Gort to Dublin. The ice, having stripped away the shale, had time only to round and smooth the profiles of the slopes of The Burren and not to do any more than that before it melted and the climate warmed.

Once the cap of shale had been breached, water could easily percolate into the limestone, seeping through the myriad hair-cracks that form naturally in this rock. Limestone is soluble, so melt-water from the glaciers and every subsequent drop of rain dissolved the exposed rock, widening the fractures and, as millennia passed, the minute fissures enlarged to form the network of underground tunnels and caverns which are characteristic of karst in areas of substantial rainfall. The process continues. Every shower of rain that washes The Burren steals some of its surface: the water removes an invisible layer of limestone from the whole region, widening every crack through which it trickles, leaving behind less and less. Slowly–very, very slowly–The Burren is disappearing back into the Atlantic Ocean, and its hills are being lowered. Some day, millions of years in the future, The Burren will be gone, washed away; a flat plain will remain where today are the beautiful, proud, pale grey whale-backs of Cappanawalla, Moneen Mountain and Turloughmore. They will have flowed back into the ocean.

Elegant experiments have been carried out to attempt to quantify the present-day rate of erosion of the Clare limestones.[6] Many environmental factors affect this; air and water temperatures, the acidity of rainwater, the chemical composition of the rock, even the plant species that are growing on the surface and the soils in which they are rooted. Some calculations have yielded figures as high as half a millimetre of surface removed per annum or half a metre every one thousand years, a very rapid rate of erosion. But it is evidently not always so rapid, and it is not necessary to be a scientist with modern equipment to see the effect of rain during the last twelve millennia. The erratics, dumped by glaciers, have served as sturdy umbrellas protecting the limestone immediately underneath them from the rain and therefore from some of the natural erosion. The depth of limestone removed by rain since each erratic was set in place at the end of the last glaciation is clearly demonstrated by the pedestals or platforms on which the boulders sit. Some boulders that I have seen on the slopes of Cappanawalla have obvious pedestals; the difference in level between the rock immediately under the boulder and that of the surrounding pavement can be ten to fifteen centimetres. At its simplest, fifteen centimetres of rock removed in less than ten thousand years represents an erosion rate equivalent to the thickness of a sheet of paper every decade.

Fifteen thousand years ago The Burren was still icy; its climate resembled that of present-day Greenland. If there were any patches of vegetation anywhere, the plants growing in The Burren then will have been typical of the severest tundra, a few lichens, maybe a handful of resilient shrubs. The general view of the history of Irish vegetation affirms that as the glaciers retreated, the tundra-like environment ameliorated and over a couple of millennia, shrubs and trees began to colonise the deep glacial soils, while creeping herbs including mountain avens flourished where there was a thinner covering. Arctic plants were dominant in Ireland until about nine thousand years ago. Aided by the return northwards of the North Atlantic Drift, further warming led to the invasion of plants from southern Europe, and the extirpation of the remnants of the tundra flora; forests of oak and ash cloaked most parts of Ireland until Neolithic farmers began felling the trees. Some of the Arctic plants were not ousted because they alone could colonise exposed habitats on the highest peaks, and remarkably some also survived near sea-level in The Burren region. As the climate continued to change, becoming mild and equable, plant species of southern affinities expanded their ranges and in a few localities found congenial niches alongside the Arctic survivors. Thus the extraordinary tapestry of The Burren flora was woven, an amalgamation of the ancient residue of a tundra vegetation and recent interlopers with less tolerance of cold. It is this strange mixture of plants that attracts the attention of botanists and wildflower enthusiasts.

However The Burren is not just a hunting-ground for botanists. Its rocks have their student-admirers too–geologists come to examine the rock strata, palaeontologists search for fossils, geomorphologists attempt explanations of the landforms, and spelaeologists burrow deep to study the caves and underground rivers. And potholers enjoy this 'classic' region.[7] Caving, like botanizing, is a minority sport, indulged by a select band who can put up with wet, dark tunnels that perhaps end in a squeeze, a swallet, or a measureless cavern. It is not a sport I feel I would enjoy, although I do envy those who have negotiated narrow passages into the interior of The Burren. In particular, I am jealous of the cavers who have gazed on The Great Stalactite of Pol-an-Ionain. To reach this wonder, you must enter an ivy-wreathed hole (hence Poll an Eidhneán (Pol-an-Ionain), cave of ivy) under a cliff-face, and follow an 'intricate course…over and under boulders' to a small watershoot. Then 'a stream canyon is followed…a knee-wrecking crawl' along a passage about 150 metres long. The Main Chamber, one of the grandest caves in Clare, is eleven metres high and forty metres long. Floating from the ceiling is the seven-metres long Great Stalactite, cited (with exaggerated dimensions) in the *Guinness Book of Records* as the longest free-hanging stalactite in the world (I am reliably informed that it isn't!). This natural curiosity has 'another four metres potential growth before it reaches the mud floor of the chamber (if left undisturbed for another few millennia)', according to Charles Self.[8] If it achieves that tranquil end–a doubtful prospect as I write–it will be a stalactite no longer but a column of pure calcite (dissolved and redeposited limestone). The Great Stalactite was first seen in 1952 by members of Craven Pothole Club; in the artificial light from the cavers' torches it was suffused with cream and pale gold.

Cavers and spelaeologists, when tracing the labyrinths of channels and caverns within the limestone, explore a barony that is bereft of light–no sunshine penetrates beyond the entrance passage of each cave. In the silence and complete darkness, when no-one is in the cave, the Great Stalactite of Pol-an-Ionain has no colour, because colours are fractions of white light, and then, perhaps, it does deserves its scurrilous, derogatory name–'The Soggy Dishcloth'.

Green plants cannot survive without sunlight; there are no growing plants in the pitch-black caves. When permanent artificial lights are installed plants do grow–visitors to the show cave at Aillwee can see the dramatic consequences of mankind's interference with Nature for around the lights illuminating the cave trail are swards of young maidenhair ferns, a few hart's-tongues and (very, very occasionally) a shamrock. Turn off those lights for ever and the plants will wither and die.

So cavers do not have any chance to botanize beyond the mouth of a cave; they may encounter animals such as eels, trout and very pale frogs which, like the potholers themselves, have come in from the 'open air', and even an occasional life-less ivy leaf or a bobbing hazel nut floating past. There are no true troglodytes in The Burren because the caves are too young to have a unique fauna of albino, eyeless spiders, woodlice, fish or frogs. Yet the caving fraternity, who admire The Burren for its darkness, do not eschew plants, and one in particular has merited their special attention.

Swallets and cave-mouths represent a habitat that is moist and sheltered; the potholes of my home county, Fermanagh, are similar, and often contain prodigious ash trees, ferns in abundance, and a luxuriant sward of golden saxifrage (*Chrysosplenium oppositifolium*). Poll na gColm on the eastern slope of Sliabh Eilbhe is like the Fermanagh potholes–large ash trees fill it. Another splendid mature ash stands in one of the swallets that fringe the limestone-shale boundary on the south-western fringe of Poulacapple in Cullaun townland. Around it are dark twigged sallies, which in the winter sunlight glow in shades of maroon and plum.

This particular sally is the eared willow, *Salix aurita* (*crann sniofa* is its Irish name, meaning withy tree); the Latin name alludes to the pair of stipules, resembling little green ears, attached to each leaf-stalk. By April the sallies have become 'pussy willows' (see plate, p. 310)–they are covered with catkins, each one being a cluster of several hundred flowers all of one sex. Some bushes are the males: each tiny male flower has two stamens carrying a yellow anther. These catkins, burgeoning with yellow anthers, soon shed clouds of pollen that may be wafted towards the catkins of the female willows. The female catkins are generally longer than the males, and do not produce yellow anthers. Once the male catkins have withered and fallen off, and the females have been pollinated and begun to droop and to ripen their seed, the leaves unfold; these are oval and about twice as long as broad, softly and persistently covered beneath with grey down. The seeds are released in May, each one with a parachute of long silky hairs enabling it to float on the breeze.

Willows, so the potholers noted, frequented the entrances to many well-known caves, especially around Doolin and Cullaun. As exploration of The

Burren cave systems progressed during the early nineteen-fifties, the spelaeologists reasoned that by investigating places where there were sallies, they might discover entrances to new cave systems. Thus a thicket of willow was 'looked upon as an indicator of where to find a cave.'[9]

Cavers have a wry sense of humour especially when devising names for caverns, underground channels and their features—who else would give a beautiful stalactite a name like 'The Soggy Dishcloth' or 'The Bloody Guts', or call warm, cascading streams 'The Piddles'? One of this fraternity, Straun Robertson, even decided to give the willow of the cave mouths a new name—spelaeodendron—cave tree.

> Now all you good Spelaeos listen to me, away down Doolin,
> And I'll sing you a song of a cave near the sea
> Level down at Doolin Strand.
> Way theories away; away from Doolin
> For the Spelaeodendron
> It grows with its end on
> The entrance to Doolin Cave.[10]

The original spelaeodendrons were those growing about the swallets at Cullaun, and they are indubitably eared willows.[11] So the spelaeodendron provides a whimsical link between the underworld, frequented by spelaeologists, and the surface paradise of The Burren which is tramped by botanists. Caves endure monotonous, eternal night: my haunts are sun-lit, a realm of changing colours.

Leamaneh Castle

WHO CAN HAVE TROD IN THE GRASS?

*He could not avoid dwelling upon and detailing the valuable researches of
the older botanists especially with reference to Dr. Eaton. Much was accomplished
formerly that were of late recorded as new discoveries.*

Francis Whitla: address to Dublin Natural History Society, 1852

William Butler Yeats knew The Burren and set one of his *Two Plays for Dancers*
in the Abbey of Our Lady of the Fertile Rocks at Corcomroe, surrounded
by the hills of 'Agate or of Jade'. A young fugitive waits for a boat to the Aran
Islands. The first musician sings, asking these questions:

> Why does my heart beat so?
> Did not a shadow pass?
> It passed but a moment ago.
> Who can have trod in the grass?[1]

The grass of Burren has survived the treading of an army of botanists, young and
old, and will endure–and survive–the footfalls of many more. Who has trod on
that grass?

Francis Whitla went botanizing in The Burren during July 1851 in company
with Thaddeus O'Mahony. A year afterwards they addressed a meeting of the

Dublin Natural History Society, the earliest recorded lecture about The Burren given to any audience. No exact transcript now exists of Whitla's remarks about the history of plant exploration in The Burren; he '…went very fully into this subject, of which he appeared to possess much information, and to have taken up with great zeal.'[2] Whitla's reference to a Dr Eaton does indeed display an intimate knowledge of bygone collectors, although he, or the society's secretary, got Eaton's name a little garbled.

To repeat: about The Burren enigmas abound. One of the most startling is that two of its wildflowers along with juniper were the first of Ireland's native plants reported in a properly scientific way.[3] That happened in 1650, yet substantial exploration had not taken place, and moreover was not to be undertaken until two more centuries had elapsed.

By modern standards the entries in *Phytologia Britannica*, a slim pocket-book published during 1650 by the London bookseller Octavian Pulleyn, are terse and imprecise, but brevity does not alter priority. The author was Dr William How. He reported mountain avens and Spring gentian from the 'Mountaines betwixt *Gort* and *Galloway*' and juniper creeping 'Upon the Rocks neer *Kilmadough*', and attributed the records to one Mr Heaton. This muster-roll reveals that sometime in the first half of the seventeenth century a man imbued with botanical curiosity travelled between Galway and Gort and diverted to Kilmacduagh perhaps to view the ancient ruined cathedral with its perfect, leaning round tower. Can we identify Mr Heaton, and be more precise about the date of his journey?

Richard Heaton[4] was born in Hooton Pagnell, a hamlet about ten kilometres northwest of Doncaster in Yorkshire. He was baptized on 14 February 1601 in All Saint's Parish Church. Richard was a clever lad and eventually gained a place as a lady-foundress scholar in St John's College, Cambridge. He first signed the College register on 7 November 1621, graduated with the degree of Bachelor of Arts in 1624, and remained at Cambridge for another three years, obtaining his master's degree in 1627. Like most graduates at that time, Heaton was ordained a minister in the Anglican Church and, professing Royalist sympathies, entered the service of King Charles I as chaplain in Colonel James Strangeway's Regiment of Foot. Heaton soon transferred to Wentworth's Life Guards of Horse, also as chaplain.

Sir Thomas Wentworth was appointed Lord Deputy of Ireland in January 1632, but did not move here until the summer of 1633–his regimental chaplain accompanied him, and shortly thereafter the Revd Richard Heaton was appointed

Prebendary of Iniscattery. In September, by royal warrant, Heaton was made Rector of Birr being instituted on 4 October 1633. Thus he had charge of two parishes, one in Queen's County (Offaly), and the other, Iniscattery, in south County Clare encompassing Scattery Island (Inis Cathaigh) and the town of Kilrush; the law obliged him to reside in his parish, but obviously Heaton could not have lived in Birr and Kilrush at the same time.

'A man of competent skill in Botanicks', Richard Heaton was keenly interested in plants. He collected several in the central lowlands–wintergreen (*Pyrola rotundifolia*) in 'a bogge by Roscre', stone bramble near Edenderry, and a helleborine at Lisnageeragh (one of the townlands about Roscrea). As for the juniper, Spring gentian and mountain avens, surely he gathered these while on the way to visit his Clare parish during one May month in the late 1630s? The journey from Birr, crossing the River Shannon at Portumna, to Iniscattery cannot have been swift or comfortable, considering that in those days it took at least four days to ride from Limerick to Dublin.

The Revd Mr Heaton's life in Ireland was full and complicated. He had a living from his parochial benefices and property near Roscrea, but with rebellion and war he felt safer far away from the diocese of Killaloe and returned to England in 1641 where he stayed throughout the Civil War and the Commonwealth. Before 1650 he told William How, who incidentally was a captain in one of the Royalists' troop of horse, about his Irish botanical discoveries in sufficient detail for Dr How to include them in *Phytologia Britannica*.

Following the restoration of King Charles II in 1660, Richard Heaton returned to Ireland to resume his rectory of Birr, to become Dean of Clonfert and receive a doctorate in divinity from the University of Dublin. He was in his late fifties by this time, and survived only a few more years, dying towards the close of 1666.

The commotions that caused Heaton to return to England eventually brought Oliver Cromwell with the Commonwealth army to Ireland. Cromwell's campaign has left bitter folk-memories, and a famous diatribe which ever since has sullied the barony of Burren, echoing as a refrain to every mention of the region. Cromwell himself left Ireland in June 1650, having installed Lieutenant-General Edmund Ludlow (c. 1617–1682) as one of the commissioners for the civil government of Ireland and second-in-command to the Lord Deputy, Henry Ireton. On their bloody campaign through Ireland, Cromwell's troops laid siege to Gort, Limerick and many isolated fortified houses and castles in the Limerick-Clare region.

General Ludlow commanded the horse during this particular campaign. Many years later, most probably between 1663 and 1673[5] while exiled in Vevay in Switzerland, he composed memoirs that remained unpublished until 1698, six years after his death, and almost half a century after the campaign in Limerick and Clare. Ludlow's memoirs cannot be regarded as a thoroughly reliable record of seventeenth century Ireland and his recollections are confused, yet the passage describing The Burren has been quoted so frequently that it has acquired a gloss of almost infallible authority.

Having captured Limerick, the Lord Deputy commanded Ludlow to march troops into Clare 'to reduce some places in those parts'. On 1 November 1651 with two thousand foot and fifteen hundred horse Ludlow crossed the River Shannon and headed for Clarecastle, which surrendered, and thence to retake Carrigaholt in the extreme south-west of Clare. As he was returning to Limerick, Ludlow was met by Ireton who wanted to view the country and winter-quarters. Together, Ireton and Ludlow headed north.

> After two days' march, without anything remarkable but bad quarters, we entred into the Barony of Burren, of which it is said, that it is a country where there is not water enough to drown a man, wood enough to hang one, nor earth enough to bury him; which last is so scarce, that the inhabitants steal it from one another, and yet their cattle are very fat; for the grass growing in turfs of earth, of two or three foot square, that lie between the rocks, which are of limestone, is very sweet and nourishing.'[6]

The Commonwealth force reached Leamaneh sometime in mid-November, and finding it '…indifferent strong, being built with stone, and having a good wall about it,…put a garison into it, and furnished it with all things necessary.'

Is it significant that General Ludlow used the phrase *of which it is said…*? Was he merely reporting hearsay, or perhaps as one writer suggests, a local proverb? Is he blameless for this slur? In mitigation I will allow Ludlow this; he was not well, having sweated with a severe fever for several days before and during his night at Leamaneh–Ireton also caught a severe fever. Moreover the weather was foul; the day after the force reached Leamaneh '…there fell abundance of rain and snow…accompanied with a very high wind.' Poor man, chilled to the bone, wrapped in 'a fur coat over my buff, and an oiled one over that', he experienced the invigorating delights of early winter in Burren without being able to enjoy them. He could not appreciate the splendid isolation, on the southern fringe of the limestone fastness, of beautiful Leamaneh with its new walled gardens, deer park and fish-ponds,[7] and presumably he did no more than gaze blearily from its stone-mullioned windows over the sweet, nourishing, gentian-enriched turf that the natives, so he averred, stole from one another. According to his own memoirs he did not venture beyond Leamaneh nor did he pace the limestone pavements. Moreover, like so many twentieth century invaders–tourists–Ireton and Ludlow had no time to linger; two days after sequestrating Leamaneh the army marched back towards Clarecastle over such rocky country that most of the horses were unshoed. The Lord Deputy died from the fever on 26 November 1651. Ludlow lived to damn the barony from afar, and his hollow words now echo from every tourist brochure.

Lieutenant-General Ludlow's memoirs were reprinted many times and went through at least five editions following the first printing of 1698. There is no way of telling whether Edward Lhuyd, Welsh antiquarian and natural historian, read Ludlow's famous jeremiad before he began an extensive journey through western and northern parts of Britain and Ireland that year. By the summer of 1700 Lhuyd had reached Connacht and, like many travellers in succeeding centuries, crossed to the Aran Islands where he recorded the vocabulary of the inhabitants for his English-Irish dictionary. Lhuyd's curiosity extended to botany and flotsam, and he made one of the earliest surviving collections of Irish plants gathering mountain avens for it '*prope Sligo in Hybernia*' [near Sligo in Ireland]. In Connacht he picked St Dabeoc's heath (*Daboecia cantabrica*) and also the plant now known as Irish heath (*Erica erigena*). On the Aran Islands, the Welsh naturalist discovered 'great plenty' of maidenhair fern.

Lhuyd visited Clare too: recalling juniper, he wrote 'Iur Creige Juniper. In the County of Clare I observ'd them to pronounce it uar cregu.' When he published the first report of bearberry (*Arctostaphylos uva-ursi*) in Ireland, Lhuyd also reported that 'I observ'd this plant to be…called…Lusradh na geire bornigh…in the County of Clare',[8] but did he walk on the limestone of The Burren? There is circumstantial evidence in a letter that he wrote describing some of his botanical discoveries; it was published in the *Philosophical Transactions* of the Royal Society of London and contained this sentence:

> Mr. Heaton's Chamaedrys Alpina is a common plant on those Hills the Mountains of Ben Bulben and Ben Buishgen, as also on divers other Mountains and Heathy Grounds in Connacht and Munster.[9]

Mountain avens has a restricted distribution in Ireland; it is *not* abundant throughout Connacht and Munster, and while Ben Bulben is in Connacht, The

Burren is in Munster. That suggests Lhuyd did visit the barony, because the mountain avens does not grow on any of the Aran Islands, or elsewhere in Clare.

Edward Lhuyd travelled on to Kerry, where tories disrupted his botanical and linguistic work, and Cork whence he returned to England with extensive notes and many pressed plant specimens.

The new century brought new impetus to botanical studies in Ireland. A professor of botany was engaged by the School of Physic in the University of Dublin, although he did little work on native plants. The Revd Dr Caleb Threlkeld, a native of the English Lake District took up residence in Dublin in 1718, and in 1726 published the first flora of Ireland—it contains no additions to The Burren floral census. Many of Threlkeld's records were repeated, without acknowledgement, in the Revd John Keogh's strange work titled *Botanalogia Universalis Hibernica, Or, A General Irish herbal...*, printed in Cork during 1735. Keogh's family came from Strokestown in County Roscommon, and he went to Trinity College, Dublin, before his ordination and appointment as chaplain to Lord Kingston at Mitchelstown, County Cork. Keogh garnered a strange confection of plants into his herbal, paying special attention to those grown in Lord Kingston's garden, so his accounting of native plants must be suspect especially when included among species from The Burren is *Palma Christi* (an archaic name for *Ricinus communis*, castor-oil). Be that as it may, this eighteenth century divine knew that dropwort (*Filipendula vulgaris*) grew 'wild in the barony of Burren.'

A much more reliable witness of The Burren was Keogh's young contemporary, Charles Lucas whose family home was Ballingaddy, situated a short distance to the northwest of Ennistimon. As a youth he was apprenticed to an apothecary to learn the skills of preparing medicines which at that period were mostly concocted of plants. Presumably he learned some of the efficacious herbs of the limestone hills from local folk, for Charles Lucas certainly gained a remarkable knowledge of the plants of The Burren before he was a quarter of a century old. He was adventurous, visiting caves like the legendary Cave of the Wild Horses at Kilcorney, not far from Leamaneh. He wrote a long letter about Kilcorney and the plants of Burren to that doyen of naturalists in the early eighteenth century, Sir Hans Sloane, and this was eventually published in *Philosophical Transactions*. For my present purpose I need only quote a short portion of Lucas' account of his native Clare:

> The Part of Ireland called Burren, is a small Barrony in the Northwest part
> of the County of Clare, & bounded on the North side by the Bay of Galway.

Dr Charles Lucas

It is from one end to the other a Continuation of very high, Rocky, Lime-stone Hills, there being little or no plain Land throughout the whole. It is that part of which it is reported that Oliver Cromwell said (when he come to storm a few Castles in it) that he cou'd neither see Water enough to drown a man, Wood enough to hang a man or Earth enough to bury a man in; Notwithstanding it is most fertile & produces immense quantities of Juniper & some Yew, besides great variety of the Capillary herbs, Virga Aurea, Verbena & some other comõn plants I have found the Teucrium Alpinum magno flore of Caspar Bauhin & a large Shrubby Cinquefoil answering the Description Mr. Morison gives in his Second Volume of Hyst. Oxon. of his Pentaphilloides rectum fruticosum Eboracense.[10]

Lucas, only twenty-three years old in November 1736 (the date of the letter), was the first to report shrubby cinquefoil ('Pentaphilloides': *Potentilla fruticosa*), yew, goldenrod ('Virga aurea': *Solidago virgaurea*) and vervain ('Verbena': *Verbena officinalis*). His reference to a plant which Caspar Bauhin called *Teucrium Alpinum magno flore* is perplexing–this name seems to refer to *Scutellaria alpina* which is not recorded in Ireland–but the phrase-name is so close to '*Teucrium Alpinum Cisti flore*' that it must be an error for mountain avens. As he does not mention the ubiquitous *Dryas octopetala* elsewhere, I feel this is a reasonable interpretation.

23

By 1736 Lucas was living in Dublin, yet he returned to Clare occasionally and continued to take a substantial interest in the botany and general natural history of the county. During 1740 he collected rue-leaved saxifrage, bearberry, stone bramble and what may have been sea wormwood[11] and by 1742 had completed a manuscript, alas now lost, about the natural history of Clare. He was elected to Dublin city council and conducted a vigorous campaign to stop abuses in the preparations of medicines. He was forced to go into exile and then took up the study of physic–medicine–graduating in 1752 from the University of Leiden. Eventually Dr Lucas returned to Dublin and became one of the city's members of parliament. So well-regarded was he in certain circles, as a patriot and campaigner against corrupt practices within Dublin Corporation that his statue, 'a queer, tormented figure which does its author [Edward Smyth] little credit…' was placed in the entrance vestibule of City Hall.[12]

Charles Lucas was a Clare man, not a stranger in a hostile landscape. While travellers were welcomed and treated civilly on the fringes of The Burren and could find board and lodgings in villages and towns such as Gort and Lisdoonvarna, inns and hostelries were few and far between within the barony. The poor roads also acted to deter travellers. Barren limestone hills and 'tracts of naked rock' did not draw even the most curious visitors, and the botanical delights, clearly known to well-informed men by the middle of the eighteenth century, do not seem to have counteracted the difficulties. Lord Chief Baron Willes skirted the barony in 1761 and one of his letters to the Earl of Warwick gives a flavour of the eastern fringe of the region–

> From Ennis to the City of Galway is a long day's journey–30 computed Irish miles. We dined at Gort… When we left Ennis and got into the county of Galway, the face of the country was quite changed: the roads rocky and rough, scarce a gentleman's house upon the whole road; the miserable cabins at 3 or 4 miles distance one from another presented themselves; not an hedge or a tree to be seen,… The whole country I pass'd thro' is very thinly inhabited. 'Tis not at all mountainous, some gentle risings but pretty much flat. In some few places little patches of barley and oates, but in general the whole country consists of rocks and large limestones, which cover the ground and stand much closer than the Grey Weathers in the road to Bath. What grass that springs up among the stones is extremely fine, and 'tis surprising to see the numbers of sheep that feed upon it. I enquir'd when I came to Galway what this rough ground set for. I was told by different persons that the occupiers pay from 5 to 7 shilling per acre. Had I rec'd

that account from one or two persons only I shou'd not have believ'd it but they say that all the rock being limestone, the grass is very sweet and the large stones are so good a shelter for sheep in winter, that it fattens them prodigiously. The sheep graze there all winter without any fodder. I am told the grass is so nourishing that a sheep fatten'd and kill'd from these rocky pastures has near double the tallow of a sheep of the same size fed upon rich pasture ground. I saw likewise horned cattle feeding among the rocks.[13]

Not even the most enthusiastic field botanists of the late 1700s and early 1800s, intrepid men like James Townsend Mackay of Trinity College Botanic Garden in Dublin, who visited many other regions within Ireland, went into the heart of The Burren. Furthermore, while numerous botanists from overseas are known to have been in Connemara in the first decades of the nineteenth century, and some also took the ferries to the Aran Islands, hardly anyone ventured into The Burren.

James Mackay probably relied on Bindon Blood of Rockforest for much of the information on The Burren that was incorporated in *A systematic catalogue of the rare plants found in Ireland*, issued in 1806, but a handful of annotations therein suggests that Mackay did some botanizing between Gort and Corrofin (whence he reported the flowering rush, *Butomus umbellatus*, a waterside plant which was still thereabout at the turn of the last century but has since vanished) and on the northern coast near Gleninagh.[14] Walter Wade, Professor of Botany to the Dublin Society and head of the society's botanical gardens at Glasnevin when Mackay was in charge at the College Botanic Garden, is not known to have visited Clare.

The only botanical traveller to leave an account of the barony in the early nineteenth century was Joseph Woods who kept a diary[15] while he visited the south of Ireland in the late summer of 1808, travelling from Waterford to Cork and thence to Killarney before heading north towards Limerick. He wended a remarkably round-about route to Galway, calling at Newmarket-on-Fergus where he 'changed horses at an inn most charmingly situated', Ennis and Milltown Malbay, before striking north-eastwards into limestone country. On 8 September, Woods walked from Milltown to Ennistimon and at noon reached Kilfenora, a cathedral town consisting '…only of a few miserable cabins.' On Saturday 9 September he was at Leamaneh,

an ancient tower with an addition comparatively recent. The addition is a mere shell, the old tower is still inhabited by some poor families. The situation of the castle is neither beautiful or romantic, among barren

Joseph Woods

looking limestone hills forming the extremity of that singular tract of country called the barony of Burren.

Near Kilfenora, Woods encountered one of the region's uniquely intriguing turloughs, and then trudged westwards again towards Doolin, passing through Lisdoonvarna where he was shown the chalybeate spa and another spring which appeared '…by the taste to be aluminous. The peasantry wash their ulcers in it & think they receive great benefit.' He was not particularly impressed by the village although 'considering the accom[m]odation, [it is] very much frequented.' Eventually Woods reached Doolin. It had been a profitless walk:

> I was too late for the tide to search for seaweeds on the rocks but hunted a long while in vain for the maidenhair on the shore and returned from a long and dreary walk without meeting any botanical recompense…'

From his lodgings at noon on 11 September,

> I began my walk thro the barony of Burrin–who has not heard of the Barony of Burrin where there is not water enough to drown a man, wood to hang

him or earth to bury him and really this is never the truth in a tract of country about [14–deleted] miles long and 11 broad (Irish measure) than will readily be conceived by a person who has not seen it or some similar country. It is moreover added to enhance the wonder that the stone walls are transparent…

Woods trudged towards Corcomroe probably by the road through Carron. The vegetation was sparse. He noticed '…a deep and narrow ravine as if formed by a current of water, and not far from it a deep and narrow chasm runs up the side of the mountain much like some of those in the Kerry Mountains'–this can only be the spectacular Scailp na Seirsí, north of Turlough village.

Joseph Woods had as much interest in antiquities, cromlechs, stone ramparts and churches as he had in geology and botany. By the late afternoon, in the northern part of Burren, he neared Corcomroe:

> The abbey of Corcomroe is in the same valley but in a still more desolate part. It appears large and I should like to have visited it but I was tired, it was growing late, & I was uncertain where I could meet with any sort of accom[m]odation. Even the valley here is naked rock with scarcely any covering but straggling patches of Dryas octopetala called here the Burren rose, & I think it might almost be called Burren grass it constitutes so large a proportion of the whole vegetation. A variety of Saxifraga hypnoides, or rather perhaps a distinct species is abundant through most of the district. Yet Mr Lysaght assured me that the great part of the Land of Burrin lets for 2£ pr acre its value depends on affording good winter feed for cattle. I endeavoured in vain to find some sort of lodgings at Corcomroe. I therefore proceeded to Kilvara [sic.] where bread is sold & where I got a pretty decent bed.

From Kinvarra, Joseph Woods journeyed on to Galway and spent more than one week thereabouts before beginning his return trip that would eventually bring him back to Cork.

> At 5 oclock on the morning of the 20th [September] I found not the least preparations for my departure [from Galway] and at ½ past 7 left Galway in a Gort post Chaise which I was lucky enough to meet with. A thick mizzling rain prevented all view and I could only see that I still continued in a limestone country. After breakfast it cleared up a little and engaging a boy and horse to carry my luggage I set off on foot for Kilmacduagh. by the time I arrived there the weather was worse than ever and it was in a thick rain that I observed the following particulars. Kilmacduagh is seated at a considerable distance from the Burrin mountains… I had flattered

myself with the hope of examining their vegetable productions at a
considerable distance from my former track & especially of renewing my
search for Potentilla fruticosa but the weather and the distance united to
prevent the execution of this plan. There are however one or two Turloughs
or pieces of ground of that nature in the neighbourhood where I hunted
without success… I slept at Crusheen. At these Irish country Inns I have
usually found myself very comfortable. The accom[m]odations indeed are
sometimes but indifferent but the people are civil and attentive and the
best of everything they have is at the travellers service.

Joseph Woods' comment about searching for shrubby cinquefoil is intriguing–surely
he had read Charles Lucas' letter in *Philosophical Transactions*–and his diary is
delightful for the glimpses it gives of the embryonic tourist industry in Clare:
Lisdoonvarna had been discovered as a spa, and ruined churches were already well
established as places to be visited.

Four decades pass. Few evince interest in the botany of north County Clare;
those botanists who come to Ireland travel to Killarney and Connemara, and Ireland's
own botanists studiously avoid the region too. John O'Donovan, famous for his
work on behalf of the Ordnance Survey, was based in The Burren during the autumn
of 1839, but his attention was focused on the antiquities so that his marvellous
letters are devoid of notes about wild flowers. Would that he had had an interest
in natural history to supplement his meticulous attention to place names, folk-
tales, and artefacts. The barony held at least one painful memory for O'Donovan
which he related in a letter addressed from Corrofin on 14 October 1839:

> I returned yesterday evening from the wild rocks of Burren, where I was
> hurt by a mule, but not very seriously. Burren is the wildest and ruggedest
> district I have yet seen and I found it exceedingly difficult to cross the single
> limestone ditches (walls) with which it abounds, but I have not done with
> it yet.[16]

A solitary exception to the disdainful company was Charles Carter who in mid-
July 1846 walked from Oranmore to Ardrahan and thence to Gort where he stayed
overnight before taking '…the car that runs daily, during the summer, to New
Quay, a sweet and retired bathing-place'. Leaving Newquay, Carter walked
around the coast to the 'wretched little village' of Ballyvaghan, of which he had
lively memories:

> Such fare, and such a bed for a poor weary naturalist, who is only enlivened
> by a far too intimate acquaintance with hosts of the order Siphonaptera.[17]

Leaving at day-break 'those loving friends', he climbed the hills, viewing 'piles upon piles of large limestone blocks, and mass upon mass extended until lost in the thick mist' that covered Black Head, and thence to Ennistimon which was much more to his liking. Charles Carter added ferns, tutsan and mossy saxifrage to the roster of The Burren's reported flora during his ramble.

Five years later in the last week of July 1851 a Dublin solicitor, Francis Whitla, and Thaddeus O'Mahony who was then a student in Trinity College, Dublin, made a visit. Evidently Whitla had been to The Burren before—he was able to tell members of the Dublin Natural History Society on 10 March 1851 that broomrape grew in the area and was a parasite of thyme.[18] Their's was not so painful an experience—or perhaps they were too polite to mention the bed bugs. Unlike the disparaging Carter, O'Mahony was captivated by the scenery: at the meeting of the society in June 1852[19] he was tempted to describe in detail

> the magnificent coast and mountain scenery…the interesting antiquarian remains scattered everywhere throughout the country…[but] I shall only observe, that the lover of wild scenery, the antiquarian, and the naturalist, could all find there enough to gratify their respective tastes.

Whitla and O'Mahony climbed one of the higher hills, finding red helleborine and bearberry growing on '…limestone ridges, with surface broken and chinky, …among stones that can be separated without much difficulty, and that, when removed, rattle over each other with a peculiar metallic kind of ringing sound.' They travelled along the coast from Ballinalacken towards Fanore, and in the defile known as Kyber Pass, 'which opens towards those sand-banks that lie right opposite the Isles of Arran', found fruiting heads of Spring gentian. Ballyvaghan may have been their base for a few days, and they also visited Glencolumbkille, and Rockforest where shrubby cinquefoil and alder buckthorn were in full flower. On 3 August O'Mahony and Whitla discovered dropwort growing on the eastern fringe of the Burren, but they were wrong in supposing that they were the first to find it.

As they botanized, Francis Whitla and Thaddeus O'Mahony must have been objects of intense curiosity. They spoke with some local folk in an attempt to record the Irish names of the wild flowers; 'In this respect, I am sorry to say,' wrote O'Mahony who later became Professor of Irish in Trinity College, Dublin,

> our efforts were not very successful. That our peasantry at no remote period possessed a considerable knowledge of plants, and were acquainted with

the medicinal properties of many of them, is what will hardly be questioned; but at the present day, when medical science has introduced more efficacious remedies, and the establishment of local dispensaries in almost all districts throughout Ireland has brought discredit on the once favourite specific of the village leech, while the decline of superstitious observances, and the departure of Banshee and Sluaghshee has shaken, if it has not completely destroyed, the invalid's faith in the virtue of the fairy-woman's charmed herbs, the peasantry have become quite indifferent about those plants they formerly studied with care, and have quite forgotten not alone their virtues, once deemed so potent, but even their very names.

Whatever native names the botanists did collect–mainly of weeds 'owing, I should think, to their being obliged to remove them as weeds'–were in Whitla's possession in 1852 but have vanished. O'Mahony lamented, 'ere the events of the last few years had so fearfully thinned the Irish-speaking portion of our peasantry', that more work had not been done to record the Irish names of plants.

Thaddeus O'Mahony concluded his lecture with a plea for more work on the flora of the remoter parts of Ireland; when a brief visit can yield a sheaf of new species, what may not be expected, he asked, by a more rigorous search at all seasons of the year?

In 1851, the same year as O'Mahony's and Whitla's trip, Alexander Goodman More,[20] an English youth whose passion for natural history, especially ornithology, was considerable, came with his parents and sister to spend the entire summer at Castle Taylor, a fine mansion embracing a mediaeval tower, set in limestone pastureland northeast of Gort. The castle belonged to the Shawe-Taylors; Walter Shawe-Taylor had become Alexander's particular friend when the families were neighbours at Renens near Lausanne in Switzerland. The two boys remained in contact while at separate schools and during the summer of 1850 Alexander paid his first visit to Ireland, staying as Walter's guest at Castle Taylor; they dissipated the months from June to October in shooting woodcock, marsh harriers, sparrowhawks and other birds. In between wreaking carnage on the local birds, More caught butterflies and moths, rats and mice, and spent some time examining blackberries (*Rubus* spp.) and other flowering plants.

Both Walter Shawe-Taylor and A. G. More (as he is best known to Irish botanists) 'went up' to Cambridge in October 1850, but at the following Easter More gave up studying the classics at Trinity College when he became severely ill; he decided he was unfit '…for work of the strenuous sort to which his habits of mind inclined him.' Although he changed to natural sciences, these too had to be abandoned in 1853, and he did not graduate. To recuperate, in May 1851, More returned to Castle Taylor, and during picnics and moth-hunts succeeded in adding several species to the muster-roll of Ireland's fauna and flora including the turlough violet–that summer he did not spend so much time shooting birds.

More was at Castle Taylor again in 1854. He accompanied the Shawe-Taylors on an excursion to Lehinch, Milltown Malbay and the Cliffs of Moher, 'that dark wall that has defied the wasting ocean beyond the reach of history or of man–bulwark of earth–champion of the land!'. His description of Moher is exhilarating.

> [We] made our way to the stables, built, as well as a tower for the accommodation of visitors, close under the best part of the Cliff. Viola still growing in the grass (not sandy). On reaching the edge, we betook ourselves to one of the little safe crows' nests built expressly, and gazed down this awful height some 700 feet. The descent is quite abrupt, and in some places the cliff overhangs the bottom; the horizontal strata so well marked in most parts as to make it look almost like a built wall. There are two detached pieces, one a long narrow ridge, and the other an isolated pyramidal needle; and there is no better way of realizing the stupendous height that to look first at one of these, and after calculating the distance to carry your eye again to the water... Scores of gulls were wheeling in clamorous indignation, while the cliffsmen were following their avocation not far from the tower, and ever and anon a little Puffin or Guillemot would shoot out and describe a circle, only to return to the cliff...[21]

More's fascination for birds obviously made him the more curious about the cliffsmen who for two months each year used nooses to capture chicks. These unfortunate squabs were boiled down to produce oil; the carcasses of forty yielded enough for one bottle, sold at two shillings as a treatment for bruises. Having lingered three hours at the Cliffs, the party left, preventing A. G. More from '...attempting a descent on the rope, to which I had just made up my mind: the danger being only apparent, not real', an opinion that his sister did not endorse.

Continuing northwards, the tourists entered The Burren passing a 'most perfect square castle' (Ballinalacken) and paused at Poll Salach where More noticed sea spleenwort, sea lavender, samphire, and 'under foot the pretty [spring sandwort] spread its lovely little stars in hundreds, and in great tufts large enough to fill my hat...' Bloody cranesbills 'seemed to smile upon us as old friends', and there too grew mountain avens, blue grass and catspaw. Some of these plants had not been reported from The Burren before, but the Mores' records were not published until many years later. Furthermore, Alexander's and his sister's major

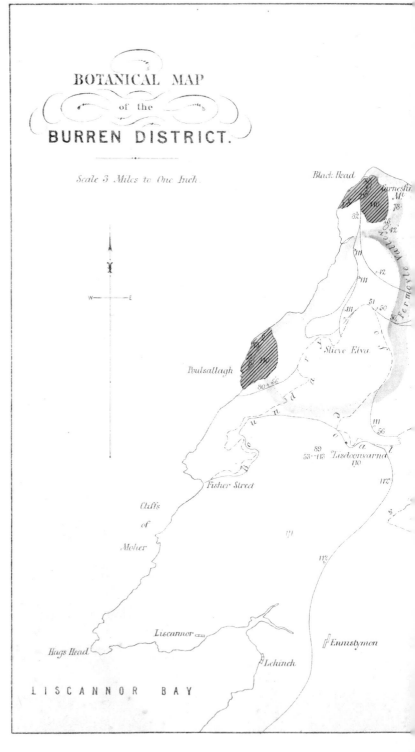

Frederick J. Foot's map showing the distribution of plants in T

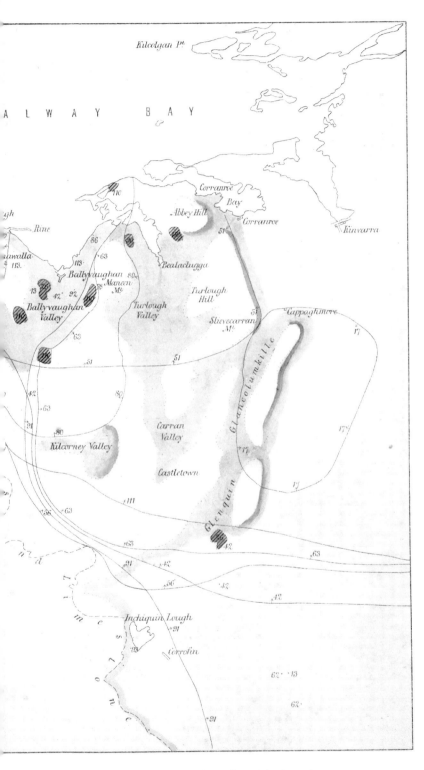

1862 (hatched areas were coloured pink on the original map).

Frederick Foot

contribution to our knowledge of the flora of the Clare-Galway limestones was another decade in the future, on another of their visits to Castle Taylor–the story of their discovery of an extraordinary orchid can be kept for a later chapter.

Undoubtedly the most important scientific visitor to The Burren during the nineteenth century was Frederick Foot, a geologist serving under Joseph Beete Jukes in the Irish Geological Survey. His father, Simon Foot J.P., M.R.I.A., of Hollybank, Rathfarnham, was a leading figure in the Royal Dublin Society and served for many years on the Committee of Botany that oversaw the running of the society's botanical garden at Glasnevin. Imbued with endless curiosity, Frederick undoubtedly relished his field-work in the early 1860s among 'the rocky tract of limestone hills…known as "Burren", or "The Burren" '–his use of *The Burren* is the probably first printed instance of this now universal sobriquet.[22]

While his principal purpose was to map rocks and geological features, Frederick Foot was most attentive to plants, and became acutely aware of the peculiar character of the vegetation of the barony, noting at the beginning of his paper 'On the distribution of plants in Burren, County of Clare', read on 28 April 1862 to the Royal Irish Academy, that many rare plants grow there in abundance, often occurring, as well as the commoner ones, in abnormal situations, that is to say, in localities quite the reverse of those usually known as their habitats...

Foot had the brilliant idea of preparing a special map showing the distributions of the 'most remarkable or characteristic plants'; this was a pioneering map–no-one had done anything like it before for any part of Ireland, and it was published by the Royal Irish Academy in 1863.

With a terrier at his heel, and accoutred with all the paraphernalia of a field-geologist, Frederick Foot walked over every hillside terrace in The Burren noting on his field maps the strike of the strata, the embedded fossils, and occasionally other geological details. He revelled in the flowers too. North of Doolin, near the coast, he found broomrape; at Kilcorney there was brittle bladder fern, and above Fanore on some cliffs he noticed wintergreen.[23] Attitudes to animals were quite different in those days–A. G. More thought nothing of shooting hawks; Frederick Foot set his terrier against the rare pine marten. This sad annotation is on one of his field maps in the townland of Deelinbeg–'Killed a Marten here January 12 1862'–and the gruesome event is related in detail elsewhere:

> This beautiful animal is now becoming rare in Burren. It was once very common, and some years ago the skin was worth 25 [shillings]. It is called by the country people Cat Krine, pronounced Cot Krine, or the cat of the woods. My dog caught one on the 14th of January [sic]; it was a female, measuring 30 inches from tip to snout; soles of the feet quite bare; throat and breast of a yellowish-white, with a brownish spot. I had great difficulty in killing it; I never saw an animal so retentive of life; it fought manfully, and bit my dog in the nose and lips.[24]

Foot worked in Clare for almost twelve months so he was privileged to observe the seasonal procession of flowers. He reported for the first time the occurrence of pyramidal bugle on the Clare coast opposite the Aran Islands at Poll Salach–it still grows there today in the exact spot that Foot marked on his field map. On the southern side of Gleninagh Mountain he discovered an isolated population of shrubby cinquefoil–it is also extant.

Frederick Foot's life came to a tragic end–he was drowned in Lough Key in County Roscommon on 17 January 1867 following a skating accident. He was survived by his wife and young family, and many years later in 1877, by coincidence, his younger brother, the Revd John Foot, became rector of the Church of Ireland parish of Kilnaboy and Kilkeedy which encompasses the northeastern part of the barony of Inchiquin on the southern fringe of The Burren.[25]

There is an uncomfortable parallel in the drowning in Lough Gill on 4 August 1883 of Thomas Corry, another promising young botanist who contributed substantially to the printed marginalia of The Burren. Corry and his companion, D. J. Calder, took a botanical ramble through County Clare in July 1879 prompted, I am sure, by Samuel Stewart who had diverted around Black Head on his way from Galway to Dingle one year earlier.[26] Stewart and Corry were already working together on *Flora of the north-east of Ireland*, and we can confidently assume that Stewart, who knew The Burren could 'afford a rich crop to the botanist', was Corry's unnamed informant–

> Vivid and glowing were the accounts that reached me of the flowers of Clare, nurtured amid the balmy breezes of the green western lands, and especially those which came from eyewitnesses of their beauty, and who described the celebrated Burren district as a spot meet to be called "the botanist's happy hunting ground"...[27]

Calder and Corry travelled from Belfast to Athenry, and thence by train to Ardrahan and Castle Taylor where Frances and Alexander More had spent their holidays. Ennis was the next stop, and then Corrofin. They stayed at Roxton, 'an old country house...covered with ivy most beautifully variegated, and in this ivy a pair of goldfinches...', situated near the south-western end of Lough Inchiquin, a handy base to explore the eastern Burren–Glenquin, Mullach Mór and Glencolumbkille and Sliabh Cairn. They saw squinancywort, madder and elecampane, and about Glenquin discovered fly orchids. On one of the hills, perhaps Mullach Mór, 'on the first great terrace', hoary rockrose and stone brambles caught their attention, and on the way down they found purging buckthorn.

> When we did arrive in safety at the base we knew not whither to turn, for an aspect of sameness prevailed, and how, or in what direction, the road lay we could not discover. I should, therefore, strongly advise anyone visiting a desolate crag country to provide himself with a good pocket compass, and to make use of it.'

They had reached Rockforest. By skirting a lough, Corry and Calder found shrubby cinquefoil, and noticed one of The Burren's botanical curiosities, the prostrate shrubs of purging and alder buckthorns.

Corry's account of his adventures is vivacious; he was only nineteen years old and it is easy to picture him striding along the rough roads and over the terraced

Thomas Corry

hills, a prototype for adventuresome teenagers of more recent decades. Time was irrelevant; the flowers and the scenery were utterly absorbing. Recalling those summer days Corry was lyrical, especially about the view from

> the new road winding up the steep hill westwards from Glancolumbekille Cottage. Beneath you lies the valley, the green fields and dark woods at this end contrasting finely with the bare rocky terraced hills of grey limestone, and far away in the background you may see the hills near Gort almost blue by reason of the distance... Never shall I forget the appearance of this valley as we saw it about three o'clock in the morning with a scarlet sun rising in the distance...

Bustling Lisdoonvarna, its five hotels thronged, was also used as a base where the ramblers enjoyed 'the beautifully clear waters of the sulphur spring through the medium of the organ of smell. but there we rested...' They walked to the Cliffs of Moher and to Poll Salach. A jarvey was engaged for the transfer to Ballyvaghan by way of Corkscrew Hill. Corry and Calder then set off on foot towards Black Head, by way of Gleninagh.

As we neared a small claghan of huts, we met two Irish girls with their long
raven hair streaming down over their shoulders, and bare feet, and, since
the day was oppressively warm, we stopped and asked them if we could
obtain some milk wherewith to quench our thirst at any of the huts. But
evidently startled as they were by our extraordinary appearance, no sooner
did they hear our mode of speech, than without stopping to answer the
question they turned sharp round and made for the huts. When we at length
arrived there also, we found every door closely locked, though we could
plainly discern the inhabitants thereof within, who eyed us with stealthy
and furtive glances of inquiry through the windows, evidently questioning
whether we were beings like themselves (though of this point they seemed
to have strong misgivings), or whether, as seemed to them far more likely,
no doubt, we were emissaries from the spirit of evil sent forth to wander
to and fro upon the earth; certainly the colour of our complexions and the
implements of geology which we carried, might have suggested such to them.

There were plenty of plants to admire too. Club moss and gentians in fruit, meadow
rue, Spring sandwort and saxifrages. And they 'made the acquaintance of some
fine specimens of the goat, known technically here as "the Burren deer."' Corry
noted crowberry near the summit of Black Head, and they trudged on to
Murrough, before returning to Ballyvaghan 'upon an open donkey cart driven
by a native, and enjoyed a most disagreeable shaking.'

Thomas Corry's delivered an account of his 'botanical ramble' in County
Clare to a meeting of the Belfast Natural History and Philosophical Society on
20 January 1880, and according to a footnote the paper was illustrated by
photographs of the scenery in the district, and by specimens of the plants
described. The photographs–we do not know to whom the camera belonged but
I suspect it was Calder's–were probably the some of the earliest taken in The Burren
but they do not seem to have survived. Robert Welch, the Belfast photographer,
whose famous black-and-white Burren landscapes and flowers–mountain avens,
Spring gentian and dense-flowered orchids–were published in several of the
books written by Robert Lloyd Praeger, visited the area in 1895 and 1907.

The Burren remained relatively inaccessible through the late nineteenth and early
twentieth centuries although it was less of an 'unbeaten track'. Undoubtedly one
reason for its isolation was the dearth of direct public transport, especially a railway
which had otherwise made travel to almost all the extremities of Ireland an easy
matter; Frederick Foot had called the area between Ennis and Galway Bay 'this *terra
incognita...*' and remarked on its isolation. In southern Clare the famous West Clare

Railway, inspiration for the ballad 'Are you right there, Michael, are you right?', and the South Clare Railway linked Kilrush, on the Shannon estuary, and Kilkee, on the Atlantic coast, with Milltown Malbay, Lehinch, Corrofin and Ennis, but it did not greatly facilitate travel in north Clare, in The Burren.[28] To be sure the railway helped to encourage more tourists to take the waters at Lisdoonvarna which became even more popular, and the Cliffs of Moher being but a short drive by side-car or jaunting-car from Lehinch developed into a major destination. Ferries steamed from Galway across to Newquay and Ballyvaghan bringing visitors to the northern parts.[29] But, trekking along dusty gravel roads into the limestone hills, even for the joy of Spring gentians, was not to most people's liking.

Towards the latter part of the nineteenth century, the character of the Irish botanical fraternity changed; somehow they assumed a more rugged, intrepid demeanour, and were not easily deterred any more; especially not by rough roads. This was the hey-day in Ireland of field naturalists clubs, when botanists, zoologists and geologists hunted the countryside in co-operative packs, on foot, seeking new county or regional records. The fact that it was also the hey-day of Irish railways aided their excursions because the trains brought them quickly and cheaply (even 'in style') to remote termini in the farthest reaches of the island; from a conveniently sited railway hotel the bands of naturalists roamed far and wide by brakes, jaunting cars, steamers, and shanks's mares. For the botanical members of this freemasonry, the mere chance of adding a new species to their herbaria was usually an adequate excuse for a field trip to some remote region.

To the reformed, pedestrian botanist with a vasculum, to this fraternity of field clubs, The Burren was ineluctably attractive, and a number of significant visitors ventured there in the 1890s. Henry Corbyn Levinge of Knockdrin near Mullingar made trips in 1891 and 1892, on both collecting vast numbers of specimens which he distributed liberally to fellow enthusiasts. Levinge was particularly friendly with the native plantsman Patrick Kelly (*alias* P. B. O'Kelly) of Ballyvaghan–a fascinating character who deserves an entire chapter to himself. Kelly's local knowledge meant he was an essential guide, and botanists venturing into Ballyvaghan and Lisdoonvarna usually met him.

In the summer of 1895 the Irish Field Club Union convened its second annual conference and excursion in Galway; this was the joint assembly of the Limerick, Dublin, Belfast and Cork Naturalists Field Clubs. The report, delightfully scripted by the Union's honorary secretary, Robert Lloyd Praeger, described the outing as if the whole affair was a military campaign: it *was*.[30] 'The members of the Belfast

Club were the first take the field…' On Thursday 11 July 1895, 'Punctually at 9 o'clock the First Class Special Train provided by the Midland Great Western Railway Company steamed out of Broadstone Station…and a very rapid journey across the Great Central Plain of Ireland was pleasantly spent in studying maps and scientific papers…' Friday dawned gloriously fine; Connemara was explored. On Saturday the honorary secretary summoned members to breakfast with a shrill whistle, and afterwards the wayfarers took to the sea:

> A morning of driving mist found the naturalists embarked on board the ss. "Duras" at 9 o'clock, which in no way lightened as the steamer passed down the river and set her course for Ballyvaughan, on the southern side of Galway Bay. However, the cheerful predictions of the conductors were duly fulfilled, for as the destination was approached the clouds broke and the sun shone out, lighting up gloriously the strange bare slopes of the Burren mountains and the great masses of vapour that still hung over the higher summits. Advantage was taken of the leisure of the passage to hold a meeting of the collectors of the party, when the work of identifying the various captures was distributed among the different naturalists, one man being responsible for the report on each group…
>
> On landing at Ballyvaughan, the party were joined by Mr. P. B. O'Kelly, a Ballyvaughan botanist, whose local knowledge was freely placed at the disposal of members, and proved of much service. Gleninagh, on the sea, three miles north-west of Ballyvaughan was the rendezvous, and the party slowly made their way along the road in this direction, with the sea on the right, and the great limestone hills rising steeply on the left. This was the field-day of the botanists, for the flora of the Burren is most peculiar as well as rich. The Maidenhair was found ere Ballyvaughan was a mile behind. On the low grounds Mr O'Kelly pointed out the Bee Orchis and the extremely rare Close-flowered Orchis, now in fruit, for which for many years Castle Taylor in County Galway was the only known British station. On the limestone hills above was found abundance of the Mountain Dryas, Bear-berry, Purple Helleborine, Bloody Cranesbill, Spring Gentian, and other rare plants. Lunch was served at 2 o'clock under the shadow of the old castle of Gleninagh. after which scientific occupations–shore-collecting, botanizing, insect-hunting, and geologizing–were energetically resumed. Some of the party drove to Black Head, where the Maidenhair was found in abundance, as well as other rarities. Mr. O'Kelly conducted one or two of the party to the home of the Shrubby Cinquefoil, which grows in much abundance not far from Ballyvaughan. Others, who ascended to the flat summit of Cappanawalla (1023 feet) brought back strange accounts of the vast stretches of bare grey limestone which extend on the higher grounds.

Robert Lloyd Praeger

At 5.30 the steamer's whistle warned stragglers to linger no longer, and when at length the last late-comer was on board, the return journey was made without loss of time. After dinner, the tables were again devoted to an exhibition of the day's spoil... It was found that a beetle, *Miaris campanulae*, new to the Irish list, and the local moths, *Anticlea cucullata* and *Phothedes captiuncula*, as well as the striking black spider, *Prosthesima Petiverii*, had rewarded the labours of the insect-hunters on this day.

Miss Matilda Knowles and Praeger both gathered 'Close-flowered Orchis', and their specimens, carefully pressed and labelled, now are in the Ulster Museum, Belfast, and the National Botanic Gardens, Dublin, testimony to the visit during which, '...at Ballyvaughan and Gleninagh, the peculiar Burren flora was seen to full advantage' although the plant-hunters had found nothing so novel as the striking black spider.

Praeger, thirty years old in 1895, was not yet famous as an author nor yet was he doyen of Irish naturalists. To be sure, he had already written over eighty articles mainly on botanical topics, and I commend the engaging account of this particular excursion, but his widely-read books were all published during the first half of the present century. I must now point to another enigma of The Burren–Praeger ignored the region, or at least during the rest of his long life he was not to pay particular attention to The Burren. He wrote nearly eight hundred publications but only one was concerned solely with the area–Praeger was much more inquisitive about Connemara, Clare Island and the Aran Islands. In that solitary paper, on the flora of turloughs, read before the Royal Irish Academy on 27 June 1932, he explored one of the characteristic habitats of the limestone region; his 'preliminary account' of zonation around three turloughs in the lowlands to the north and west of Gort was not followed by a definitive study of the plant ecology of these ephemeral loughs. From the localities on his herbarium specimens we know Praeger made collecting trips in July 1895–he returned after the Field Club Union conference ended to gather shrubby cinquefoil at Ballyvaghan–July 1905, and during May and June 1907; he did not return again until May 1932 to study turloughs, and made a final collecting trip in June 1936.[31]

Although the region is of outstanding interest to plant geographers–and he is numbered among that company–Dr Lloyd Praeger passes over The Burren in *The way that I went* with almost casual brevity, as if it was so well-known he need not bother to mention the place. There is a lucid entry in *A tourist's flora of the west of Ireland* (repeated with minor alterations in the better known *The botanist in Ireland*) illustrated with Robert Welch's photographs some of which were taken during the Field Club Union excursion, yet Praeger was not rhapsodic, nor did he critically eschew the famous jeremiad:

> Burren is, indeed, the dry skeleton of a country and deserves the description said to have been given to it by one of Cromwell's officers, who, returning from a reconnoitring expedition reported that it was a savage place…[32]

For all that, Praeger was willing to admit that The Burren was a landscape of contradictions: 'though frost is here unknown, plants characteristic of the high Alps grow in great profusion…and mixed with them are others…whose home is on the sunny shores of the Mediterranean.' The display of flowers in May and June–'thousands of acres with the gay blossoms of the Dryas, Spring Gentian, Mossy Saxifrages, Bloody Cranesbill and so on…'[33]–was, he agreed, a remarkable sight but nowhere does he explain his own seeming lack of enthusiasm for 'these gaunt grey limestone hills.' The silence is confounding.

In overview, botanical studies in The Burren before the late 1950s were conducted in a desultory way by dilettantes and tourists, those 'doubled-up figures that stoop over every cranny, scramble up the hills, or crawl on all fours over the terraces', whose eyes only brightened when they spied a gentian or maidenhair fern but who rarely took more than a casual interest in other species. That is not to decry their work. Only Frederick Foot's studies in the early 1860s were systematic. By 1950, three hundred years after Dr William How had signalled the richness of the flora, no-one but Foot had written a scientific treatise encompassing all plants within the karst area. No-one had compiled an exacting modern flora, yet The Burren had been 'famous far outside Ireland' for at least one century. 'It is curious how little has been written on the flora…', mused Professor David Webb in 'Noteworthy plants of The Burren: a catalogue raisonné', published by the Royal Irish Academy in June 1962.

Disturbed by the lack of a definitive account of The Burren's flora and the want of adequate studies of the ecology of its plants, Dr Webb persuaded the British Ecological Society to establish a Burren Survey project to conduct ecological research; the decision was announced at the Society's annual general meeting in January 1958.[34] While it was hard to persuade a substantial squadron of botanists and zoologists–the British Ecological Society enfolds both–to undertake co-ordinated work, many individuals did participate, and the most important outcome of this initiative was a classic paper, published in the *Proceedings of the Royal Irish Academy*, detailing the vegetation studies of Dr Robert Ivimey-Cook and Dr Michael Proctor from the University of Exeter. Ivimey-Cook and Proctor spent two months during the summer of 1959, painstakingly recording the species present in several hundred quadrats–randomly sited, 2 x 2 metre squares. They collected and analysed soil samples from some of the quadrats and, employing modern statistical methods, used these data to attempt an interpretation of patterns in the distribution of plants. They were particularly interested in how the individual plant species associated with one another to form distinct communities–some never grow side by side, others frequently are companions, so that a community can be defined by the presence of certain 'key' plants. Ivimey-Cook and Proctor's paper is a masterly record of the scientific investigation of vegetation patterns in one small part of western Europe.

During their work, and that by other amateur and professional botanists for the Botanical Society of the British Isles' *Atlas of the British flora* initiated separately in 1953, new information was accumulated on the occurrence of ferns and flowering plants in The Burren. Webb's catalogue raisonné of 1962 summarised this, bringing up to date Frederick Foot's paper of a century before. But there was still no flora of the area. In 1963 the Irish Regional Committee of the Botanical Society of the British Isles decided, following a suggestion by David Webb, to concentrate on the production of such a book, combining The Burren with Connemara. For almost twenty years, botanists laboured in the field accumulating records for the flora which was compiled and edited by Professor Webb and Miss Maura Scannell, and published in 1983. Like the monograph by Drs Ivimey-Cook and Proctor, Webb and Scannell's *Flora of Connemara and The Burren* is essential for serious students; it is a scientific catalogue of the higher plants with adjunct chapters on the mosses and liverworts, lichens, algae and fungi.

Thirty years ago, David Webb wrote that in The Burren '…botanical visitors keep to the well-worn track, admire, photograph and collect the same plants from the same stations year after year…'[34] I venture to suggest that that is still true, in part, and therefore comforting. The spectacular, alluring wild plants have survived in well-trodden places despite the attentions of innumerable visitors over many years: The Burren and its flora are resilient. That visitors do not often venture far from the beaten tracks is also reassuring; the pressure from tourists on the wilder areas has heretofore remained small. On the other hand, there is still a lot to be discovered about the flora of this 'savage place', and there can be no doubt that The Burren has changed greatly since that first botanical visitor, the Yorkshire man who was rector of Iniscattery. Farming practices have altered and are changing the ancient landscape. Tourists are more numerous than ever before. Plants have disappeared. Unique plant communities have been damaged and some have been extirpated.

The Burren remains a contrary land—there is no chance of seeing *Alpes Felwort of the Spring time* nowadays in the silage fields that border the highway between Gort and Galway, and no point in following Dr Caleb Threlkeld's suggestion that 'such as go to that Place may inquire for it'.[35] Yet you may still chance on a creeping juniper at Kilmacduagh, maidenhair ferns at Black Head, and Welsh poppies where the cartographer marked them.

Kilmacduagh: cathedral ruins and round tower

STRANGE, EFFECTED PAVEMENTS

…between us and Black Head lay the mysterious brooding moonscape country of *the Burren*, that great region of grey, sinister naked limestone where even the rivers shun the light of day to flow in a dark underworld and where Slieve Elva raises its unearthly head above crowding terraces of frightening desolation to dominate a terrain the like of which is not to be seen anywhere else in these islands.

Richard Hayward: *Munster and the city of Cork.*

William Butler Yeats' grey, much-trodden pavements were those of cities and towns, artefacts that are deserts for plants, noisy flagstones that have no soul. The Burren has natural pavements of pure limestone, more extensive, wonderfully fecund pavements, worn down by water, ice and wind, not by the soles of shoes, pavements splashed with the blue and green, purple, white and gold of flowers, ferns and lichens, musical pavements of flags that 'emit a metallic sound when struck with a hammer', even pavements of fragments 'so nicely balanced, as to quiver in the breeze with a tinkling noise, which, in very retired situations, has a strange effect.'[1]

Yeats was a frequent visitor to the home of Lady Gregory at Coole Park, a short ride north of Gort, and later he bought, for thirty-five pounds, a mediaeval tower-house at Ballylee. At Coole he was able to recover from illness, and Thoor Ballylee

45

was his summer home for a dozen years. From Coole Park and Thoor Ballylee, and more especially from Vernon Lodge at Newquay, which was the Gregorys' summer house, Yeats surely explored the natural pavements of The Burren. That he found inspiration in this place is obvious from his writing, the woods of Coole Park and the nine-and-fifty wild swans on the turlough behind it, and, as already mentioned, the setting of 'The dreaming of the bones' at Corcomroe Abbey.

The pavements of Burren vary from naturally level platforms partitioned into slabs by small cracks and fathomless crevices–the scailps–which may run perfectly parallel or crisscross like lines marking out irregular squares on a bizarre chessboard, to terrain that resembles a badly made road strewn with gravel and stones of all sizes[2]–the latter type is termed 'shattered pavement'. In between there are many variations. In places the limestone is water-worn into forms that look organic, reminiscent of the skeletal back-bone of a slumbering whale. Elsewhere are terraced rock-gardens, stepped more elegantly than anything gardeners have achieved and impossible to emulate.

Scailp deserves further explanation–I prefer this Irish word which is used locally for the crevices in the pavement–grike (or gryke) is the vernacular English term for the same feature.[3] In an Irish landscape *scailp* is more appropriate than grike for these natural fissures, and it is more familiar than may appear at first sight. A steep-sided defile in the Wicklow Mountains through which the road between Dublin and Enniskerry passes is named The Scalp–that is one anglicized version of *scailp* which means a cleft, a fissure or a chasm (it has no connection with the crown of the head).[4] In The Burren there is one remarkable place called Scailp na Seisrí, a small yet impressive chasm on the eastern flank on Moneen Mountain, northwest of Turlough. Here again the term is used for a specific natural feature, about which Frederick Foot recorded that 'some of the peasantry have a tradition that it is artificial, and that from it the stones were quarried to build Corcomroe Abbey…'[5]

Solid rock does not provide any habitat for flowering plants and ferns. Only between the stones and in scailps is there space for soil to develop and plants to grow. Where soil does accumulate, even in minute quantities as in cracks or in the solution cups, communities of higher plants will become established. Mosses, lichens and many microscopic plants including fungi and algae, will thrive on the living surface of the limestone but for the present they must be overlooked.

Drs Robert Ivimey-Cook and Michael Proctor of the Department of Botany, University of Exeter, described a series of broadly defined plant associations. These abstract associations, given extraordinary pseudo-Latin names, fit into an artificial hierarchy of plant communities enumerated by botanists working in continental Europe. Each one is characterized by the species it constantly contains–the principal assumptions underlining the hierarchy are that plants with similar ecological tolerance will grow together frequently, and that throughout its range each species behaves in an entirely predictable manner. By creating an artificial hierarchy based on species' constancy, some botanists argue that each plant community within the same floristic region–in this case western Europe–can be pigeon-holed into a precisely defined nodum (a series of 'related' vegetable associations). The Burren would seem to be one of the least suitable places to test those hypotheses.

Be that as it may–I personally treat this artificial system of abstractions and its burden of names with reservation–Ivimey-Cook and Proctor sorted thousands of plant records and circumscribed twenty vegetation 'classes' occurring in The Burren. One of these (Festuco-Brometea) encompasses the grassland communities developed on calcium-rich, well-drained soils and includes an association characterised by lady's bedstraw and squinancywort (*Galium verum–Asperula cynanchica* Nodum; Campothecio-Asperuletum cynanchicae) which develops on stable sand dunes. Ivimey-Cook and Proctor noted particularly that the squinancywort–lady's bedstraw community covered a large proportion of the dunes at Fanore and that it was heavily grazed. But *Asperula cynanchica* is not confined to this one association that includes its name; squinancywort also is a constant plant in Ivimey-Cook's and Proctor's *Dryas octopetala–Hypericum pulchrum* Nodum (the same community was named Asperuleti-Dryadetum by Braun-Blanquet and Tuxen, but subsequently others changed its name to Asperuleti-Seslerietum!) which is the most extensive grassland community even cloaking, in a degraded and extraordinarily depauperate form, the summits of the hills where scattered plants of mountain avens and squinancywort, with perhaps some red helleborine, are almost the only signs of vegetable life.

Squinancywort (*lus na haincise*), a herb with a somewhat woody root-stock, is one of The Burren's most characteristic plants, as quintessential as mountain avens and Spring gentian, but being smaller, with unspectacular flowers and none of the frigid, alpestral romanticism of those others, it tends to be forgotten. The leafy shoots usually are more or less prostrate, and the leaves are evenly spaced in whorls of four and within each whorl are unequal in length ranging from about half a centimetre long to over two centimetres; the lower leaves are broad, while those on the upper part of the stems are linear with a distinctly pointed tip. The

Asperula cynanchica: squinancywort

small flowers are clustered towards the stem tips; each one is tubular and the four petal lobes spread horizontally. They open white or pale pink depending on the weather, and are delightfully scented, like vanilla.

Asperula cynanchica belongs to the family Rubiaceae which also includes *Galium* (woodruffs, lady's bedstraws and weeds such as robin-run-the-hedge (or goose-grass or cleavers, *G. aparine*)) and *Rubia* (madder). Its English name comes from quinsy, a sore throat–squinancywort made into a gargle was said to cure that complaint.

James Mackay when he was about Corrofin in August 1806 was the first to report *Asperula cynanchica* as a denizen of The Burren–'Very abundant among the lime-stone rocks near Corrofin, and in other parts of the county of Clare'.[6] Frederick Foot affirmed that it 'spreads freely all over Burren, from the sea-shore to the tops of the hills'.[7] It is certainly common, sometimes wedged firmly into the tiniest cracks on tops of boulders, sometimes hidden among the herbs of the grassy places. Yet squinancywort is at its finest when the pale pink flowers glow against the smooth, grey flags of the pavement.

Madder (*garbhlus na Boirne*) looks like vigorous goose-grass, glossier, often with rich red and bronze tints especially on the young shoot-tips, and with the same armament of minuscule hooks on the margins of its leaves. Shoots of madder

Rubia peregrina: madder

will cling to clothes but not as tenaciously as those of its weedy cousin, goose-grass, which also has sticky fruits bristling with hooks; they adhere to trouser-legs or become entangled in the fur of mammals, and thus are dispersed by hooking a ride on passing beasts. In contrast, madder has juicy black fruits, without hooks, and relies on birds and small animals to eat the fruits and then distribute the seeds in their droppings. There are other differences between madder and robin-run-the-hedge. The flowers of *Rubia peregrina* have five yellow-green petals, arranged starwise, and five short stamens; in *Galium aparine* flowers there are only four petals.

On the pavements, especially along the coastal fringe of The Burren, madder is more abundant that anywhere else in Ireland; the Irish name *garbhlus na Boirne*, rough herb of Burren, reflects this. Frederick Foot alluded, with slight exaggeration, to its abundance in Clare

> The most ordinary observer cannot fail being struck with the abundance
> of the Dyer's madder in Burren, every available place being occupied by it.[8]

Shoots peep above the bed-rock from the base of scailps—and when the next gale blows they will probably be broken and bruised. Madder's weak stems are more lush when growing through blackthorn and hawthorn shrubs for the woody branches provide scramble-holds and break the force of the wind. There is an abundance of it at Muckinish, on the eastern side of the bay, and at Murrough, yet madder is scattered everywhere, a plant that is seen unexpectedly when you are looking for something else.

For ages, *Rubia tinctoria*, a species similar to the native Burren plant, has an important source of a red dye, and in the seventeenth and eighteenth centuries efforts were made to cultivate it in Ireland but without any lasting success. Benjamin Worsley, an English physician serving with Cromwell's army in Dublin, reported during May 1654 that

> Hearing upon Inquiry that there was Madder grown in this country wilde of itselfe and that the Rootes were very faire and good…i imployed poore people abroad to gather what they could find of it and have got a small Nursery of the roots in my Garden.[9]

By late June, Worsley had planted and weeded his madder crop, that being '…all that is required until it comes to be gathered and mill'd.' If he actually did grow madder from Irish localities, he should have been cultivating *Rubia peregrina*. Dr John Rutty recorded that in the first part of the 1700s, over three thousand pounds was spent per year importing madder to Ireland for dyeing cloth. The Dublin Society encouraged its propagation by premiums.[10]

Wild madder will serve as a substitute for dyer's madder (*R. tinctoria*) but removing it from the scailps cannot be condoned. The roots, boiled with alum, dye linen, cotton and wool 'a sad and durable red'.[10]

As ubiquitous as squinancywort, and in some ways also as 'invisible' because it is everywhere, is *Teucrium scorodonia* (wood sage: *iúr sléibhe*)). To confound those botanists who love phytosociology, wood sage, throughout its range in Europe, grows in two entirely different habitats, in woodland dominated by oaks, birches and holly, and in open sites on well-drained soils alongside bloody cranesbill and burnet rose. Oak woodland is absent from The Burren, but suitable, open sites abound, especially on the shattered pavement.

Wood sage is a perennial herb: its Irish vernacular name perhaps alludes to this, *iúr sléibhe*, fresh-greens of the hills. The leafy shoots do not disappear entirely in winter; as tight, green rosettes they are conspicuous in sheltered scailps and among the stones of the shattered pavements throughout the short, cold months. The wrinkle-surfaced leaves, which incidentally do not have the aroma of sage, are arranged in opposite pairs along the square stem–this is a member of the dead-nettle family, Lamiaceae (Labiatae), that is characterized by four-angled stems. At the tips of the stems are orchid-like spikes of flowers, each blossom with a prominent creamy-green lower lip that acts as a landing platform for insects. There are two pairs of stamens with dark red filaments of different lengths so that two anthers are held close below the upper lip of the corolla and two project beyond it. When the flower is newly opened the style is behind the stamens and out of reach of visiting insects.

Bumble-bees pollinate wood sage. The anthers are mature and capable of shedding pollen as soon as the individual bloom opens. Pollen grains are dusted on to the head or thorax of a visiting bee. Once the pollen is shed, the style slowly bends downwards below the empty anthers so that the stigma is positioned to receive pollen from any pollen-laden bee that subsequently visits the flower. This arrangement ensures that cross-pollination takes place.[11]

Wood sage was sold by the herb-women of Dublin in the early eighteenth century and evidently was prized for its efficacy in 'preventing Mortifications and Gangrenes', as a diuretic and as a cure for gout, rheumatism and scurvy.

Water germander (*Teucrium scordium*) is recorded from the margins of a few of the loughs in the eastern sector of The Burren where it was discovered by Patrick O'Kelly in 1892; it is a rare plant both in Ireland and Britain, confined to the Shannon valley, and the fens of East Anglia, and is a protected species.[12]

Like wood sage, the burnet rose grows profusely on the shattered pavement. It is conspicuous in early summer when the clumps of thorny shoots are bedecked with sunlit cream-white or blush-cream five-petalled flowers. Burnet rose is also conspicuous in autumn when its neat, ferny leaves turn the richest plum-purple; mixed with the creamy-gold foliage of blackthorn, blue-black sloes, and scarlet haws from the hawthorn, these dark leaves form one of the most remarkable colour patterns of The Burren. The solstice sunlight enriches the colours—the dying leaves glow rich burgundy against the ashen rocks.

Rosa pimpinellifolia has upright, woody stems armed with rapier-straight thorns. As this rose produces underground 'suckers', thickets of shoots congregate along the scailps and around larger slabs. In exposed sites the stems are rarely more than half a metre tall, but in hedges and among other shrubs, some shoots will grow much longer. The winter buds are ruby-red. In spring these burst to unfurl leaves like those of the salad burnet (*Sanguisorba minor*) which also inhabits the pavements of Clare. The individual leaflets are round or oval with finely serrated margins and they are evenly disposed along a central rhachis. *Rosa pimpinellifolia* usually begin to blossom in late May, although a mild spring might cause a few

Teucrium scorodonia
wood sage

52

Rosa pimpinellifolia: burnet rose

blooms to appear earlier. The main flowering is in June and July with a scattering of waifs into August and perhaps September. Five heart-shaped petals, and a coronet of many golden stamens encircle the cluster of styles. The petals vary from pure white to rich pink (this latter can be called *Rosa pimpinellifolia* f. *rosea*[13])–on the slopes of Moneen Mountain I have seen burnet roses with white petals streaked with pink yet the common state is milky cream.

Unlike all other native roses, the burnet rose or, in Irish, *briúlán* has squat, black heps crowned with the crisped and withered sepals. Inside are numerous seeds encased in their protective fur of hairs which as schoolboys we delighted in using as a particularly irksome itching-powder. In bygone days rose hips were widely made into syrups and conserves, taken 'to strengthen the Stomach, cool the Heat of *Fevers*, good for Coughs, spitting of Blood, and *Scurvy*.' They are a rich source of Vitamin C, a deficiency of which we now know causes scurvy. Dr Threlkeld advised that the hips of the burnet rose were 'of the Vertues of the other *Wild Roses*.'[14]

There are other roses in The Burren. The pure white-flowered *Rosa arvensis* is native in the eastern lowlands especially in and about Garryland west of Gort–it is not recorded from the high Burren. Dog rose, *Rosa canina*, is common

53

throughout, while the pink-blossomed *Rosa sherardii* which has resin-scented blue-green leaves grows around Carron and Lough George. But roses are difficult plants to name and it is possible that more detailed work may indicate the presence of other species. One especially beautiful plant that I know, with deep pink flowers, grows beside the road leading in to Glencolumbkille from the New Line. It is certainly not a garden escapee, but whether it is *Rosa sherardii* or another species, I have not yet been able to decide.

Rosaceae, the rose family, is represented in Ireland by trees, shrubs and herbs: later I will mention hawthorn, rowan and whitebeam as examples of native trees; tormentil, salad burnet and mountain avens are a few of the herbs; among the shrubby genera are *Rosa* and *Rubus,* the roses and the brambles respectively. The invasive, weedy blackberry briars are not the sole representatives of *Rubus* in Ireland–the wild raspberry is a member of the genus too, as is the elegant, and only slightly thorny stone bramble, one of the characteristic plants of Burren scailps.

Richard Heaton knew stone bramble because he noticed some in a wood at Edenderry, County Offaly, but he did not, as far as we know, record it from the limestones of Clare. Professor Wade, of Glasnevin Botanic Gardens, was aware stone bramble inhabited The Burren, reporting that 'The commons of Killinboy, barony of Burren, afford it in great profusion'[15]–two townlands, one to the north and the other to the east of Kilnaboy village, still bear the name 'Commons'. As Wade most probably never set foot in The Burren, I imagine that a fellow member of the Dublin Society, Bindon Blood, D.L., J.P., *alias* 'The Vampire', who lived at Rockforest House, north-east of Kilnaboy, told him about this plant.[16]

Stone bramble roots run deep into the soil of the scailps. The shoots are neither woody nor perennial as in some brambles, but are annual; wandering, wispy stolons with rather weak prickles grow in spring from the rootstock. Leaves sprout at the nodes; each leaf has three leaflets with wedge-like bases and is irregularly toothed, and the central one is the largest. The leaf-stalk will bear small prickles like the stolons. Stone bramble blooms in June and July but the flowers are not particularly brilliant; each one–true to the family pattern–has five white-green petals about the same length as the five sepals. The flowering shoots are somewhat stouter and more erect than the stolons, and usually bear a cluster of three or more flowers.

Translucent scarlet fruits develop in late summer; they 'shine like cabochon garnets'.[17] Consider a raspberry or a blackberry: each seems to be composed of many juicy sacs, each containing a single seed. In fact each sac is an entire fruit (a drupe) so the blackberry or raspberry is a compound fruit composed of an aggregation of drupes. The stone bramble's berry is like a raspberry; instead of a large number of small, juicy drupes, *Rubus saxatilis* only has two to six large drupes that are separate—they don't coalesce into a cup-like raspberry. No matter, the juicy berries are nice to eat and the birds usually get there first! Even to a geologist, clambering over the 'parched-up crags' of The Burren, the stone bramble's 'pretty berries, though without much flavour, are very acceptable in hot weather…'[18]

Rubus saxatilis is found in many other counties in Ireland and in a variety of habitats including woods, but nowhere does it forms so prominent a part of the native vegetation as in The Burren. All areas of pavement yield the tell-tale stolons and trefoil leaves of this species which ranges from Greenland and Iceland into northern Russia, southwards to the Pyrenees and eastwards into the Caucasus, the Himalayas and onwards to Japan.

The Revd Richard Heaton provided an opaque footnote for this plant. In *Phytologia Britannica*, William How quoted Heaton as learning that the Irish name was 'Soon-a-man-meene: In English the Juyce of a faire Woman.' In modern Irish this can be rendered *sú na mban min*[19]—literally, juice of the courteous woman. Dr Threlkeld was informed that it signified '*Juice for a fair Woman*' and explained that 'No vegetable exceeds this in curing the *Scurvy*, either eaten Raw, or in an Electuary prepared of them: Whence it took its *Irish* Name among the Bells.'[20]

There are fine brambles of other species throughout The Burren and a choice crop of blackberries in season. Indeed one of the great pleasures of a Burren autumn is the harvest of hedgerow fruits—blackberries, rose heps, sloes, and juniper berries—and more of that anon.

My usual 'hunting ground' for ripe juniper is on the rocks by the Garryland turlough, on both sides of the causeway that carries the road from Gort towards Kinvarra. Thereabouts, a short distance from Kilmacduagh, is a fine population covering many hectares; some of the shrubs tumble over the rocks, while many have shoots that arch in elegant sprays. Such diverse habits, enhanced by a variety of foliage shades, indicate that this community is vigorously reproducing from seeds—if the plants were only being perpetuated by vegetative means there would be more uniformity.

Professor Webb and Miss Scannell suggested that all the junipers in The Burren belong to one subspecies, *Juniperus communis* subsp. *communis*, but I think

Rubus saxatilis: stone bramble

that is too sweeping a generalization. The taxonomy of the variants of common juniper is not simple, and our wish to see every organism assigned to a precise 'pigeon-hole' obscures patterns of variation that are more complicated than they appear at first sight. I have propagated prostrate junipers from cuttings obtained at random in several localities in The Burren and grown the plants for over ten years in my garden. Some of these gardened shrubs were vigorous and bushy with arching shoots, but others remained prostrate with stems that were never going to rise from the rock surface. The latter could be assigned to a separate subspecies, now correctly named *Juniperus communis* subsp. *alpina*. But it would be equally acceptable to assign then to *Juniperus communis* var. *hornibrookii*, a juniper described by Murray Hornibrook from a prostate, mat-forming juniper he collected in western Ireland. Thus the Clare populations are not easily 'pigeon-holed', and it is especially important to remember that plants which are prostrate in the wild may not retain that habit in cultivation demonstrating that, in some cases, the beautiful earth-hugging mat is an artefact of wind, hares and goats.

The junipers of Garryland are interesting for an historical reason; could it be that they are successors of those admired by Richard Heaton–William How reported his record thus: 'Iuniperus repens. *Creeping Iuniper*: Upon the Rocks neer *Kilmadough. Mr. Heaton*'.[21] Juniper (*aiteal*) is not a flowering plant. In common parlance it is often called a 'conifer'; more pedantically it is a gymnosperm, a member of Cupressaceae, the family of cypress (*Cupressus*) and arbor-vitae (*Thuja*). While some members of Cupressaceae bear woody cones (female strobili)–and may adequately be described as conifers–species of *Juniperus* have fleshy or leathery, not woody, strobili containing one or more seeds. The ripe 'berry' of *Juniperus communis* is composed of three or more scales that remain quite moist and oily instead of developing into separate woody scales. I harvest them to use in cooking, and they have long been used to give the flavour to Hollands Geneva (gin).

In The Burren juniper shrubs can be three metres tall, although many plants, especially on the most exposed pavement, are entirely recumbent, pruned to rock-level by nibbling animals and by winter gales. The leaves are awl-shaped, sharply pointed, with a bright grey-white band on the upper side yet rich green below; they are borne in whorls of three on grooved shoots which are triangular in cross-section. Juniper shrubs are either male or female. Male junipers produce tiny catkin-like strobili that consist of stamens attached to a central stalk; these last only as long as they take to mature and shed pollen into the wind. Female shrubs bear strobili that once fertilized by wind-blown pollen grains swell slowly to about the size of a pea and change colour from dull green through pale grey-green to stupendous blue-black bloomed with silver.

The plants from the pavement that I have described so far are all perennials. Juniper shrubs undoubtedly survive for many decades, if not centuries, especially when they are rooted tightly between rocks. Individual stone brambles and burnet roses are unlikely to survive for such long periods, yet because they can propagate vegetatively by stolons and suckers the separate plants in any area may be offspring from a single, now-vanished parent; a lineage can be endlessly perpetuated and is potentially eternal. Some denizens of The Burren pavements seem to be perennials–at least they are always obvious–but many of these are annual or biennial herbs.

There is not a day in the year when the carline thistle, *Carlina vulgaris*, disappears from sight on the pavement. It seems almost as permanent as the limestone. In the middle of winter the silver carapaces of bygone thistles stand erect and proud, defying obliteration; they will not melt softly away to yield humus for a new generation, and if you try to pluck them their vengeance is painfully

Juniperus communis: juniper

sharp. All around these relicts are young plants, green starfish among the rocks and short turf. In the summer from the centre of their cobwebby, spine-encrusted rosettes rises the flowering stem bearing a group of two or more buds that look like silver and green sea-urchins and are just as vicious as the winter skeletons or the ocean creatures they resemble. The spiny buds open in June, unfolding into a golden sunburst, rays formed by parallel-sided bracts, their inner surfaces shining, a bright yet pale straw-gold. The disc in the centre of this shimmering circlet is formed by countless minute florets–before they open these are yellow-green, but when they bloom their tiny throats are purple, darkening with age. The florets around the rim open first, and eventually the whole disc is deep purple. By September the thistle head has changed into a fluffy, fawn dome burnished with darker brown, just like a fine, old-fashioned teddy-bear. The fluff replacing the florets is composed of feather-like bristles, joined in threes at their bases, that are attached to the tops of the fruits; the bristles form a pappus that will assist the fruit (each one containing a solitary seed) to float in the breeze.

Carline thistles (*feochadán mín,* fine thistle) may be visible all the year round, but each individual thistle has a precise life-span. The seeds germinate in the spring and through the first summer a rosette with a strong tap root develops. This is

Carlina vulgaris
carline thistle

59

the stage that will survive through the winter. In the late spring when the central stem begins to grow, the rosette leaves wither, but there are other leaves on the rising stem which serve the plant through the second summer. After the flowers have faded and the seeds have formed, the whole thistle dies, its life cycle almost completed. The fruits on their feathery 'parachutes' then blow away, leaving silver skeletons to decorate the winter pavements. Thus carline thistles are biennials, taking two summers to complete their life-cycle.

One of my delights–apart from walking in The Burren–is collecting old books about botany. Some years ago I was given a most handsome present of the five volumes of Anne Pratt's *The flowering plants, grasses, sedges and ferns of Great Britain*, one of the more accurate of the Victorian books about natural history and quaintly illustrated with bouquets of wildflowers. Perusing Miss Pratt's tomes I read that the flower heads–at least the 'fleshy receptacles'–of carline thistles were once eaten as a vegetable and were 'often preserved as a sweetmeat with honey and sugar'–so small and viciously prickly a thistle could hardly make an edible vegetable. Furthermore, the name *Carlina* is supposed to signify a connection with the Emperor Charlemagne who, directed by an angel to this thistle, used it to cure the army of plague.

Anne Pratt's books can be dipped into for entertaining morsels of floral lore and horticultural wisdom, and I wonder if anyone can confirm another of her reports:

> Our common Herb Robert is believed to be obnoxious to many insects,
> and is by cottagers often placed near beds to repel them; and the strong odour
> is probably disagreeable to these intruders.

Garlic has a considerable reputation for keeping greenfly at bay, and some of the marigolds (*Tagetes* species) are said to act as 'weedkillers'; nowadays they are often planted in flower beds by folk who dislike using chemicals in their gardens. How much more delightful would be a rose-bed carpeted with delicate herb Robert, than with garish French marigolds?

There is no corner of The Burren that will not yield herb Robert and hardly a day passes when this plant is not in bloom–I have seen herb Robert in blossom on New Year's Day and Midsummer Day. By the stile into Corcomroe Abbey, along the roadside at Newtown, deep in a scailp in the shadow of Mullach Mór, and on the stormy brow of Black Head, everywhere, herb Robert flourishes. Among the juniper at Garryland, where there is shelter, it grows vigorously forming a haze of pink and claret in spring. The Black Head plants are fascinating because many have almost white flowers, or very pale pink, with pallid green leaves and green stems. These belong to a variety, *Geranium robertianum* var. *celticum*, originally described as a subspecies by the Danish botanist Carl Ostenfeld, that is restricted to western Ireland and south Wales. A. W. Stelfox collected it in 1955, brought seeds to his garden in Newcastle, County Down, and grew it alongside the local red-stemmed variety–the Burren plant seeded about and remained distinct although it lost its succulent character.[22]

Dr Peter Yeo, in his definitive book on hardy cranesbills, describes herb Robert as 'a usually overwintering evil-smelling annual',[23] an unflattering description for a glorious plant. The leaves are divided into three lobes–almost into five–each of which is further divided into stalked segments which are also lobed. The leaves have long stalks which are somewhat succulent and form a rosette from the centre of which the branched flowering stems arise. All *Geranium* species have five sepals forming a goblet-like calyx, and five petals. In the centre of each flower, a lovely contrast with the purple or palest pink petals, are ten red anthers; *Geranium robertianum* and its close relatives produce yellow pollen. The calyx is hairy but not ribbed in herb Robert, and is usually red-brown–in the pale-coloured variety it is green. Following pollination, the characteristic ridged cranesbill fruit is formed by development of the style and ovary; at the base are the five seeds, each enclosed in a mericarp.

In cranesbills the seeds are scattered from parent plants explosively; in some species, such as bloody cranesbill, the seeds are slung from the mericarp as a stone is from a sling, while in those related to herb Robert, the whole mericarp (with the seed inside) is propelled from the plant.

There is another small-flowered *Geranium* native in The Burren and frequently it grows alongside herb Robert–this is the shining cranesbill, *Geranium lucidum*. They cohabit at the stile by the Abbey of Corcomroe, and on verges of the bohreen to Newtown Castle beyond Ballyvaghan. Each pale lavender petal has three prominent paler streaks running towards the base; the petals are less than half a centimetre long without an apical notch. In the centre of the flower are ten lemon yellow anthers, and the flower sits in a bulbous green calyx which is ribbed. The most noticeable difference between shining cranesbill and herb Robert is the smaller, glossy, grass-green leaves, round in outline, the size of a thumb-nail and devoid of hairs apart from a few bristles. As in herb Robert the mericarp containing the seed is slung from the plant.

Geranium robertianum: herb Robert

In Connemara and The Burren, herb Robert is called in Irish *earball ri* (the tail of the king), although its 'official' name is *ruithéal ri*, which has no obvious connection with the English one. Stinking Robert–an allusion to its fetid odour when crushed–is a name recorded from Donegal. Geoffrey Grigson, whose book *The Englishman's flora*[24] is a treasury of information about the vernacular names of plants and a joy to explore, suggested that *Herba Roberti* does not signify a link with St Robert of Salzburg, but more probably indicates an association with the house goblin, Robin Goodfellow in English lore, Knecht Ruprecht in German. The name may also link this cranesbill with the robin redbreast, which for all the sentimental gloss of the present times, was formerly a bird of ill-omen especially if he was abused or when he flew indoors. Ill-treated, the robin would wreak revenge; kill a robin and your cow's milk will turn to blood. On the other hand, treat a robin with kindness and you will have good luck and he will protect your house from lightning. Perhaps, Grigson suggested, herb Robert was the vegetable counterpart.

Carved capitals: Corcomroe Abbey

HER WINTER WEEDS OUTWORN

Now feathered fingers of the fern unfurl
Beside the bell-loud stream where waters spill
In crystal loneliness where sculptured crags
Are etched in evening silver on the hill.

Soon will the gentian and the crane's bill bloom
In stony spaces where Dawn's sea-borne showers
Slant through the rainbow's arch, and noonday brings
The bagpipe drone of bees among the flowers.

B. P. O'Connor: 'The Burren (for S. P. Irwin)'

Few outlanders venture to The Burren in winter: local folk have it all to themselves. Even botanists seem to shun this wilderness until the gentians begin to bloom towards the close of April. 'Lord, what fools these mortals be!' They will never know what they are missing.

63

The winter landscape is a myriad of metallic greys, silvers and golds, and lusty greens lit by ever-changing light which, streaming at a shallow angle, highlights the sculpted surfaces of rocks. The limestone, clouds and ocean often conspire to unite in a single glittering mass–only by the movements of waves and clouds can the eye distinguish solid earth. At other times, Atlantic showers change the pavement into a black mirror. Quickly afterwards, fractured sunlight gilds the rain-washed rocks and the silver carapaces of carline thistles, and in this light the bare trunks and twigs of trees and shrubs glow with hues of astonishing beauty. The sinuous leaves on the holly bushes glint and sparkle with rain drops. During these bright days, sun-shafts dance with the wind on the sea. In between are the gales that sigh over the dunes, combing through the marram grass which scratches at the sand flashing the white and furrowed backs of its long leaves. Overhead gulls breast the wind, hovering, rising, gliding down to skim over the crashing breakers.

On New Year's Eve, a west wind chills my fingers, ears and nose, and brings tears to my eyes as I lean into it and buffet my way across the limestone terraces to the cliffs above Fanore. Winter is a harsh, rasping season, and also invigorating, exhilarating, rewarding. Yet only to warm-blooded creatures does that wind feel cold, for it is a warm, moist wind that warms the stones and liberally waters the whole countryside.

The present-day climate of the north-western corner of Clare can be described as mild and equable, moist and windy.[1] The average (mean) daily temperature in January is 6°C around the coastal fringe, and about half a degree lower inland; the comparable July temperature is 15°C; the annual mean temperature is just over 10°C, which is also the mean temperature of the air in the caves and the water in the underground streams. Frosts are not infrequent, but are rarely severe, and if snow ever falls it is unlikely to lie for more than a day. The equable climate means that The Burren has an extraordinary growing season–grass starts growing about mid- to late February and continues into late December so that only for about eight weeks is there potentially no growth. Thus pastures grow for not less than ten months every year, allowing farmers to leave cattle and sheep on the hills and pavements in winter without provision of fodder. 'Winterage' connotes this and is the age-old practice in The Burren.

Rainfall varies according to elevation and distance from the coast–mean annual precipitation is about 1100 mm (c. 45 inches) near the sea, rising to over 1400 mm (c. 55 inches) on the highest hills. Rainy days are frequent–between 175 and 200 each year–and the driest months generally are February, March and April.

The prevailing winds blow from the south-west to west quadrant. There are few calm days; the mean annual wind speed is between 18 and 24 kilometres per hour, and gales roar on one in every twenty days. Robert Lloyd Praeger was succinct–'...winter on the west coast might be described as a succession of westerly gales with westerly winds between.'[2] However, it has to be remembered that brisk winds, even the moisture-laden winds of western Ireland, can rapidly dry the surfaces of wet rocks and desiccate any soft stems and leaves that are exposed.[3] The warm westerlies are not always kind to plants.

In the scailps, protected from wind and well-provided with moisture–mean rainfall figures are irrelevant as there is so much run-off from bare rocks and seepage from underground–microclimates are significantly different. Various attempts have been made to quantify the climate of the scailps; Professor Heslop-Harrison of Queen's University, Belfast, gathered climatological data from pavements, scailps, hazel scrub and cliffs, to demonstrate that even shallow cracks in the limestone provide consistently humid habitats with relatively constant temperatures.[4] Students from the Department of Botany, University of Nottingham, studied scailps and woodlands too, and found that hour-by-hour fluctuations in temperature and relative humidity are much less dramatic in these sheltered crannies than on the pavement surface.[5]

Protected in the scailps, warmed and watered, plants thrive. For them the most potent signal of the march of the seasons is the changing length of each day, yet some herbs take no notice even of day-light hours: hawkweeds and herb Robert continue to bloom through winter, and these occasional blossoms seem more intensely coloured than the summer ones perhaps because they are lonely in the grey landscape. On scattered boulders and on the walls, soft green pads of mosses and rippling saffron lichens also declare that life continues here through all weathers. In winter the rusty-backs have soft, unfurled, silver-margined fronds, so these delightful, diminutive ferns are conspicuous on the shattered pavements. Other plants too stand out in the winter light: pale grey thorns spike the claret stems of the burnet rose whose sealing-wax-red buds promise flowers in the summer to come. Among greyness, green leaves are most brilliant, and the evergreens–mosses, wood sage, the statuesque holly and wreaths of ivy–have their heydays.

At the foot of the walls along the green roads, and in the shelter of the hollies and hazels, there are almost always flowers. One of the first herbs to blossom is the barren strawberry (*sú talún bréige*, false strawberry), that 'small and charming

Potentilla sterilis: barren strawberry

liar of the spring, posing as a Strawberry'[6] which ranges through Europe from southern Sweden to Greece. It has a rosette of strawberry leaves, and small, five-petalled white blossoms that look so much like the flowers of the alpine strawberry; seeing the barren strawberry bloom, it is difficult not to think of strawberries and cream, but such a dream is vain.

Potentilla sterilis is a cousin of the strawberry (*Fragaria vesca*) but it does not produce succulent, red strawberries; its 'fruits' are dry and small, most unappetizing. The barren strawberry's leaves have a bluish tinge that serves to distinguish the two species when they are not in flower or fruit–the other strawberry has pure green leaves. There are other differences–the terminal tooth of each leaf is very much smaller than all the other teeth in *Potentilla sterilis*, but not so in *Fragaria vesca*.

Like wild strawberry and some other herbaceous species of *Potentilla* including silverweed (*Potentilla anserina*), the barren strawberry produces stolons which can root at the tips and thus it reproduces easily without any need to produce seed. It inhabits crannies on cliffs and pavements, scrub and open woodlands, and, according to botanical sources, is more abundant on dry soils–the habitats in The Burren certainly fall within that category.

Barren strawberry blooms most profusely from the beginning of the year into early spring when it heralds primroses and cowslips, yet flowers are to be found at almost any time without too much searching. In September I have seen this delightful herb blossoming by the stream which trickles from the bowels of Sliabh Cairn beside Tobar Mac Duach.

Erophila verna: whitlow grass

In general flowering plants have narrowly synchronized flowering seasons; in The Burren most species bloom between May and September but a small number keep the barren strawberry company during the first months of the year. One of these is whitlow grass, formerly *Draba verna* but now placed in the genus *Erophila*, 'lover of spring'.

Whitlow grass (*bosán anagair*) is not a grass but a distant relative of wallflowers, of cabbages and kale. All species in the cabbage family (Brassicaceae) have flowers with four petals arranged as a cross (hence the family's other name Cruciferae). Whitlow grass has four tiny white petals, each deeply notched at its apex–the individual flowers are only a few millimetres across, and the whole plant usually little more than a thumb-length tall. It is an annual, germinating usually in the autumn and completing its entire life cycle within about six months–its seeds are scattered and the parent plant withered by early summer.

Despite its diminutive stature, whitlow grass is prolific, and can be found on tops of walls and on the pavement throughout The Burren; it has even invaded the tarmacadamed surfaces of hotel tennis-courts in Lisdoonvarna. Frederick Foot was the first to report *Erophila*, using its old name *Draba verna*:

> …never have I seen it in such rank abundance as in Burren. I at first imagined that it flowered twice…in early spring and at the end of autumn; but I find that it is out of flower during the summer months, generally commencing about September, and lasting through the winter, till the middle of May, or so.'[7]

In 1989 I found it blooming on Black Head during early September, and in 1991 on 3 August, whitlow grass was in full flower thereabout.

Dr S. Clark studied whitlow grass and some other winter flowering annuals, and found that this little plant produced flower-buds from mid-November irrespective of the temperature—in other words, even if November and December are cold, whitlow grass has buds by the turn of the year. He noted that the flowers only opened when the temperature was relatively high, and warmer conditions had to persist for proper maturation of seeds.[8] It is indeed noticeable that whitlow grass has open flowers only on warm, sunny winter days—when it is overcast, they remain tightly closed. While this ordered life-cycle is the norm, it is possible to find *Erophila verna* blooming in late autumn if the summer has been especially dull, cool and damp.

Erophila verna can only be confused with one other Burren plant, the rue-leaved saxifrage (*Saxifraga tridactylites*), which also inhabits the tops of walls and bare patches of soil on the pavements. They can be distinguished easily by looking at the rosette of tiny leaves and the fruits: in the saxifrage each leaf is usually deeply divided into three, occasionally five, segments; the fruits of whitlow grass are flat discs. While whitlow grass resembles few other species, there is an unresolved discussion in botanical circles about *Erophila verna*—is there just one species or are there several? Professor David Webb and Miss Maura Scannell allude to this inconclusive debate in *Flora of Connemara and The Burren*, suggesting that two, perhaps three subspecies—veritable species in some botanists' opinion—grow in The Burren. I have yet to be convinced that whitlow grass needs to be subdivided, so I will not venture an opinion, merely suggesting that those who are inclined to peer down microscopes at dwarf plants looking for differences between them will find this weed endlessly diverting. There is enough of it on the Burren's walls and pavements to keep you happy till the cows come home.

There is no point in looking on the tops of walls for mudworts—they inhabit watery places. Like whitlow grass, *Limosella aquatica* (*lus lathaí*, herb of the mud) is an annual and blooms most profusely during the winter although standard botanical books will aver that it only flowers in summer. This is so improbable most years in The Burren that I wonder it is repeated so frequently. For the record I have noticed mudwort in bloom at Poll Salach in September, November, January, March, April, May, and perhaps because of the dull, wet summer of 1991, in August.

Mudwort grows in the shallow pools that form where the limestone is sculpted into basins, maybe a finger-length deep. In some of these natural bowls, called solution cups, there are small accumulations of fine loam, and during the wetter months water fills them, the depth being sufficient that sun and wind do not evaporate the pools entirely at any period—the combination of constant wind and sun-warmed rock means that the pavement dries rapidly after showers of rain. In a 'normal' summer, these basins may contain water for a few days, maybe a few weeks, but the annual mudwort cannot complete its entire life cycle in so short a time.

Patrick O'Kelly discovered *Limosella aquatica* at Lough Inchiquin in July 1893, and shortly thereafter not far from Gort. Henry Levinge wrote an interesting account of the plants at Lough Inchiquin, where mudwort has not been seen for many years (it may yet be rediscovered at the lough).

> About one month after the discovery of this plant by Mr. O'Kelly, being in the neighbourhood of Corofin, I visited the lake, which, owing to heavy rain, had in the interval risen about three feet, and submerged the Limosella to a depth of nearly two feet. I was able, however, with the help of a boat and my drag, to procure some plants, which then presented a totally different appearance to that of the specimens sent me by Mr. O'Kelly, having apparently, after submergence, cast off most of the old leaves with the ripened fruits, and developed a fresh crop of bright green young leaves, the stems of which were in some instances elongated as much as four or five inches.[9]

In 1900 mudwort was collected at Fisherstreet by a Mr Richardson and it still grows there. The plant is also known in solution-hollows on the pavement at Poll Salach, a few kilometres further north along the coast. Outside The Burren, *Limosella aquatica* is rare; until 1985 the only other Irish stations were in my home county of Fermanagh, but recently it appeared in The Gearagh, County Cork. Professor Walter Wade's record of this plant from Ballynahinch in Connemara is generally dismissed as an error, although he accurately described the habitat and habit of this minute annual.

Limosella aquatica has a rosette of paddle-shaped, pallid green leaves, the fragile stalks of which elongate just enough to allow the mature blades to break the surface of the water. Stolons spring from the rosettes and these may root at the nodes. The flowers are minute, perhaps two millimetres long, and usually remain submerged so that mudwort blooms underwater. Each blossom has an outer whorl of five green sepals which are longer than the five mauve petals that,

Limosella aquatica: mudwort

fused, form the corolla. If you are lucky to find a few mudworts flowering in an almost dry puddle, the tiny, pale flowers sparkle in the centre of the rosette. After pollination–I suspect the species is self-pollinated–a torpedo-shaped capsule develops, twice the size of the flower, and the seeds, once shed, will lie dormant in the solution-hollows until late summer when the basin fills again. I know of no experimental studies that seek to explain what triggers germination in this annual. While the plants growing around loughs and turloughs may not have such a precarious existence as those in the Poll Salach and Fisherstreet pools, they too are most likely to be autumn and winter-flowering rather than high summer plants.

Whereas the mudwort is rare, or at least inconspicuous and probably fleeting, *Sesleria albicans* (blue grass; in Irish *féar Boirne*, Burren grass) is one of the most abundant plants on The Burren, and not likely to be overlooked. If, like me, you have an blind-spot for grasses and sedges, a few minutes spent looking closely at the young flowering spikes of this grass might convert you into an enthusiastic agrostophile.

The stalks of the flower spikes of *Sesleria albicans* begin to elongate in March and April, so that the startling steel-blue, tightly clustered spikes emerge from

Sesleria albicans
blue grass

71

the short tufts of grey-green leaves about Easter. The individual leaves are distinctly keeled, with parallel sides and a hooded tip–they resemble a very long currach. On the upper side is a greyish, glaucous bloom. The spikes, or panicles, are stumpy, at most about three centimetres long and usually less than a centimetre in diameter, and are made up of numerous (ten to more than three hundred) spikelets each composed of paired florets only one of which will produce a seed. The colour of the panicle is at its richest just before the anthers emerge–on the sunlit side it is deep purple-green melting into gun-metal blue, while on the shaded side the colour can be green. The anthers are creamy-green with purple tips which fade when their pollen is released to a pale whitish-green.

Grasses are always wind-pollinated, so the pollen grains float on the breeze from anther to stigma. Pollen is released and fertilization occurs in April or May, and all the while the stalk (culm) of the panicle continues to elongate. The colour fades from the flower-spike after pollination, so that when the seeds begin to ripen through June the blue grass does not live up to its name. Eventually, the stalk stops growing and dies–it can be more than thirty centimetres long–but it and the spike itself remain attached to the plant so that in high summer the blue grass is as conspicuous as it is in spring. Now the stiff dead flower-spikes, resembling feathered arrows stuck in the soil, are straw coloured. The seeds will fall on to the pavement around the parent grass.

Blue grass is grazed by the cattle, goats, sheep and hares of The Burren, and undoubtedly provides food for other beasts. Dr J. Dixon has recorded that on cliffs and screes in Britain, this species provides habitats for at least twenty species of snail–undoubtedly Irish snails find as congenial homes among the grey-green leaves.[10] In Scotland and the north of England, the caterpillars of the Scotch Argus butterflies (*Erebia aethiops*) feeds on *Sesleria albicans*; there are no Scotch Argus butterflies in Ireland, but this grass gains my complete respect because it is believed to be the food plant of caterpillars of a most beautiful moth known today as The Burren Green, *Calamia tridens* subsp. *occidentalis* (formerly *Luceria virens*).[11]

While this is a book about plants, the story of The Burren Green is worth telling. In August 1949, Captain William Stuart Wright was botanizing at Black Head, and while answering a 'call of nature', noticed a moth resting on a bracken frond. Wright had an all-round interest in natural history and he could not resist collecting the sleepy moth and bringing it home to Lurgan in a match-box. Unable to identify it, Stuart Wright enquired of Eric Classey what this green moth might be, later suggesting that it tallied with a species called *Luceria virens*. This news intrigued Classey and when the moth 'arrived in England (together with Capt. Wright), for a short visit', he confirmed that the beast was indeed *Luceria virens*. Thus a new moth had been discovered in the British Isles, and in a most unexpected locality, the west of Ireland. A major expedition had to be mounted to confirm that *Luceria virens* was indigenous and not a blow-in, so the following summer Stuart Wright, Eric Classey and some others met at Gort.

Setting up their brightly illuminated traps near Black Head and at another inland site, the moth-hunters attracted audiences of up to twenty people, who watched enthusiastically; some folk walked ten miles to see 'the great lights and the gintlemen catching flois.'[12] The visitors took every precaution to ensure success, even adorning themselves with sprigs of white heather. The first night, Sunday 6 August 1950, they trapped all sorts of insects. At 11.15 pm a moth fluttered in the grass and was soon trapped–it was a freshly emerged, malachite-green female *Luceria virens*. The entomologists were elated.

The expedition was a success; male and female moths were trapped, proving that the original was not a chance migrant. Later studies by E. Cockayne led him to conclude that the Burren population represented a distinct subspecies of the moth, characterised by grey hind wings and a red-brown line on the fore wings, and that its closest analogue came from the Iberian Peninsula,[13] a distribution pattern that is not unfamiliar to botanists. This exquisite jade-winged moth–the colour is dazzling–is known to inhabit mainland Europe from Portugal to Finland, and to occur also in Asia, but it has never been seen in Britain although its food plant does grow in the north of England and the Scottish Highlands. In Europe, the caterpillars must feed on other grass species; *Sesleria albicans* does not grow in Finland nor in Portugal.

Richard Haynes kindly showed me a Burren Green one summer–he kept a nice specimen in a match-box, but I have not seen another despite my best endeavours including a fruitless late-night sortie to Carron in company with a bewildered visitor from England.

A walk over The Burren in spring will soon reveal to the observant that some *Sesleria* plants do not have blue spikes. A small proportion of the tussocks have pallid green ones–the flowers are not metallic blue–and these have been assigned to a distinct variety, *Sesleria albicans* var. *luteo-alba*. I am not aware that anyone has calculated the frequency of this variant, but in some places in The Burren it is not infrequent–a large erratic boulder in Rockforest townland has a handsome clump.

Primula vulgaris: primrose

When blue grass is just beginning to display its spears in early March, there will already be a sprinkling of primroses on the green roads, in the shelter of the great walls that stride over the hills, particularly where the stones form suntrapping nooks. Primrose is the first rose of the year–*prima rosa*: 'The queenly flower that opens the lock to let in summer'.[14] In Irish, primrose is *sabhaircín*, the May flower. Is there another pleasure to vie with that of The Burren springtime, wandering southwards on the green road that rises from the valley of the Caher River, between the high walls built by master craftsmen, and softly to thread a pathway through the clumps of golden-eyed, butter-petalled primroses? They are, after all, 'good against Melancholy'[15] especially when left unpicked.

Whereas the primrose has been eradicated from many parts of Ireland and Britain, The Burren hills remain a stronghold. Even on the summit plateau of Cappanawalla, primroses are plentiful in the short turf. It was there, in July 1989, that I found an albino, a startling pale cream plant, with only a tincture of green along the mid-veins. It was not in blossom, but stood out because of its unusual hue. Such things, green plants without chlorophyll, rarely survive beyond the seedling stage,

Primula veris (entire plant and lower inset) and *Primula* x *tommasinii* (middle inset)
cowslip and false oxlip

but this was a healthy vigorous primrose showing no signs of being scorched in the summer sun. Its leaves must have contained sufficient chlorophyll to enable it to carry out some photosynthesis–the process whereby plants utilise the sun's light to convert water and carbon dioxide into sugars and oxygen.

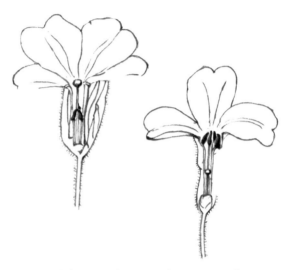

'Pin' (left) and 'Thrum' (right) primrose flowers

There are few habitats in The Burren that contain no signs of primroses; they abound in the hazel copses, on the open pavement among heather, wood anemones and mountain avens, and by the coast on the sand dunes. As in all other places too, two sexual forms, the 'pin' and 'thrum', exist side by side; the first with the female stigma like the head of a pin just visible at the mouth of the flower and concealing the anthers; the 'thrum' has a cone of anthers, the male, pollen-producing organs, at the mouth overtopping the stigma. For fertile seed, pollen from a 'thrum' must reach the stigma of a 'pin', and *vice versa*.

In many of the open habitats primroses grow alongside cowslips, and because cowslips and primroses are not too distantly related, pollen from a primrose may, by accident, land on the stigma of a cowslip. Occasionally such a chance happening results in viable seeds and a host of hybrid seedlings. It is equally possible for cowslip pollen to reach a primrose flower but Professor David Valentine showed that this reverse cross rarely results in viable seed.[16] In The Burren there are swarms of false oxlips, as the progeny of this inter-specific cross are known; the individual plants vary considerably because the hybrids are sometimes fertile, and can set seeds if pollinated by their own pollen or pollen from one of the parent species. Some have orange cowslip-like blooms, whereas others resemble the true oxlip (*Primula elatior*) having many-blossomed heads of pale yellow, primrose-like flowers.

Bainne bó bleachtáin, literally milk of the milch cow, is one among many Irish names for the cowslip (and in some parts for the primrose too), and a more poetic name than the old Anglo-Saxon one which today we use without blushing. To put it delicately, as Geoffrey Grigson did, the English name arose from the notion that a cowslip would take root in a meadow 'wherever a cow lifted its tail'; it is the polite form of cow-slop, in Old English cu-sloppe, a cow pat.[17] The beautiful Irish name surely had the same conception, but we had more panache in disguising the ordure. Among countless other names, cowslip has been called Lady's fingers and Lady's keys, St Peter's herb and St Peter's keys; in Welsh it is *dagrau Mair*, tears of Mary.

There can be no doubt that in The Burren cowslips are still plentiful, while in other counties these beautiful flowers have been picked to near extinction; in Northern Ireland, it is now illegal to gather cowslips and to interfere with plants in any way because populations are declining so rapidly.

Cowslips with primroses drift through the barony; they traipse in the company of violets and water avens along the green roads. But they do not stay with the tracks and highways; there are cowslips on the peaty hummocks crowning the summits of Dobhach Bhrainín, Cappanawalla and the other hills. And they seem bigger, more robust than cowslips from other parts of Ireland.

The structure of the individual flower of *Primula veris* is the same as that of the primrose (*Primula vulgaris*); 'pin' and 'thrum' plants occur in all the populations. However cowslip flowers are smaller and clustered atop a stem, the petals form a cup, and are a deeper hue, lemon- rather than butter-yellow, usually with prominent orange spots near the mouth. The leaves tend to be shorter than those of the primrose, with a distinct stalk and blade, and fine down on both sides.

The cowslip's disappearance is sometimes ascribed to over-collecting to make cowslip wine, but changes in agricultural practices must be more to blame. In the old days, when meadows were grazed and maybe scythed late in the summer, not harvested for silage and then dosed with fertilizers for a second silage crop, cowslips and other meadow plants could blossom and set seeds with a good chance that the seeds would ripen and fall to the soil before the reaper came. There is no chance of that in a silage field. Fortunately vestiges of the old ways of farming survive among the small stone-walled Burren fields, as at Fanore, and there still are cowslips by the acre. Who will preserve this way of life, the cowslipped meadows a-hum with bees, the cow pats and the scythes? Dr Threlkeld asserted that cowslips are 'Friends to the Nerves'; to be sure he intended that to be understood in a different way, but what can be more soothing that the sight of a meadow brimming with *bainne bó bleachtáin*?

In times past cowslips were believed to be 'serviceable against an Epilepsy, Palsy, and Pains in the Head; they have a Tendency to procure Sleep; for which purpose a Thea is made of the Flowers'–folk in The Burren know this old receipt.[18] But please do not pluck cowslips for tea, even on drowsy April days. Leave them to spring again as the ghosts of cow pats.

> The honeyed cowslip tufts once more
> The golden slope;–with gradual ray
> The primrose stars the rock, and o'er
> The wood path strews its milky way.

Aubrey de Vere: 'Spring in Ireland'

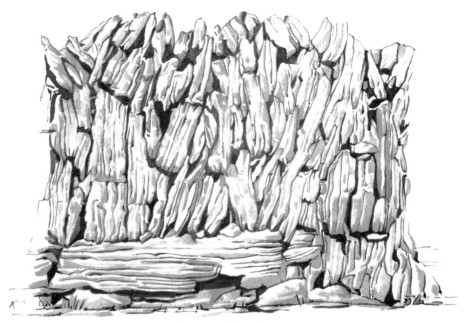

Dry-stone wall: Formoyle West

ON THE GREEN ROADS

We know the pathways that the sheep tread out,
And all the hiding-places of the hills,…

W. B. Yeats: 'The dreaming of the bones'

Between walls of deliberately laid stones, the bohreen, a rough track, meanders off to nowhere in particular! *Boithrín an ghorta* GREEN ROAD is engraved on the signpost, but that topically evocative English name is not a translation of the Irish–bohreen of hunger, famine road would be more accurate, but only literally. And the Irish name is a spurious, recent invention.

The Burren's hills are crisscrossed by these verdant tracks and the walls that mark their routes. Why are these roads here? Nobody really knows. Despite the road signs, the green roads are not famine roads. Furthermore they are not futile artefacts, the grand scheme of some demented landlord, a landscape-sized folly created to employ starving peasants in times of hunger. They lead nowhere nowadays only because their beginnings and their ends are obscured by a network of seemingly purposeful modern roads driven across the antique landscape during recent centuries to link new towns and villages. Undoubtedly in unrecorded, unremembered times the green roads served as cattle tracks by which herdsmen drove their beasts down to the lowlands in summer and returned them to the high ground in winter. Undoubtedly too they linked the many clachans which were dotted throughout the barony of Burren, settlements betrayed today only by the tumbledown ruins of stone cottages. But in which era the greatest of the green roads were built—the broad highways through Gleninagh down into the Caher Valley and over the hills to Ballinalacken, or the one which circumscribes Black Head and surely led on to Béal an Chloga and Abbey Hill, or the road that reaches Mullach Mór and Lough Gealáin—and by what authority, are questions we cannot answer. Who knows what traffic long ago was trundled along these broad roads, how many hundreds, or hundreds of thousands of cattle and sheep have been driven between these walls? Only the mute walls could testify if horses and donkeys passed by in number.

Organized communities of considerable wealth existed in The Burren in pre-Christian centuries, and their monuments abound, the wedge tombs and the great dolmen at Poulnabrone, and the stone forts such as the spectacular fastnesses of Cathair Dhúin near Poll Salach, and Cathair Dhúin Irghuis on Black Head. Christian monks chose the fertile valleys and sheltered expanses of glacial till as the sites for their monasteries—Corcomroe, Oughtdarra and Oughtmama, Rathborney and Glencolumbkille, and even in the shadow of Cinn Aille. Each of these civilizations had sufficient cause and could have commanded sufficient labour to build the walls of the green roads and the many other walls that mark out boundaries of townlands and fields.

Lord Chief Baron Edward Willes was fascinated by stone walls of Clare and Galway, and in his letter of 1761 to the Earl of Warwick gave a lucid description of them which is well-worth quoting:

> …the land was enclos'd in very large pastures with stone walls of a very singular construction. They are piled one upon another, but not flat and like the stone walls in Glocestershire, solid; but the stones are placed in such a manner, that there are interstices thro' out the whole length of the wall of about 5 or 6 inches diameter, so that when you look upon a wall on a rising ground and see the light thro' the different vacancies, it very nearly resembles a net set in the sea to catch fish, only with this difference, that the meshes, if I may call them so, are generally triangular and not square. I wou'd defy a London mason to build one of them without

serving an apprenticeship to the trade, and yet every cottager makes them in this manner. This is the only county in Ireland, or perhaps the only place in the world, where they build these kind of nettwork walls. They are so particular a construction that I am afraid you can have no idea of them by my description, but they are really so odd that I can't describe them better. I ask'd several persons why they made walls of this kind; the only answer is that it has been their antient custom to make them so, and that they are as strong and as good as a fence as solid walls, and I can asure you that its being an antient custom is an invincible argument with the native Irish to continue it.[1]

Joseph Woods was also impressed.

It is moreover added to enhance the wonder that the stone walls are transparent–& it is the custom of the country to build their walls with stones that shall touch if possible only by the angles and this is said to be done under the notion that the wind passing thro the intervals will not blow them down. Every field is encumbered by stones which in many abundantly cover the surface so that it certainly is not from any want of materials.[2]

Today the *boithríni an ghorta* are largely abandoned to the wild flowers. In a few places they have been blocked and are impassable, and in others they come to abrupt, meaningless ends. For an intrepid naturalist, these obsolete highways provide easy access to the high limestone terraces and to out-of-the-way localities of considerable interest and breath-taking beauty. Where there is no traffic, except for the occasional scampering hare or a herd of goats, and maybe the tramp of a foot-loose botanist, from wall to wall the tracks are carpeted with plants. There is no species unique to the green roads, but as the pathways are a 'happy hunting ground', they should be explored.

I have wandered many kilometres of green road, and been thankful that they lead nowhere except into the heart of the wilderness. I have walked on carpets of violets and primroses in spring and tried in vain to avoid trampling too many gentians. Knee-deep in blue scabious and aromatic yarrow during a mild September is a different experience to a winter walk, sailing in a westerly gale that billows my coat like the spinnaker of an ocean yacht. On still sunny summer days I have sat on the turf and listened to the bees and the skylarks, and watched blue butterflies flounce from bloom to bloom. Leaning against one wall I have stared across at the opposite one, and wondered idly what the craftsman, who had so carefully placed each stone on stone, had thought of his task. Had he also marvelled at the butterflies, mountain avens and Spring gentians? Had he apprehended the

Polygala vulgaris: milkwort

mosses and lichens, or the rusty-back ferns and wall-rues that sprout from the blocks that he was setting up? Why had he deliberately tried to make this fragment of wall a work of art, a gossamer wall to wither the winds of winter.

The little chapel at Formoyle is silent now, its roof gone and most of its walls, but the carefully crafted arches of the windows are mute testimony that this was not a farmhouse. Striding the green road towards the summit of Sliabh Eilbhe, I am in the company only of the breeze and the grasshoppers; perhaps in the distance a dog barks, or the cattle low. In between the silence is real. Underfoot unrolls a tapestry of eyebrights and tormentil, milkwort and meadow-sweet, thyme and ox-eye daisies, dormant harebells and squinancywort, and the drying stems of quaking grass. It is in such a place that Reginald Farrer would have found 'the whole department of a lady's plenishing'[3]–Lady's mantle, Lady's bedstraw, Lady's fingers and Lady's tresses.

My earliest memory of milkwort is as a schoolboy, on an outing with the Field Club in the mountains above Carrick Lough in County Fermanagh. We had found it growing with eyebrights, beside a track, and I remember being told that some milkworts have pink flowers and others white. Common milkwort, *Polygala vulgaris*, does exhibit that range of colours–in The Burren the predominant colour is bright royal blue but pale blue, lavender and even pink blossomed milkwort do occur very occasionally.

There are two, closely similar species of milkwort native in Ireland, namely *Polygala vulgaris* and *Polygala serpyllifolia*. They are not easy to tell apart, and even

Geum rivale
water avens

83

experienced botanists can be thoroughly confused. However only *Polygala vulgaris* is common in The Burren, it being the species that abounds on limestone soils–the other one inhabits peaty places where there is no lime in the soil (and it does not have the same capacity to produce flowers of different hues).

Polygala vulgaris is a low, wispy herb, rarely more than ten centimetres tall. The paddle-shaped leaves are always arranged alternately along the stem and the uppermost one will be the longest, reaching perhaps a couple of centimetres in length. The little flowers are clustered in a lax spike at the tip of the stem. The individual blossom is complicated, composed of three white petals fused into a tube that is enveloped by two coloured inner sepals and three green outer sepals. The inner pair of sepals are petal-like and much larger than the three green outer ones–these are the parts that can be blue or shade towards pink.

Dr Threlkeld noted that he could discover no vernacular Irish name for this plant and suggested that 'luss baine' could be used as that was a literal translation–the current Irish name is indeed *lus an bhainne*.[4] The herb, by ancient repute, increases milk yield in cattle and nursing mothers.

Milkwort is abundant along the green roads, blooming from May into autumn–in spring 1991 milkwort blossomed with such profusion it almost outshone gentians–and being a plant of open habitats, such as grassland, it is common throughout The Burren except in shady hazel woods. Water avens, on the other hand, inhabits both shaded and open habitats as long as the soil is moist and rich in lime.

The dainty pendant flowers of water avens, cups of dusky red petals, possess a subtlety of which I never tire. Again, this is a plant I knew well as a boy growing up in Fermanagh. In The Burren water avens is almost ubiquitous. On the green road from Formoyle to Ballinalacken clumps of them mingle with cowslips in the lea of the walls; there are few other flowers that can match that chance pairing for beauty. Water avens also grows in sunny woodland glades, and in the sheltered valleys, pot-holes and declivities that pockmark the uplands of The Burren; often these are damp places, with springs that flow continually, providing the moist habitats that, as its name suggests, this plant prefers.

Geum rivale is a relative of *Dryas octopetala*–both genera belong to the rose family (Rosaceae) and to its tribe Potentilleae–*Potentilla* and *Rubus* (the blackberries) are also assigned to this tribe. The structure of the individual flowers demonstrates the similarities and serves to distinguish the genera from each other. *Geum* has a whorl of five petals, inside a whorl of five sepals with five intervening epicalyx segments. There is no epicalyx in *Dryas*, only five sepals, and of course, there are more than five petals–usually seven or eight, sometimes many more. The flowers of both *Geum* and *Dryas* have twenty or more stamens and numerous carpels–in *Geum rivale* the carpels are clustered into a globular head atop a short stalk. While related, no intergeneric hybrids are recorded between these genera, so they are not very closely allied.

Frederick Foot reported water avens from The Burren in 1862: '...at all elevations, and in most exposed and dry places. The Floras give as its habitats marshes and wet ditches, but nowhere does it grow in greater luxuriance than in the arid limestone of Burren'.[5]

Herb Bennet or wood avens (*Geum urbanum*) also grows in the region–it has small starry yellow flowers quite different from, and not nearly as beautiful as those of water avens. Where the two avens grow together hybrids can arise.

By the bye, the name *avens* is impossible to explain–while there are analogues in mediaeval Latin and in Old French, according to the *Oxford English Dictionary*, their meaning has not been fathomed. In Irish, *machall* is shared by both species of *Geum*; water avens is *machall uisce*.

Mountain everlasting is the 'official' English name of a diminutive relative of the daisy that grows on high mountains throughout the northern hemisphere–Siberia, Russia and Scandinavia, and North America–yet in western Ireland flourishes within splashing distance of the ocean. Cat's-foot is another of its names, although somehow I always think of its as cat's-paw–Geoffrey Grigson helpfully records that the latter version is recorded from Somerset, Rutland and Yorkshire, but not, it seems, from Ireland.[6] Where did I pick it up from? I had often pondered cat's-paw–what was there about this plant which merited such a name? Some flowers have names which are so simple to understand that they become obscure, especially to professional botanists! Such was this one to me, until a kind friend, hearing me remark that I could never see what there was about *Antennaria dioica* to merit any allusion to cats, pointed out gleefully that from above the clumps of pink female flowering heads, when arranged in fives as they often are, look like the soft pads of a kitten's foot. So simple, inspired! The Irish name is *catluibh*, and that does not need to be translated.

Why mountain everlasting? The flowering stems can, it is said, be dried and used in posies. But I would never suggest such barbarous treatment for this endearing and intriguing plant and I still prefer cat's-paw as its name.

Antennaria dioica: cat's foot

Antennaria dioica is abundant in The Burren. Take any square metre of pavement or pasture, at any season, any altitude, and peer among the congregations of leaves and stems–almost certainly you will find tell-tale rosettes of deep green leaves silver rimmed because their silvery backs are showing at the recurved margins. This is the foliage of cat's-paws. From the rosettes every May the flowering stalks rise, reaching perhaps ten centimetres. At the tips of the shoots are several clusters of florets. Each of the heads is composed of many minute flowers because this is a member of the daisy family (Asteraceae, or Compositae). Cat's-paw plants are dioecious–the flowers produced are not hermaphrodite with both male (stamens) and female (stigma, style and ovary) reproductive organs, but are unisexual, at least functionally. The flower-heads of female plants usually are delicate rose-pink, and of course they do not produce anthers and pollen. The intensity of the colour varies–some plants, as Frederick Foot noticed, have bright pink, almost red, heads. The male plants tend to have smaller flower-heads, only about half the diameter of the females, and may be white or pink; the males can be most easily distinguished by the presence of pollen-yielding anthers.

Viola riviniana: common violet

Professor Josias Braun-Blanquet, the Swiss botanist whose system of vegetation classification is much used by European botanists, visited Ireland in the late 1940s and collected *Antennaria* in several localities; seeing *Antennaria dioica* thriving on lime-rich soils, in stark contrast to its habitats in Europe, he was 'scandalized' and decided that the Irish plants must represent a distinct species. Thus he described *Antennaria hibernica*, stating that the Irish populations had longer stalks to the flower-heads which were always white, never pink.[7] However, Irish populations of cat's-paw are not sufficiently different to warrant separation from those elsewhere, and therefore Braun-Blanquet's *Antennaria hibernica* is rarely mentioned nowadays. Anyone visiting The Burren can easily find cat's-paws with white or pink flowers, so colour constancy will not distinguish Irish plants; the length of the flower stalks varies substantially and is also an unreliable character.

Antennaria dioica grows in full sun and on well-drained soils, with mountain avens, mouse-ear hawkweed (*Hieracium pilosella*), and gentians. Cat's-paw behaves as a calcicole species, but does not eschew the hummocks of peaty soil that sit on the limestone pavement. Thus it frequently occurs with lime-hating species, including ling (*Calluna vulgaris*), that form part of the enigmatic tapestry of The Burren's flora. Common violets are abundant on these peat mounds too.

🌿 There are several species of violet native on the limestones of Clare and Galway; some are rare and fleeting, including *Viola hirta* (hairy violet) which is relatively common on the Aran Islands but is known from only one place in The Burren, and is a protected species. The turlough violet (*Viola persicifolia*) occurs around the margins of some of the turloughs, a peculiar habitat because of the widely fluctuating water regimes. *Viola canina*, dog violet, often grows nearby, but beyond the winter high-water mark–Robert Lloyd Praeger noted this zonation in his seminal paper on turlough plants. The two other abundant violets are wood violet (*Viola reichenbachiana*) and the common dog violet (*Viola riviniana*).

Wood violet is a plant of sheltered sites, demanding shade and a lime-rich soil; it does not, in general, venture to colonize areas of pavement, yet can be seen with barren strawberries in hazel scrub and woodland, and in the scailps. Wood violet and common dog violet are difficult to distinguish when in leaf but their flowering times are staggered–wood violet tends to blossom a few weeks before the common dog violet which accompanies the earliest gentians. The individual blossoms are distinctive: wood violet has widely separated petals and the backwards-pointing spur is purple, smooth, flattened and slender; in contrast the stout spur of common dog violet is furrowed or notched, and cream-white or pale violet, and the much broader petals usually overlap.

Cats and dogs, and cuckoos! No-one seems to agree a vernacular English name for *Viola riviniana*, the violet from Rivini. Common wild violet, common dog violet, common violet, and dog violet are all used in botanical books. It is a scentless violet, inferior to the fragrant sweet violet, a degraded thing, a worthless dog-end of a violet.[8] In Irish violets are called *sailchuach*, literally the heel of a cuckoo and presumed to be a reference to the spur, or *goirmin*, a much more pleasant word meaning little blue flower. The standard Irish name for *Viola riviniana* is another of the native names for a violet, *fanaigse*.

Names can be as vexatious as they are amusing and diverting. The purpose of carefully regulated Latin names is, in part, to overcome both the fanciful multiplicity of vernacular names, in uncomprehended languages, bestowed on many plants over the centuries, and also the total absence of such names for uncounted others. The two-word Latin botanical name was a brilliant invention that serves everyone and is universal. Each species recorded in Ireland has a unique Latin name, a simple binomial made up of a generic name, like our surname, and a specific name which serves, as does our Christian name, to distinguish that one species from its fellows in the same genus. These plants may have Irish names too–many species have no time-honoured Irish name although the anonymous ones have all been shamelessly given invented ones! The same pertains for English vernacular names. Of course, just as Irish or English names may now have meanings so obscure that our folk-memories cannot explain them, the Latin names, being nothing but universal tags, need not mean anything. *Viola riviniana*, the violet from Rivini, no longer has any significance as this particular violet is much more widespread than Heinrich Reichenbach thought. Quite often, however, a Latin name serves as a concise mnemonic, a miniature description of considerable merit–*Dryas octopetala* would be a good example but for the fact that many, many mountain avens flowers have more than eight petals.

A plant badly in need of a memorable, universal label was *Lotus corniculatus*, which has about seventy English names, including the quite misleading bird's foot trefoil–'When a species has been endowed with more than seventy names, and when it is a small plant (however common) to which people could very well have been indifferent, one has to look for reasons.' Bird's foot and its Irish version, *crobh ein*, king's finger, *pied du bon Dieu* and a host of others are listed by Geoffrey Grigson. One may infer, he suggests, that this was not a plant to be picked: *pied du bon Dieu* disguised the notion that this is the plant of the goblin Tom Thumb; after all it bears the devil's fingers.[9] For all that, this particular herb does not have any good or ill uses; it was passed over by Dr Threlkeld without a murmur.

Lotus corniculatus was first reported from The Burren by Frederick Foot, who said bird's foot was to be met with in every direction. Any green road will be carpeted with it from the coastal dunes at Fanore to the summits of the high hills. When in full blow, there can be few sights more splendid that the coastal grassland ablaze with the brilliant lemon of bird's foot trefoil. An Cloch Scoiltithe, the spectacular, crumbling erratic perched between the road and the ocean beyond Fanore, was engulfed by a golden lawn in May 1991 after one of the fiercest winters on record when massive waves moved huge slabs of limestone several metres inland, and sprayed brine over all the coastal grassland between the Cliffs of Moher and Black Head

A member of the pea family, Fabaceae (Leguminosae), *Lotus corniculatus* resembles a clover and has even been used, but very rarely, as shamrock. Its shoots entwine with those of the other turf-hugging herbs that compose the Burren

Lotus corniculatus: bird's foot trefoil

grasslands. The individual leaves have five leaflets–not three, despite the vernacular tag 'trefoil'. Usually the flowers are a pure yellow–rarely have I noticed red streaking on the petals that is a characteristic of this plant elsewhere, and even rarer are clumps with orange flowers (this form is relatively common at Muckinish). Once pollinated, the petals wither and the ovaries elongate to form the bird's foot, a splayed cluster of about five pods that darken to chestnut brown as they ripen.

There are true trefoils in The Burren, a plethora of shamrocks! The common white and red clovers are everywhere. So is the diminutive yellow-flowered *Trifolium dubium*, the plant most commonly used nowadays to represent the mythical shamrock. One of the finest is hop trefoil (*Trifolium campestre*) which produces beautiful small puffy flower-heads on erect stalks, pale lemon yellow when in their prime, fading through fawn to tan as the tiny, individual flowers are pollinated and their petals wither. Hop trefoil can easily be recognized by its flower-heads which do look like miniature hop fruits when they are ripe and papery brown.

Lotus corniculatus is a short lived perennial and requires a well-drained soil, not necessarily rich nor calcareous; in The Burren it is one of the most catholic species, included in vegetation associations ranging from shrubby cinquefoil dominated turlough margins, to peaty hummocks with ling, and coastal grassland on stable dunes. It is absent from the wettest and the driest places–for example it does not grow in the hollows of the turloughs, and it is unlikely that you will

Saxifraga tridactylites: rue-leaved saxifrage

find swards of it on the tops of walls or in the shallowest solution cups. The latter habitats are the preserves of annual species.

We tend to think that saxifrages are perennial herbs making mossy hummocks among the rocks, and there are two species with this habit in The Burren, *Saxifraga rosacea* and *Saxifraga hypnoides.* But rue-leaved saxifrage is an annual, found in cracks on the flattest, bare pavement, on walls (*mórán balla* means wall saxifrage), anywhere there is a small accumulation of soil, a reasonable certainty of water and wide open sky; there is no point in looking for *Saxifraga tridactylites* in woodland or scrub.

Rue-leaved saxifrage looks a bit like whitlow grass (*Erophila verna*) with which, as Frederick Foot noticed, it is often associated, but they differ particularly in foliage. While both are annuals and rarely more than a finger-length tall, most of the rosette leaves of *Saxifraga tridactylites* are three-lobed like Neptune's trident–a few of the earliest leaves will be undivided and some may be five-lobed. They turn bright red, particularly during the latter weeks of the plant's growing season, and are cloaked with sticky, glandular hairs, just like the rest of the herb–when the glands catch the sunlight there is no larger plant that can compare with this glittering, carmine saxifrage. In its early stages during the winter, *Saxifraga tridactylites* forms a compact rosette of lobed leaves. In spring from the

91

centre of the rosette rises the flowering stem, which has a few, minute, lobed or entire leaves along it. The little white flowers are clustered in a branched inflorescence; the height of the plant, the number of flowers produced and other characters are determined by such factors as the richness of the soil and the rainfall at crucial stages in the plant's growth. While the flowers are no more than a half centimetre across, a clump of these saxifrages growing in a solution cup amongst grey rock will stand out–vivid red and pure white, sparkling against dark grey.

The vernacular name, rue-leaved saxifrage, does not seem entirely appropriate–as noted, the specific epithet might be translated as trident, or three-fingered. David Webb and Richard Gornall remark in their monograph on European *Saxifraga* that rue-leaved saxifrage being 'too inconspicuous and without medicinal reputation'[10] is not mentioned in mediaeval herbals. The silence was broken by the early eighteenth century when Dr Caleb Threlkeld, at least, wrote a detailed description. He had found the Jagged-whitlow-grass growing on houses in Dublin, and because it was 'accounted a Specifick against the *Kings-evil,* or *Strumae'*, especially by the Hon. Robert Boyle, Threlkeld repeated this wonderful receipt:

> Take an Handful of it, Boil it every Morning in a Quart of small Beer, strain it, and drink it for your ordinary Drink for a long Time.[11]

I am tempted to suggest that the page and a half written about this herb by Threlkeld means he suffered from king's-evil (scrofula, a chronic condition in which the lymphatic glands enlarge and degenerate) and had personally used the cure.

Charles Lucas undoubtedly had read Threlkeld's flora and thus must have known the medicinal reputation of rue-leaved saxifrage. In July 1740 he found Sedum alpinum folio trifido, as the herb was then named, in County Clare[12]–the exact locality is not recorded, but somewhere in or near The Burren is most likely.

Caleb Threlkeld added an interesting footnote to his cure for king's-evil, about a book that he owned, the third edition of John Gerard's great herbal:

> one of its former Owners has added these Words in my Copy: This is a perfect Cure for the *Kings-evil,* it flowers in the *Spring,* and perisheth with the Heat.[13]

And that is not inaccurate. In most years, *Saxifraga tridactylites* germinates in late summer or early autumn, over-winters as a rosette, and blossoms during April and May–occasionally as early as March. By the onset of summer when The Burren rockscape is usually parched, rue-leaved saxifrage plants have ripened and shed their seed, and begun withering to straw-coloured skeletons.

Seacht Srotha na Taosca, Seven Streams

TURLOUGHS
THE HALF-DROWNED BURREN

The province of Connaught has one species of curiosity in it
which I do not know that I have read of in any country. They call them
Terloughs… The superstition of the country people is that they begin
to break out upon a certain day and likewise to decrease at
a certain time, but that is apocryphal and fabulous.

Lord Chief Baron Edward Willes, 1760

urlach is a dry lough or, to use a more colloquial idiom, soft ground that is half-drowned. In its English form, turlough has entered the vocabulary of geography, a companion to two other Irish toponyms, drumlin (*droimnín*) and esker (*eiscir*).

Contradictory though it seems this antique word, known from mediaeval Irish texts, is remarkably descriptive. Patrick Dinneen's explanation is possibly the most succinct–he glossed *turlach* as 'a winter-lough or mere, dry or marshy in summer'.[1] As a geographical term it signifies basins within the limestone region that are occasionally full of fresh water, and occasionally dry; they alternate from being small loughs to being green grassy hollows depending on the rainfall and the season. During summer, a turlough is a small field, and in winter it will overflow with water.

Potentilla anserina: silverweed

Turloughs are happy hunting grounds for anyone interested in *Potentilla.* Five species inhabit the margins of these ephemeral ponds. Tormentil (*Potentilla erecta*) and creeping cinquefoil (*Potentilla reptans*) are familiar herbs with small yellow flowers, four petalled in tormentil and five-petalled in creeping cinquefoil. Marsh cinquefoil (*Potentilla palustris*) has brown-purple flowers and is a taller, stouter perennial. The fern-like, silvery-green leaves of silverweed (*Potentilla anserina*) will betray its presence down as far as the edge of the summer water, so it can survive a subaquatic existence for most, if not all of the winter. Around some turloughs, there is so much silverweed that it excludes almost every other herb. Yet if you venture to walk along the beach at Bishop's Quarter or The Rine you will see silverweed creeping out onto the sand where it can never be submerged in fresh water, and it grows in many other localities throughout the limestone hills.

Silverweed (*briosclán*) is a versatile species, capable of invading an open habitat by means of far-reaching, leap-frogging stolons that sprout roots and a new

Potentilla fruticosa: shrubby cinquefoil

rosette of leaves, and then grow on. The leaves are composed of deeply toothed, ovate leaflets arranged in opposite pairs. Some plants have especially silvery leaflets because of a dense covering of silky hairs; others may have leaflets green above but silver beneath, the hairs being so thinly distributed on the upper surface; in turlough populations, the leaves may appear green all over as there are few hairs on either surface. From nodes on the stolons and from rooted rosettes, more long stems arise bearing solitary, buttercup-like flowers that are identical with those of the shrubby cinquefoil, the fifth of the *Potentilla* species colonizing the turlough rims.

Charles Lucas was the first to report that shrubby cinquefoil grew in Ireland in his letter to Sir Hans Sloane, published during 1740 by the Royal Society. Lucas clearly knew the region east of his home well, and his magnificent description of the Cave of the Wild Horses at Kilcorney was prefaced by some remarks about plants; I noted this earlier but repeat it again. Lucas told Sloane that the barony of Burren

> produces immense quantities of Juniper & some Yew, besides great variety of the Capillary herbs... I have found the *Teucrium Alpinum magno flore* of Caspar Bauhin & a large Shrubby Cinquefoil answering the Description Mr Morison gives in his Second Volume of *Hyst. Oxon.* of his *Pentaphilloides rectum fruticosum Eboracense.*[2]

That paragraph contains unfamiliar plant names, which need to be translated into modern botanical Latin, because Lucas wrote before the modern system of naming was published by Carl Linnaues in 1753. Capillary herbs were plants used in medicines, and were thought especially useful in treating respiratory complaints–at the time Lucas was an apothecary practising in Dublin and would necessarily have been familiar with such plants. *Teucrium Alpinum magno flore* of Caspar Bauhin is the same as Richard Heaton's *Teucrium Alpinum Cisti flore*, 'Alpine Germander with a Cistus flower', in modern parlance *Dryas octopetala*, mountain avens. The shrubby cinquefoil–we still use that vernacular name–was called *Pentaphilloides rectum fruticosum Eboracense* by Professor Robert Morison in *Historia Oxoniense*; the phrase-name may be translated as 'Five-leafed, erect shrub of York'.

The colony of shrubby cinquefoil that grows nearest to Charles Lucas' home is the one about the margins of Lough Gealáin, at the foot of the vortex of Mullach Mór, north-east of Kilnaboy. From the lough, the cinquefoil colony extends some distance through the townland of Rockforest to the shores of Lough Bunny, Castle Lough and Lough George. This is the most extensive of The Burren's populations; the other two have many fewer plants. On the south-western slope of Gleninagh Mountain shrubby cinquefoils grow in bed of an intermittent stream; this colony was discovered by Frederick Foot in 1861 and is marked on his vegetation map of The Burren (see pp. 32-33).[3] It probably remains much as he saw it. The third one, south of Ballyvaghan village, was also recorded first by Foot and shown on the same map. He reported shrubby cinquefoil covering 'upwards of two acres of low-lying ground, or *Turloughs*'. Robert Welch photographed this particular population and his picture was printed in Robert Lloyd Praeger's book, *A tourist's flora of the west of Ireland*, with this caption

> *Potentilla fruticosa* at Ballyvaghan, Co. Clare. An almost continuous low growth, about two feet in height, extending over several acres of flat heathy limestone ground occasionally flooded.[4]

In 1988 and 1989 I walked the area shown on Frederick Foot's map, and found some woebegone cinquefoil shrubs around a hazel-ramparted turlough, but I could not trace anything like the 'almost continuous' carpet photographed by Robert Welch. Later, in December 1989, armed with an excellent print of the original, I set out to find the place where Welch had stood with his camera–it was not difficult given the various landmarks, especially the spire of St John's Church. No colony of shrubby cinquefoil surrounds Welch's camera site, just improved, artificial grassland in which sleek cows grazed contentedly, and a dense growth of hazel in the rockiest parts.

Last century, farmers would not have allowed cattle to graze the cinquefoil; Thaddeus O'Mahony and Francis Whitla learnt this from the people about Rockforest where they saw *Potentilla fruticosa* in 1851–'The peasantry believe it to be most deleterious to such cattle as browse upon it. They told us of cattle having died in consequence of having eaten thereof.'[5]

This is not the only tale of a curse on shrubby cinquefoil. While O'Mahony and Whitla were not regaled with other legends, Frederick Foot gleaned from natives of The Burren a more elaborate tale. In his paper 'On the distribution of plants in Burren, County of Clare', Foot retold the fable.

> The peasantry have a superstition, that it formerly grew to a great height, and bore thorns; and that from it the crown of thorns of the crucifixion was made, ever since which time it has been under a curse, lost its thorns, and become stunted in growth.[6]

Potentilla fruticosa is an intriguing, widespread species that circles the northern hemisphere in temperate latitudes; eastwards from The Burren, colonies survive in the English Lake District in Cumbria, at Teesdale in Yorkshire, and on Oland, Gotland and in the eastern Baltic; in southern Europe, slightly different races inhabit the Pyrenees, a very restricted area in the Alpes Maritimes, and one locality in Bulgaria; thence, continuing eastwards, populations are reported in the Caucasus and Ural Mountains, and through Siberia; across the Bering Straits, shrubby cinquefoil marches into Alaska, and Canada and the United States of America extending eastwards to Newfoundland; thereafter The Burren.

The North American plants that have been studied possess fourteen chromosomes in each cell and hermaphrodite flowers: they have fertile, pollen-laden stamens, and fertile, seed-bearing carpels.[7] Similar genetic races are known in the Pyrenees, Bulgaria, the Caucasus and central Siberia. But the Irish, English

Viola persicifolia: turlough violet

and Oland shrubs have a double set of chromosomes, twenty-eight in each cell–they are termed tetraploids–and the flowers are functionally single-sexed. A male flower has numerous fertile anthers containing pollen but hairs where the numerous carpels should be. In contrast each female blossom has fertile, swollen carpels and shrunken anthers incapable of producing pollen. Flowers of only one sex are produced by each plant. These different sexes are easy to spot in The Burren colonies; even with the naked eye, it is quickly evident if the carpels, in the centre of the blossom, are fertile, or if they are moribund.

There is a substantial variation in flower size and fullness–some petals are broad and overlap giving the blossom a rounded form, while others are starry with narrow petals that do not even touch. A proportion of Irish plants produces rather small flowers, just over one centimetre across, yet many have flowers twice that in diameter. A walk through the stands of shrubby cinquefoil will yield all these variants, and perhaps, if you are eagle-eyed, you will spot blossoms with more than five petals. As far as I can trace, double-flowered *Potentilla fruticosa*,[8] with ten or more petals, has not been reported from the wild, yet I found a clump beside Lough Gealáin in July 1987–it stood out for its striking large, frilly flowers. Alas my cuttings failed to root, but the original is still there, perhaps to be found by someone else. In the summer of 1990 I stumbled upon another shrub producing ten-petalled, well-rounded flowers, and also one with more than fifteen narrow petals in each blossom.

Shrubs of *Potentilla fruticosa* rarely exceed one metre in height, and being deciduous, the brown-grey twiggy stems do not look very attractive in the winter

98

Taraxacum palustre: marsh dandelion

if they happen to be above water–however many plants are submerged during winter as the shrubby cinquefoil only inhabits the belt of ground between the summer low-watermark, and the winter flood-mark. When the turlough levels drop in late spring, and the shrubs emerge from their underwater hibernation, the leaves begin to unfurl, and by the end of May the first blooms should be out. Some plants have green foliage but, as in silverweed, the density of hairs varies, and therefore other plants appear pale and silvery; the leaves are composed of three to seven leaflets, and as its names (cinquefoil, and in Irish *tor cúigmhéarach*) suggest the usual number is five. Flowering does not reach a peak until August, although occasional shrubs are in full blow at the beginning of July. By late September most will be out of bloom. At the peak of the season, the lough nestling below the sweep of Mullach Mór has a lemon-gold band like a Celtic torc about it.

As the water drains away through the underground channels during April and May, grass and other herbs begin to grow. Rapidly, bright green young leaves break through the encrustation of lime deposited by the retreating water. By late May, there are new flowers among the green leaves, and prime among the early summer blossoms are the grinning faces of the delicate turlough violets.

Turlough violets (*Viola persicifolia*) are rare outside Clare and southern Galway, but they make up for this by growing in considerable profusion in some of The Burren turloughs. In England this species is called the fen violet (*sailchuach uisce* is its Irish synonym), and populations there have declined so much that it is protected by law. Its other Irish stations are in Fermanagh (therefore this is also a protected plant in Northern Ireland), Mayo, Longford and Roscommon.

Like all The Burren's violets, when not in bloom this little creeping herb is easily overlooked, its toothed leaves melting in among the other lush foliage of the sward. Turlough violet flowers however cannot easily be forgotten–the smiling face comprises five broad, short, blunt-tipped petals, pale duck-egg blue, lightly lilac-tinted, with a pure white throat. The large, middle petal of the lower lip is delicately marked with dark lines that run back into the spur, and there are similar but less prominent markings on the two upper petals.

Dog violets (*Viola canina*) also grow around turloughs; they inhabit a zone above the turlough violets and the distances quoted by Praeger in his paper on the botany of turloughs, suggest that the two species are usually separated by about one metre.[9] Dog violets are in blossom first, and have darker flowers with a yellow spur, and more distinctly heart-shaped leaves. Hybrids between *Viola canina* and *Viola persicifolia* are not uncommon where they grow side by side.

Several botanical visitors to The Burren mentioned the tricolor of white, blue and red–mountain avens, Spring gentians, and bloody cranesbill–that 'flew' from the limestone hills (to suggest this was a politically motivated vision is far-fetched[10]). I fancy that the flags are changed with the seasons and from the poetic rainbow yellow, indigo and purple are as frequently displayed. As befits western Ireland, green in myriad shades is never absent. Summer by a turlough is yellow with marsh marigolds, yellow worts, silverweeds and cinquefoils; purple is provided by bog thistle, pyramidal orchids and bloody cranesbill; the indigo buds on devil's bit scabious complete the new tricolor.

Dandelion flowers are yellow–there is no more colourful display than a unkempt sidewalk bordered by dandelions in full bloom on a sunny day in early spring. The large-headed, far too-familiar dandelions of gardens are unwelcome weeds–plants in the wrong place at the wrong time–whereas the petite dandelions of The Burren, including *Taraxacum palustre*, are neither out of place nor untimely.

I found a strange little dandelion, with narrow, linear leaves growing in the soapy grey mud towards the north-eastern corner of Lough Gealáin during June 1987. It was all by itself, and evidently had just emerged from submerged hibernation. The flower-head was smaller than that of the common dandelion, and deeper yellow verging on gold. The flower-stalk was red, and emerged from the rosette horizontally turning upwards towards the tip. I had not knowingly encountered a dandelion like it before, and certainly not one which was capable of surviving for part of the year underwater, and soon identified it as *Taraxacum palustre* (marsh dandelion). I have seen the same dandelion elsewhere since in much greater profusion and in places where the mud does not so closely resemble over-cooked porridge. It blooms in April and May and is easy to distinguish–nothing else like it grows about the rims of the turloughs.

There are no fewer than twenty-one different species of *Taraxacum* listed from The Burren, mostly from the western sector, and none bears a familiar name such as the much-loved binomial *Taraxacum officinale*. That there can be more than one species of dandelion, and that they can be so different from the garden weed will surprise some people.

This mud-lark of a dandelion belongs to *Taraxacum* section Palustria, a section represented in Ireland by only two species, *Taraxacum palustre*, and *Taraxacum webbii*;[11] the second one was named as a tribute to Professor David Webb, doyen of Irish botanists, who was responsible for stimulating so much of the recent research in The Burren. *Taraxacum webbii*, described by Dr John Richards of the University of Newcastle-upon-Tyne, has been collected amongst *Potentilla fruticosa* near Ballyvaghan, at Lough Bunny and near Ballinderreen, and from habitats in County Mayo and County Cavan.

There is little use turning to any currently available flora of Ireland for help in naming dandelions–Professor Webb's *An Irish Flora*, which is the standard manual, contains only three very broadly defined 'aggregate' species. So it is comforting to read in John Richard's monograph that *Taraxacum palustre* occurs 'in considerable abundance around most of the turloughs from Carron and Turlough village to Ballinderreen, Gort and Mullaghmore.'[12] However the marsh dandelion is rare

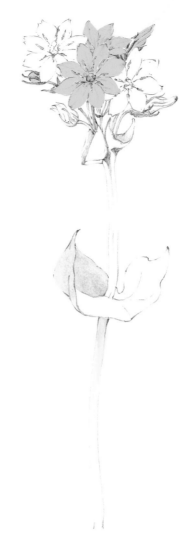

Blackstonia perfoliata: yellow wort

and apparently declining throughout the rest of Europe, so much so that in 1972, before he knew about its exuberance in The Burren, John Richards was prompted to write that 'the world population may well number less than 1,000 plants.' There are many gardeners, plagued by *Taraxacum officinale* in its grossest guise, for whom such a state of affairs would be heavenly bliss.

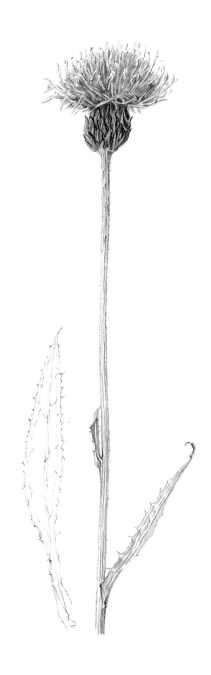

Cirsium dissectum
bog thistle

Of yellow-flowered plants few can vie with yellow wort; in older accounts, this delightful flower is noted by the name *Chlora perfoliata*. Its current name, *Blackstonia perfoliata*, commemorates an English apothecary and botanist, John Blackstone. The Irish name, *dréimire buí*, yellow ladder, is a perfect description of yellow wort. It is an annual herb about ten centimetres tall, with a cluster of lemon-coloured flowers atop an erect, unbranched stem; both stem and leaves are dusty grey-green. Each flower is formed from eight petals united at their bases into a short tube that is concealed within an eight-lobed calyx; there are eight stamens and a two-lobed stigma. The most distinctive character of yellow wort, apart from its flowers, is the perfoliate arrangement of the leaves which are paired along the stem, and each pair is fused together so that the stem appears to be threaded through a single boat-shaped leaf–a similar, perfoliate arrangement is found in some species of the Australian genus *Eucalyptus* (gum-trees).

Blackstonia is not related in any way to *Eucalyptus*, but is a close relative of the Spring gentian. Other representatives of the gentian family (Gentianaceae) in The Burren are common centaury (*Centaurium erythaea*), another annual, not so tall as yellow wort, with coral-pink flowers that is abundant especially on the sand-dunes at Fanore, Autumn gentian (*Gentianella amarella*) which is seen in its full glory and in a remarkable range of hues on the dunes at Bishop's Quarter, and the much rarer field gentian (*Gentianella campestris*).

While *Blackstonia perfoliata* is strictly confined to habitats rich in lime, it is not necessarily restricted in The Burren to turlough rims. It grows throughout, from the slopes of Black Head to the lowland pavements around Gort.

Turloughs are unique to Ireland, but not unique to The Burren; there are examples from Limerick northwards to Mayo, and even a couple in north Kilkenny.[13] They share one common characteristic, subterranean drainage, but otherwise they can vary both in their structure and origins. Some are basins in the limestone rock, yet many are not floored by rock and instead occupy hollows in the glacial deposits which remain on top of the limestone. Dr P. Williams recognized two other general types of turlough:[14] lowland turloughs are those which fill with water in winter as the ground-water level rises and they may not become completely dry in summer; upland turloughs fill with water after heavy rainfall at any time of the year because water, unable to drain through the underground channels quickly enough, backs up. The lowland type are abundant especially in the eastern part of The Burren near Gort–just west of the town the road to Kilmacduagh traverses the edge of one example–while upland turloughs are much less numerous and occur only in The Burren hills–examples include Lough Aleenaun a short distance north of Kilfenora.

From the botanical point of view, the more interesting plants of the turloughs are those that colonize the margins, especially between the winter high-water and summer (permanent) low-water levels. Robert Lloyd Praeger paid particular attention to this zone and its plants[15]–his paper is one of the very few published accounts of the flora of these remarkable habitats. He commented on the soils and sward: 'the vegetation of the turloughs is usually nibbled to the last leaf–often much more closely shorn than could be done with a lawn-mower.' Some of the most attractive wild flowers of The Burren inhabit only the seasonally-submerged margins of the turloughs. Contrariwise, the alternating waterlogged and dry conditions are not congenial for the majority of species that grow on the pavements–Spring gentian, mountain avens, and bloody cranesbill cannot abide sodden wet soil nor even occasional floods, and will not grow below the winter high-water mark.

Those turloughs that do not empty completely in the summer have flotillas of white and yellow waterlilies and maybe fringing clumps of bog-bean (*Menyanthes trifoliata*); reeds, club-rushes (*Sparganium*) and the great fen-sedge also flourish at the water's edge. Among the plants making up the fine, closely-munched sward between the water-marks are sedges, plantains, water-mints, buttercups, watercresses and yellow-cresses (*Rorippa* spp.). These flowering plants, and some mosses, grow contentedly in the 'soapy loam' (to borrow Praeger's description[15]) and wet clay which form the soil in the flooded areas, a glutinous, sucking mud which is best avoided for not only will it stick messily to boots and clothes, it is far too soft to walk on.

Two aquatic mosses, *Cinclidotus fontinaloides* and *Fontinalis antipyretica*, are particular to turlough rims; they are most obvious as black patches when water-levels are low in summer. Dr Praeger measured the relative positions of the upper limits of these and found that *Fontinalis* did not reach so far from the permanent low-water level, indicating that it needs a longer period of submergence than *Cinclidotus*–he also noticed that unlike *Cinclidotus*, *Fontinalis* colonized the sides of rocks. *Cinclidotus*, on the other hand, is tolerant of a longer period of desiccation, and can grow much further from the low-water level, but it does need a considerable period of winter flooding for survival.[15]

The flora of a turlough and its rim, particularly one with limestone pavement encircling, is not summed up by the few plants selected here. Grasses and sedges are present in abundance and there are possibly unique forms of shrubs, even of trees. At Lough Gealáin, the scailps on the eastern shore harbour an unusual, apparently prostrate blackthorn (*Prunus spinosa*) that has slender stems and soft spines, and blooms many weeks after its erect, hedgerow siblings. Prostate forms of purging buckthorn (*Rhamnus catharticus* var. *prostratus*[16]) and alder buckthorn (*Frangula alnus*[17]) also inhabit these scailps; both have thin flexible shoots that spread horizontally and lie closely appressed to the rocks. No research has been carried out, as far as I am aware, to discover if these variants remain prostrate when cultivated in a 'normal' environment. Perhaps, if water did not ebb and flow with the seasons, submerging both rocks and shrubs for many months, the buckthorns and blackthorns would adopt again an erect habit.

A common associate of turlough violets, silverweed, and marsh dandelion in the zone below the winter high-water level is a thistle of elegant simplicity with vivid purple blossoms. Like silverweed, bog thistle is not too particular about the length of time it is inundated, and so it can be encountered anywhere between the winter and summer water-marks, and it is not confined to turlough sward.

As the summer advances and the grasses and sedges grows more rankly, the beautiful flowers of the bog thistle appear above the greenery. The flower-heads are solitary atop thin, straight stems which are coated with white hairs. A few softly-prickled leaves clasp the stem, but the larger ones are clustered at the base; the leaves usually are entire with a white felt on the lower side. The rich purple flowers are tightly clustered into a single head enclosed within an involucre of dark bracts.

This is not by any means a rare plant in the north and west of Ireland, but it is not nearly as common in eastern counties. In The Burren *Cirsium dissectum* is frequent, but bog thistle strangely does not occur on the Aran Islands, and while flourishing in the lime-rich soils around turloughs, is equally abundant on the lime-free peatlands of Connemara. Praeger, in his marvellous book *The botanist in Ireland*, noted that where wet grassland was enriched with lime *Cirsium dissectum* (as *Cnicus pratensis*) occurred with grass of Parnassus and a suite of orchids. He also noted that on exposed rocky heathlands beside the ocean in Connemara bog thistle was equally at home mingled with cross-leaved heath and bog asphodel.[18]

Among the various associations delimited by Ivimey-Cook and Proctor is one characterised by black bog-rush (*Schoenus nigricans*) and bog thistle; it is a community found in calcareous fens, at the edges of loughs. As well as these two plants, tormentil, devil's-bit scabious (*Succisa pratensis*) and several grasses (for example, the famous *feorainn* or creeping bent (*Agrostis stolonifera*), and purple moor-grass (*Molinia caerulea*)) are constant members. This community will not last for ever–it is not a 'climax' association, but one that is a staging-post. Ivimey-Cook and Proctor projected its future thus: as a peaty soil accumulates and the ground level rises slowly above the influence of lime-rich water, the soil surface becomes more and more acidified and eventually lime-tolerant plants disappear; purple moor-grass then becomes the dominant herb and bog myrtle (*Myrica gale*) begins to invade followed by cross-leaved heath and sphagnum moss. Once these plant are established, the calcareous fen has been converted into a raised bog.[19] This progression has already begun in the subsidiary turlough at the foot of Mullach Mór where bog myrtle is well established with black bog-rush and bladderwort (*Utricularia intermedia*).

Be that as it may, raised bogs are not a feature of The Burren–it will be many millennia yet before the turloughs are submerged below heather covered peatland.

The earliest account of turloughs that I can discover is by one of the members of the Dublin Philosophical Society, William King, later Bishop of Derry and Archbishop of Dublin, published in the *Philosophical Transactions* of The Royal Society of London during 1685;[20] 'Of the bogs and Loughs of Ireland' was republished in the 1726 reprinting of Gerard Boate's *A Natural history of Ireland*. King did not mention turloughs in The Burren, but avers that 'they are chiefly in *Connaught*…' Be that as it may, the strange 'vanishing' loughs of Ireland have been on record for more than three centuries.

Several subsequent observers never got around to publishing their observations on turloughs. Edward Willes' description and explanations, even his ingenious (but neither original nor correct) attempt to derive 'terlough' from Latin,[21] were not published until 1990; Lord Warwick tried but failed to persuade Willes to have his letters about Ireland printed. Lord Chief Baron Willes was told about turloughs when he passed through eastern Clare in 1761–without knowing, he rode across one, over a bridge that seemed to him pointless because there were fine meadows, not water, on either side. After making diligent enquiries he wrote to the Earl of Warwick:

In many parts of this province every year, may lakes rise out of the ground, the water of which covers the ground for 30, 40 nay to 500 acres, and continues till the end of spring, when they gradually sink again into the ground and it throws up the finest pasture and grass, and is the best meadow ground in the county... In many of them are visible apertures of 6 or 8 inches diameter. In some they know of no apertures, but suppose [water] sokes thro' the ground; where there are appertures it bubles up like a great spring, and in some throws up the water above a foot high; when the water subsides and retire into the earth, the country people catch eels and large trouts in them. The superstition of the country people is that they begin to break out upon a certain day and likewise to decrease at a certain time, but that is apocryphal and fabulous. The truth is they break out sooner or later in winter according to the greater or smaller quantity of rains that fall and subside sooner or later for the same reason. Why these terloughs are peculiar to this part of the world may be very dificul [sic] to determine. The most probable account seems to be this: this country is a great rock of limestone, and by the multitude of subterraneous rivers, which run thro' the cavities of the rocks, and which break out above ground and sink again in so many places in this country (and indeed in so many that they are not consider'd on as any kind of curiosity by the inhabitants) I presume that when towards winter more water falls in rain than the subterraneous rocky channels can contain, it forces the water out into these several low meadow grounds; what makes this more probable is the quantity of els and trouts which are found in the terloughs and which are seen and known to be in great plenty in these kind of amphibious rivers which run above and below ground.[21]

Also unpublished was Dr Patrick Browne's flora of Ireland; this Mayo botanist knew turloughs in north-eastern Galway, and noticed that they were habitats for meadow rue (*Thalictrum*).[22] Joseph Woods was perhaps the first botanist to employ 'turlough' in a description of The Burren, but his account remained as an unprinted manuscript until recent years.

A little below Kilfenora is a large Turlough and there are several smaller ones in the neighbourhood. These are among the singularities of the country. They are pieces of flat land generally of very fine and rich pasture. After continual rain the water issues through some holes or under some rocks on the borders and presently covers them with lakes. After a time the water runs off again generally by the same openings. The subterraneous rivers whose overflowings supply the Turloughs are the only streams in the limestone country. There is no continued stream of water and no constantly descending valley in which such a stream could run. Mr Lysaght has cut through a hill and drained one of these Turloughs at the expense of about 150£ and converted a property of 15£ pr annum into one of a hundred. Indeed it is impossible to conceive a finer & richer black mould than that of these turloughs or a closer and more luxuriant herbage. How far this latter might suffer by the drainage I cannot tell but I conceive that one advantage is the throwing into one hand what before was common to many, for these Turloughs are mostly in commons and they are the only commons I met with in Ireland.[23]

Botanic Gardens and Fern Nurseries
Glenarra House, Ballyvaughan, Co. Clare, Ireland

The Botanic Gardens and Fern Nurseries
are situated within 20 minutes walk of Ballyvaughan,
and one hour's drive from Lisdoonvarna. Visitors are
respectfully invited to inspect the stock and select
their desiderata on Mondays, Wednesdays
and Saturdays, if possible.

P. B. O'Kelly: A catalogue of plants, 1893

PATRICK B. O'KELLY

While Charles Lucas, physician and patriot, was a native of Clare he did not come from the ancient barony of Burren, and whereas his contribution to knowledge of the county's plants was singular it was nevertheless insubstantial. There was another man, born in Burren, who by devoting his time to the pursuit of wildflowers made a lasting impact on knowledge of the region's flora. He was a farmer, a Ballyvaghan man, Patrick Bernard Kelly; his alias was Dr P. B. O'Kelly, nurseryman, botanist.[1]

Patrick, one of the sons of John and Bridget Kelly, was baptised on 1 August 1852; he may have been the eldest in the family which at that time lived in Kilweelran, a mountainy wedge of a townland in the parish of New Quay between Ballyvaghan and Kinvarra, a rock-strewn place like most other townlands in the barony. Today Kilweelran has only three inhabited houses, but abandoned fluorspar workings at the head of Gleann na Manach proclaim a more industrious, if not a more populous past. By 1855 John Kelly and his family had moved to the adjacent townland of Ballyhehan, nowadays cloaked with a mixture of hazel scrub and pasture; it also has just three houses. By the time Patrick's brother Stephen was born in 1861, they had moved again, into Aillwee townland, immediately south of both Kilweelran and Ballyhehan. No-one lives there today although derelict houses, redundant calcite workings, a disused lead and silver mine dating from 1836 and a tumbledown mill that is hidden in a secret valley beside a flowing spring, betray a lively history.

Patrick's childhood is mysterious beyond those few facts, but two things may be deduced with some certainty–he learned to read and write, and he gained a considerable and accurate knowledge of the ferns and flowers of The Burren hills. Eventually he left the townlands of his childhood, and by the early 1890s, approaching his forties, had taken up residence in Glenarra House, a two-storey cottage south of Ballyvaghan about halfway along the Lisdoonvarna road towards Corkscrew Hill. Patrick Kelly conducted his nursery business from Glenarra and created a garden which boasted an astonishing collection of exotic trees, shrubs and herbs–he had, for example, herb Paris (*Paris quadrifolia*),[2] miniature daffodils and one of the rarest British orchids, the lady's slipper (*Cypripedium calceolus*).

Kelly was a big man, tall, robust, with huge hands, and a fine bushy beard. He enjoyed a pint of stout and is remembered as a skilful exponent of the pub-game called 'corks'. Ballyvaghan lads knew he liked rabbit stew, and they could earn a few pence from him by supplying a brace for his pot. The parochial register records that Kelly was a farmer and while this probably was so, He was also an inveterate plant-hunter. Perhaps he had independent means and thus could afford to spend his days botanizing rather than farming, but it is hard to fathom how any farmer's son, living in such a remote region in the late 1800s, could have accumulated or inherited a fortune. There was, however, that other side to Patrick Kelly–his universal alias, P. B. O'Kelly, botanist and nurseryman, and salesman extraordinary.

Some time before 1884 Patrick adopted the surname O'Kelly; he was perhaps doing nothing more than reverting to the original, or perhaps following the current fashion for all things Celtic. As P. B. O'Kelly he is still remembered by older folk in the Ballyvaghan area for the countless parcels of plants he sent to places far from Clare–thanks to him Ballyvaghan post-office must have been a busy place early this century. People still speak highly of his knowledge of the local wildflowers; incidentally, as a service to distant customers O'Kelly offered to identify any native plant, asking only that 'proper' specimens be forwarded with a one penny stamp for the reply. Tourists who frequented the resorts of north Clare nick-named him 'The Doctor'; indeed not only is Dr O'Kelly retained as his title by respectful Clare folk in recognition of his botanical learning–there is not a shred of evidence that he studied at university, nor that he was granted a doctorate–but there are even specimens in botanical institutes in Britain labelled 'collected by Dr P. B. O'Kelly'.[3]

Patrick O'Kelly was most probably self-taught, his botanical knowledge accumulated simply by observation of the plants growing in the wild, for he is reputed to have walked on the limestone hills most days–Thomas O'Donoghue of Ballyvaghan, who often drove O'Kelly to remoter parts on botanical quests, recalls him carrying that singular badge of the field botanist in bygone days, a vasculum. Boulee was among his favourite places; the townland encompasses part of the low ground on the eastern side of Turloughmore Mountain. Frequently O'Kelly went to Lisdoonvarna to meet visitors before escorting them in The Burren and he showed Burren plants to many erudite, visiting botanists. George Claridge Druce of the University of Oxford was so guided in 1907, and O'Kelly certainly accompanied Henry Levinge during the 1890s. Robert Lloyd Praeger also knew him. In fact, it is probable that any half-inquisitive traveller who bothered to seek botanical advice locally between the 1880s and 1930s encountered P. B. O'Kelly.

This big man is unlikely ever to be forgotten. In the company of a select band of botanists–Druce, Levinge and Praeger, for example–he has attained a certain immortality because his name, Latinized, has been wished upon a flower; *Dactylorhiza fuchsii* f. *okellyi* is the white-flowered variant of the spotted orchid that abounds in The Burren. Moreover, O'Kelly was the first to collect a somewhat perplexing hybrid pondweed (*Potamogeton* x *lanceolatus*)[4] in the Caher River during 1891, water germander (*Teucrium scordium*) and mudwort (*Limosella aquatica*) in Ireland. He also claimed to have found a natural hybrid between common bugle (*Ajuga reptans*) and pyramidal bugle (*Ajuga pyramidalis*)[5] but, as I will explain later, I believe he was mistaken.

Among the earliest evidence of O'Kelly's entrepreneurial skills is a small folded leaflet (opposite), offering plants for sale. A copy reached the editors of *The Irish Naturalist*, who were incensed and printed a sarcastic rebuke in September 1893: among their ripostes was this comment on the identification service offered and, *inter alia*, some typographic peculiarities of the list–

> …if plants are returned labelled with such appellations as "*Anemone nemorosa purpurea Livingrii*," "*Berberis vulgaris superbum*," or " *Trifolium repens purpurea folins*," we fear that serious injury may be caused to the enquirer's nervous system.[6]

Undaunted, O'Kelly about 1895 issued a much expanded catalogue, an elaborate booklet of twenty-nine pages printed by Littlebury & Co. of Worcester. *Catalogue of choice hardy perennial, alpine, and herbaceous plants & evergreen shrubs…* bears the address 'Burren Nurseries & Botanic Gardens', but sadly lacks an expansive explanation on the contents, although the phrase 'gems of the first water' does appear three times, and 'rare' and 'very rare' are liberally applied to plants throughout. Plants, exotic and native, were offered either singly or by the dozen (with a suitable reduction in price): thus the 'extremely rare' *Ajuga pyramidalis* cost one shilling and six pence each, or twelve-and-six pence per dozen; *Epilobium alpinum* was 'very rare' and O'Kelly asked two-and-six for a plant or one pound (twenty shillings) for a dozen; large tufts of *Gentiana verna* could be supplied for four shillings per dozen; and 'Evergreen Irish mosses, 12 clumps in six sorts' were available for four-and-six pence. Ferns generally cost from three to six pence each; the 'very rare' *Adiantum capillus incisum*–whatever that was–had the highest tag, nine pence per plant or six-and-six a dozen.

The most interesting page is the second wherein O'Kelly advertised two other publications, *Catalogue of 1042 Species and varieties of British ferns* (it cost three pence) and *Catalogue of the flora of County Clare* (only two pence a copy).

> These two interesting Catalogues contain about 600 new sorts of Irish Ferns and plants which were never before discovered in any part of the World. They are just now ready for commerce. Please note that the two Catalogues cannot be obtained elsewhere. They will be sent post free to any part of the United Kingdom on receipt of 5 Penny Stamps.

What glories were there among the 1042 species and varieties of ferns on offer? We may never know for nowhere can I trace copies of the catalogues; they *must* be 'gems of the first water' and their discovery would be more than welcome.

A Complete List of the Rare
Perennial Plants & Shrubs

Of the Burren Mountains of Ballyvaughan, Co. Clare.

By *PATRICK B. O'KELLY*,

Glenarra House, *BALLYVAUGHAN*,

County Clare, *IRELAND*.

☞ The Names and Prices are as follows :—

No.		Each. s. d.	No.		Each. s. d.
1	Achillea Millefolium purpurea, purple flower	0 6	37	Carex lævigata	0 6
2	Ajuga pyramidalis, very rare	2 0	38	—— pendula...	1 6
3	—— reptans purpurea, purple flower, new	1 6	39	—— remota ...	1 0
4	Alliaria officinalis	0 6	40	—— stellulata	1 0
5	Allium Schœnoprasum...	1 6	41	—— ampullacea	1 0
6	—— Sphærocephalum ...	1 6	42	—— sylvatica	1 0
7	—— vineale ...	1 0	43	—— vesicaria	2 0
8	Althæa officinalis	1 6	44	—— riparia ...	1 6
9	Anemone nemorosa purpurea Livingrii, new	1 0	45	—— Pseudo-cyperus	2 6
10	Antennaria dioica	0 6	46	Carlina vulgaris	0 6
11	Anthemis nobilis	0 6	47	Centaurea Scabiosa	0 6
12	Aquilegia vulgaris	0 6	48	Cerastium arvense	0 6
13	—— alba, white flower, new	1 6	49	—— —— Andrewsii...	1 6
14	—— cærulea, blue flower, new	1 6	50	Chærophyllum anthriscu	0 0
15	Arabis hirsuta	0 6	51	Chenopodium Bonus Henricus	0 6
16	—— Thaliana	0 6	52	Chlora perfoliata	0 6
17	Arctostaphylos Uva-ursi, sh. rare	1 0	53	—— aureum, new	2 6
18	Arenaria verna, rare	1 0	54	Chrysanthemum Leucanthemum...	0 6
19	Artemisia Absinthium ...	0 6	55	—— segetum	0 6
20	—— maritima, rare	1 0	56	Circæa alpina	1 6
21	Asperula Cynanchica, rare	1 0	57	Clematis Vitalba, an Exquisite Climber	1 0
22	—— odorata...	1 0	58	Comarum palustre (Shrub)	0 6
23	Aster Tripolium, very nice	0 6	59	Cornus sanguinea (Shrub), rare ...	1 6
24	Atriplex portulacoides, (Shrub) ...	0 6	60	Cytisus scoparius (Shrub)	1 0
25	Barbarea vulgaris, variegata, new	1 0	61	Dipsacus fullonum	1 0
26	Berberis vulgaris superbum, new	2 6	62	—— pilosus	2 6
27	Butomus umbellatus, very pretty	2 0	63	Drosera anglica, carnivorous plant	1 0
28	Cakile maritima	1 6	64	—— longifolia	1 0
29	Calamintha officinalis ...	0 6	65	—— rotundifolia	0 6
30	Calluna vulgaris alba, white flower	1 0	66	Dryas octopetala (Shrub)	1 0
31	Campanula rotundifolia, alba	1 6	67	—— fl. pl. ...	2 0
32	Cardamine pratensis fl. pl.	1 6	68	Empetrum nigrum (Shrub)	0 6
33	Carduus nutans	2 6	69	Epilobium montanum ...	0 6
34	—— Marianus	1 0	70	—— hirsutum	0 6
35	—— pycnocephalus	0 6	71	Epipactis latifolia (Orchis)	1 0
36	—— pratensis	0 6	72	—— palustris (Orchis)	1 0
			73	Equisetum sylvaticum ...	1 0
			74	Erica cinerea, alba, white flower	1 6

No.		Each. s. d.
75	Erigeron acris	0 6
76	Eriocaulon septangulare	1 6
77	Erodium cicutarium	0 6
78	—— —— alba,white flower, new	2 0
79	—— maritimum	1 0
80	Eryngium maritimum (Sea Holly)	0 6
81	Eupatorium cannabinum	0 6
82	Euphorbia Paralias	0 6
83	—— portlandica	1 0
84	Euonymus europæus (Shrub)	1 0
85	Filago minima	0 6
86	Fœniculum officinale, very rare	1 6
87	Fragaria vesca, fl. pl.	1 0
88	Galium boreale	1 0
89	—— Mollugo	1 6
90	—— pusillum	0 6
91	Gentiana campestris	0 6
92	—— verna	1 0
93	—— —— alba, white flower	5 0
94	Geranium molle alba, white flower	0 6
95	—— lucidum	0 6
96	—— sanguineum, very pretty	1 0
97	Geum rivale	0 6
98	Glaucium luteum	1 0
99	Glyceria maritima	0 6
100	—— rigida	0 6
101	Gymnadenia albida (Orchis)	1 0
102	—— conopsea (Gnat Orchis)	0 6
103	—— —— alba, white flower	2 0
104	Habenaria albida (Rare Orchis)	1 0
105	—— chlorantha (Butterfly Orchis)	1 6
106	—— bifolia (Orchis)	0 6
107	—— viridis (Orchis)	1 0
108	Hedera canariensis, variegata new	2 6
109	Helianthemum canum	1 0
110	—— canum vineale	1 6
111	Hesperis matronalis	0 6
112	Helosciadium inundatum	1 0
113	Hieracium alpinum	2 0
114	—— iricum	1 0
115	—— murorum	0 6
116	Honckenia Peploides	0 6
117	Humulus Lupulus(The Hop Plant)	0 6
118	Hyacinthus nonscriptus	0 6
119	Hydrocharis Morsus-Ranæ	0 6
120	Hyoscyamus niger	1 0
121	Hypericum Androsæmum, berry-bearing	1 0
122	—— elodes	0 6
123	—— humifusum	1 0
124	—— pulchrum	0 6
125	—— montanum	1 0
126	—— perforatum	0 6
127	—— calycinum (Rose-of-Sharon)	1 0
128	Hypochœris glabra	1 0
129	Ilex Aquifolium (Shrub Holly)	0 6
130	Inula Helenium, rare	1 0
131	Iris fœtidissima, rare	1 0
132	Jasione montana	0 6

No.		Each. s. d.
133	Juncus maritimus	0 6
134	—— squarrosus	0 6
135	—— glaucus	0 6
136	—— acutus	0 6
137	Juniperus Nana, shrub	0 6
138	Kœleria cristata	0 6
139	Lathræa squamaria(Toothwort) rare	1 0
140	Lavatera arborea, very rare	1 0
141	Leontodon hispidus	0 6
142	Ligustrum vulgare (Shrub Privet)	0 6
143	Linaria Cymbalaria	0 6
144	—— Elatine, rare	1 6
145	Linum catharticum	0 6
146	Lathyrus maritimus, very rare	2 6
147	Listera ovata (Orchis)	0 6
148	Lithospermum officinale	0 6
149	Lonicera Periclymenum (Climbing Shrub)	0 6
150	Lotus major	1 0
151	Luzula pilosa	1 0
152	—— sylvestris	0 6
153	Lychnis Dioica, rare	1 0
154	Lycopodium alpinum, rare	1 6
155	—— inundatum, rare	1 6
156	—— selaginoides	0 6
157	Lycopus europœus	0 6
158	Lysimachia nemorum aureum	2 0
159	—— Nummularia, creeper	0 6
160	—— punctata	0 6
161	Lythrum Salicaria, pretty purple flower	0 6
162	Mercurialis perennis	0 6
163	Malaxis paludosa, very rare Orchis	2 6
164	Malva moschata (Musk-mallow)	1 0
165	—— parviflora	0 6
166	—— sylvestris, pretty	0 6
167	Marrubium vulgare (Horehound), rare	1 6
168	Matricaria Parthenium, rare	1 6
169	Melampyrum pratense	0 6
170	—— sylvaticum	1 0
171	—— aquatica	1 6
172	Mentha aquatica variegata	1 0
173	—— piperita, peppermint equal to perfume	0 6
174	—— Puleginm (Pennyroyal) rare	1 0
175	—— rotundifolia	0 6
176	—— sylvestris, rare	1 0
177	—— viridis	0 6
178	Menyanthes trifoliata	0 6
179	Mertensia maritima, rare	2 6
180	Mimulus luteus (Yellow Monkey Flower)	1 0
181	Myosotis palustris	0 6
182	—— sylvaticum (Wood Forget-me-not)	0 6
183	—— —— alba, white flower	1 0
184	Myrica Gale, shrub	0 6
185	Myriophyllum spicatum	0 6

116

No.		Each. s. d.	No.		Each. s. d.
186	Nardus stricta	1 0	240	Rubia tinctoria ...	0 6
187	Narcissus major	0 6	241	Rubus cæsius...	0 6
188	Narthecium ossifragum (Day Lily)	0 6	242	—— Idæus	0 6
189	Nasturtium amphibium, rare ...	1 6	243	—— fruticosus aurens, new ...	2 0
190	Neotinia intacta, rare Orchis ...	1 6	244	—— saxatilis	0 6
191	Nepeta Cataria, very rare ...	2 0	245	Sagina subulata, rare	1 0
192	Nuphar luteum (Yellow Water Lily)	0 6	246	Salix pentandra (Shrub), rare ...	1 6
193	Nymphæa alba (White Water Lily)	0 6	247	—— repens	0 6
194	Œnanthe crocata	0 6	248	—— Sambucus Ebulus, rare ...	1 0
195	—— Phellandrium	0 6	249	Saponaria officinalis	1 0
196	Œnothera odorata (Evening Prim- rose)	1 0	250	Saxifraga hypnoides	0 6
197	Ononis camprestris	0 6	251	—— Sternbergii, rare	1 0
198	Ophrys apifera (Bee Orchis) ...	0 6	252	—— tridactylites	0 4
199	—— muscifera (Fly Orchis) ...	1 0	253	Scutellaria galericulata ...	0 6
200	Orchis latifolia	0 6	254	Scirpus acicularis, rare... ...	1 0
201	—— —— alba, white flower, (Orchis)	2 0	255	Sedum anglicum	0 6
202	—— maculata	0 6	256	—— Rhodiola	0 6
203	—— —— alba	0 9	257	—— Telephium, very rare, 2 ft. high	1 0
204	—— mascula...	0 2	258	Sempervivum tectorum ...	1 0
205	—— —— alba, white flower ...	2 0	259	Senecio sarracenicus, rare ...	1 6
206	—— Morio	1 0	260	—— sylvaticus	1 0
207	—— pyramidalis	0 6	261	Sesleria cærulea	0 6
208	—— —— coccinea	1 6	262	Silene maritima	
209	Origanum vulgare	0 6	263	Sium latifolium, rare	2 0
210	Orobanche Hederæ	1 0	264	Smyrnium Olusatrum, rare ...	1 0
211	—— minor, very rare	3 6		Plant used as cabbage by the Monks in the 13th century.	
212	—— rubra	0 6	265	Solanum Dulcamara	1 0
213	Orobus tuberosus	0 6	266	Solidago cambrica	0 6
214	Oxalis Acetosella, variegata, new	1 6	267	Sparganium minimum... ...	1 6
215	Parnassia palustris (Grass-of- Panassus)	0 6	268	—— ramosum	1 0
216	Peucedanun Ostruthium, very rare	2 6	269	Spergularia marina	0 6
217	Pinguicula lusitanica	1 0	270	Spiræa Filipendula, rare ...	1 0
218	—— vulgaris	0 6	271	Spiranthes autumnalis (Lady's Tresses Orchis)	1 0
219	Plantago media, very rare ...	2 6	272	Statice Limonium	0 6
220	—— lanceolata, variegata ...	2 0	273	—— spathulata, very rare ...	2 6
221	Potamogeton lanceolatus, very rare	1 6	274	Taxus baccata	0 6
222	Potentilla fruticosa (Shrub), rare	1 0	275	Teucrium Scordium, rare ...	1 6
223	Poterium Sanguisorba	0 6	276	Thalictrum flavum	0 6
224	Primula acaulis, alba (White Primrose)	1 0	277	—— flexuosum, rare	1 0
225	—— veris elatior, rare ...	1 6	278	Tragopogon pratensis	0 6
226	—— ——, with many colours ...	0 6	279	Trifolium repens (Shamrock) ...	0 6
227	Pyrola media, very rare ...	1 0	280	—— —— purpurea folins (St. Patrick's tears)	1 6
228	Pyrus Aria	0 6	281	—— arvense	1 0
229	Radiola Millegrana	1 0	282	Turritis hirsuta, rare	2 6
230	Ranunculus Lingua	1 6	283	Utricularia neglecta	0 6
231	Raphanus maritimus, rare ...	1 0	284	Vaccininium Oxycoccos ...	0 6
232	Reseda Luteola	0 6	285	Valeriana dioica	1 0
233	Rhamnus catharticus, rare ...	1 6	286	—— officinalis	0 6
234	—— Frangula	1 0	287	Verbascum Thapsus (MulleinPlant)	0 6
235	—— —— microphylla, new ...	7 6	288	Veronica Chamædrys, variegata...	1 0
236	Rhyncospora fusca	0 6	289	—— officinalis purpurea ...	1 0
237	Rosa rubiginosa	1 0	290	Viburnum Lantana (Shrub), rare	2 6
238	—— pimpinellifolia	0 6	291	—— Opulus (Shrub)	1 0
239	—— villosa	1 0	292	Vinca major (Creeping Periwinkle)	0 6

117

No.			Each. s.	d.
293	Viola Curtisii	... ...	1	0
294	—— odorata, very rare	...	1	6
295	—— palustris	... ...	0	4
296	Zannichellia palustris, rare	...	1	0

FILICES—The Ferns of Burren.

No.			Each. s.	d.
297	Adiantum Capillus-Veneris	...	0	6
298	—— Incisum, rare	...	1	6
299	Aspleninm Adiantum-nigrum	...	0	9
300	—— marinum	... ...	0	6
301	—— Ruta-muraria	... ...	0	4
302	—— Trichomanes	... ...	0	4
303	—— viride ...	... ...	1	0
304	Athyrium Filix-fœmina (The Lady Fern)	... ...	0	4
305	—— rubrum	...	1	0
306	Blechnum boreale	... ...	0	4
307	Botrychiun Lunaria (The Moon-wort Fern)...	... ...	0	6
308	Ceterach officinarum	... ...	0	4
309	—— crenatum	... ...	0	4

No.			Each. s.	d.
310	Cystopteris fragilis (Bladder Fern)		0	4
311	Hymenophyllum tunbridgense (Filmy Fern)	... ...	1	0
312	Lastrea æmula	... ...	0	6
313	—— dilatata...	... ...	0	6
314	—— Filix-mas	... ...	0	4
315	—— Thelypteris	... ...	0	6
316	Ophioglossum vulgatum (Adder's Tongue)	... ...	0	6
317	Osmunda regalis (Royal Flowering Fern)	... ...	0	6
318	Polypodium vulgare	... ...	0	4
319	—— semilacerum	... ...	1	0
320	Polystichum aculeatum (Prickly Shield Fern)	... ...	0	6
321	—— angulare (Soft Shield Fern)		0	6
322	—— lonchitidoides	... ...	1	0
323	—— Lonchitis (Holly Fern)	...	1	0
324	—— lobatum	... ...	0	9
325	Pteris aquilina polydactylum	...	2	0
326	Scolopendrium vulgare (Hart's Tongue Fern)	... ...	0	4

These Three Hundred and Twenty-Six rare Flowering Plants, Shrubs, and Ferns, are quite hardy, and are real gems of the first water, adapted for planting anywhere out in Gardens, Rockeries, Shrubberies, Courtyards, etc. ; also in Windows, cold Greenhouses, etc. In placing the Plants in alphabetical order, I have followed the systematic or Botanical names, to do this with their popular names would lead to great confusion, as many Plants have two or three English names. If any of my friends wish for hardy Plants not contained in this Catalogue, they will please make their wants known, as I have about Three Thousand species and varieties of hardy Exotic Plants and Shrubs from every country in the whole world. Also 700 distinct varieties of Scolopendrium vulgare, this is the largest collection of the Hart's Tongue Fern in the United Kingdom ; I have collected 500 distinct varieties of these on the Burren Mountains about Ballyvaughan, which is really the home of the Hart's Tongue Fern. Native Plants are above referred to, and I would encourage my friends to bring as many of these as are desirable into their Gardens, Houses, Lawns, etc. It may be thought that this advice is against my own interest as Plant-seller, but this is not so, as the love for Plants is never satisfied, and it is generally those who have the most that buy the most. Aside from any other consideration, I have found so much satisfaction in bringing Native Plants into cultivation, that I would point out a new source of pleasure to all lovers of Plants. To aid in this matter, I shall be very glad to name Native Plants for those who will forward proper specimens to my address from any part of the United Kingdom, enclosing 1d. stamp for a reply. The Botanic Gardens and Fern Nurseries are situated within 20 minutes walk of Ballyvaughan, and one hour's drive of Lisdoonvarna. Visitors are respectfully invited to inspect the stock and select their desiderata on Mondays, Wednesdays, and Saturdays, if possible. Any quantity supplied free by Parcel Post to any part of the United Kingdom, on receipt of Post Office Order, or Postal Orders, payable at Ballyvaughan, and small sums in Stamps.

❖ PATRICK ❖ B. ❖ O'KELLY, ❖

Botanic Gardens and Fern Nurseries,

GLENARRA HOUSE,

BALLYVAUGHAN, CO. CLARE, IRELAND.

HILLMAN AND CO., HORTICULTURAL PRINTERS, CHEPSTOW.

A crested variant of hart's-tongue fern

Customers known to have patronized Ballyvaghan 'Botanic Gardens and Fern Nurseries' include Henri Correvon of Geneva who purchased thirty different hart's-tongue ferns, and the redoubtable English gardener, Miss Ellen Willmott of Warley Place. O'Kelly tempted Miss Willmott with five shillings worth of plants from his catalogue in return for anything she could send him from a list which he furnished (it included the weedy *Cardamine bulbifera* which still thrives in the derelict Glenarra garden). O'Kelly added–

> I have a good collection of Hardy Plants about 3000 varieties. I have 50 varieties of shrubby veronicas, 30 shrubby Spireas, 31 shrubby Altheas.

And the most of our native wild flowers. I have about 100 varieties of
variegated Plants & shrubs. Also I have about 700 varieties of Scolopendrium
vulgare, The Hart's-Tongue fern.'

Miss Willmott received dozens of plants from O'Kelly in 1905: the bill for May
totalled £17 2s. 0d. and as each one cost a shilling that represents 342 different
plants, most being Burren natives. On 26 April O'Kelly had despatched five parcels
of plants, and estimated that 'it will take me closing on two months to supply
the remainder of your order as I will have to travel far distances to counties in
Ireland for some of them…' He left on this quest in late June; earlier on 9 June
Miss Willmott was asked for payment for the plants already supplied '…as I am
going to travel to distant counties for rare Aquatic plants etc.' By late October
all had been supplied, and the list makes depressing reading–grass of Parnassus
(*Parnassia palustris*), a 'colony of 12 Cardamine Impatiens' (a very rare species in
Ireland–The Burren is one of two known habitats), Spring gentians, a new
variegated ivy 'discovered by myself on the highest mountain in Burren', and orchids.

Apart from the catalogues, O'Kelly regularly published advertisements in English
horticultural periodicals. One of these, in *The Gardeners' Chronicle* late in 1905,
was reprinted by the editors of *The Journal of Botany* only because they did not
wish to '…withhold from…readers the information it contains as to the special–we
may say, peculiar–properties attributed to *Gentiana verna*.' After offering 'Hardy
Evergreen Irish Rockery Ferns', and 'the real Irish Maidenhair Fern Magnificum…no
button-hole completed without a sprig…', and 'One Golden Variegated
Scolopendrium O'Kelly', O'Kelly proffered this description of the gentian:

> The flower is heavenly-blue. It is the queen of all known Alpine plants in
> the whole world. No collection complete without this gem of the first water.
> It is the only known flower in existence that exhilarates the mind and heart
> of the fair sex.

The advertisements are revealing of other details. In 1909, O'Kelly used as his
postal address 'Nurseries, Ballyvaughan, Co. Clare', but he changed this to
'Botanist, Ballyvaughan' in 1918. Without exception his advertisements began
with 'GENTIANA VERNA, 12 first-class clumps…'; usually an orchid was
mentioned and the whole insert occupied about three lines. Longer, more detailed
advertisements were rarely published. As well as advertising in periodicals, this
enterprising gentleman used the headings on his specially printed note-paper to
promote his–The Burren's!–wares.

In 1909 one dozen gentians cost five shillings (post free), but by 1934 the price had risen to six shillings. In 1909 '6 Royal Flowering Ferns' were three-and-six pence while in 1934 (as *Osmunda regalis*, which is not a native species in The Burren) the half-dozen cost five shillings. Putting that into perspective is not easy, but consider that in those days a pint of stout cost twopence–a dozen gentians deprived the purchaser of thirty creamy glass-fulls.

Orchids were one of the staples in the advertisements–three bee orchids cost two-and-six pence in 1909, two shillings or three-and-six pence in 1915 (perhaps depending on size and season), but two-and-six again in 1934; local folk in Ballyvaghan questioned in the late 1970s recalled men earning two shillings and six pence a day digging up bee orchids at Lough Rask for 'The Doctor'. Among the 'gems of the first water' there was a pair of very special orchids–two 'Orchis Immaculata O'Kelly, new' were three shillings in 1916, while one plant of *Neotinea maculata* fetched one-and-six pence.

Even when he was over eighty years of age, P. B. O'Kelly was actively selling plants. In May 1934, he advertised 'Arctostaphylos uva-ursi, Juniperus Nana, Dryas Octopetala, Potentilla Fruticosa, the four rare Ballyvaughan shrubs' for a total of five shillings–of course, these were, indeed still are, abundant in the region.

Although some people frowned upon Patrick O'Kelly's commercial activities, many were prepared to accept the enterprise and to pay tribute to O'Kelly's botanical zeal–Dr Praeger noted that while P. B. O'Kelly was long known 'as a trader in the rare plants of the West of Ireland…he had a more reputable side–as a field botanist…'[7] And it is clear too that successive Keepers of the Royal Botanic Gardens, Glasnevin, Dublin–Sir Frederick Moore and J. W. Besant–were happy to obtain plants, particularly ferns and orchids, from him. O'Kelly regularly (almost every year) sent clumps of Spring gentians (forty in 1928, fifty in 1933) to Glasnevin.

It is easy to denigrate Patrick O'Kelly's activities, and to sneer accusingly at his statement that

> I have found so much satisfaction in bringing Native Plants into cultivation, that I would point out a new source of pleasure to all lovers of Plants.

He was ahead of the times in promoting wildflowers in gardens, but he operated in a manner now considered reprehensible; similar wholesale exploitation of the wild flora of The Burren today would rightly be condemned as totally unacceptable. However, in O'Kelly's days when living conditions in Clare were extremely harsh, he alone made a tolerable living off a rich resource in the best way he could–today he might act as a national park warden or a tourist-guide showing people the 'gems' in their incomparable wild habitats.

We cannot assess the impact of O'Kelly's collecting on the present flora of The Burren because there are no quantitative figures available for comparison, but I suggest that this solitary man did little long-term damage to The Burren during the half-century he collected plants. But, inevitably, his activities raise other questions. Did O'Kelly's gathering for sale of *Ajuga pyramidalis*, one of the rarer Burren plants, cause the population to decline? Was he gathering *Cardamine impatiens* in the wild? Whence came the *Pinguicula grandiflora* that he offered at six for four shillings? And, most importantly, did he ever operate in the reverse way, and plant exotic species in habitats which now seem completely natural?

He was 'A Character', observant, attuned to the environment in which he lived and wherein he collected. He had a keen eye and thus was able to spot unusual variants of ferns and flowering plants. He depended to a substantial extent on those wild plants for a livelihood and was a good publicist in that cause. One cannot help smiling wryly when reading that an unnamed sea-holly with '…ivory leaves, new [is] the grandest Eryngium in cultivation, in fact it is the most exquisite plant in the whole world…', or that 'No Englishman ever saw…' a daffodil like 'This Burren Trumpet Daffodil…so it is a real gem'. Nor can one truly comprehend what he meant when claiming that he had 1042 different species and varieties of ferns!

Patrick Kelly never married. He lived at Glenarra, an easy walk of Ballyvaghan, for forty years and more, until he died aged 84 on 27 March 1937. The parochial register enigmatically declares that he was a farmer of Newtown, the townland in which Glenarra is situated, but he surely was no ordinary farmer.

The shell of Glenarra House and its outbuildings still stand; cattle trample through the derelict garden, now a garlic-scented quagmire. Daffodils and several ornamental onions with *Arum italicum* and *Cardamine bulbiferum* flourish yet; two fine horse-chestnut trees, a variegated one, and a solitary Chusan palm also survive in the thickly planted grove that envelops the ruin. Some years ago herb Paris and summer snowflakes were growing there, but they have vanished.

P. B. O'Kelly was 'a gem of the first water'.[8] He is buried in the ancient graveyard beside the ruin of Drumcreehy church at Bishop's Quarter, about a kilometre east of Ballyvaghan. No headstone marks his grave, just two sentinel, wind-swept cypress trees. All around on The Burren hills, wherever there is a fine lime-rich loan, his perfect memorial, a white orchid, blossoms each and every summer.

Ballinalacken Castle

THE RECEIPT OF FERN-SEED

Out of those scenes she arrived, not from a shell
but licked with the wet cold fires of St. Elmo,
angel of the last chance, teaching us
the fish in the rock, the fern's
bewildered tenderness deep in the fissure.

Seamus Heaney: 'An Aisling in the Burren'

Deep in the scailps enveloped by a humid atmosphere and shielded from gales, deep in the ash and hazel copses likewise protected and cosseted, or taunting the rip-tides of the four winds of heaven from flat and shattered pavement, ferns are a perennial admiration of The Burren. They are in their prime through winter and summer and what they seem to deny by way of colour is amply counterpoised by the shapes and textures of their leaves, their fronds, from the first sedate uncurling of the croziers.

The fortunes of ferns have waxed and waned chaotically from decade to decade. In the first half of the eighteenth century, if one report can be believed, sack-loads were gathered in The Burren for the thriving Dublin herb-market because ferns were deemed valuable in physic. Then they fell into disfavour with the apothecaries. By the middle of the nineteenth century, ferns were again all the rage, but not as medicinal herbs; they were grown in Wardian cases that had become essential furniture in the gas-lit drawing-rooms of fashionable city houses. Not only were the rarest species hunted with extraordinary zeal, but innumerable, misshapen and contorted variants of common-or-garden ferns were removed from the wild to satisfy the thirst for novelty. The fern craze, *pteridomania*, which, incidentally, almost precipitated the extinction of the delicate Killarney fern, was indulged by Patrick O'Kelly who so imaginatively and willingly supplied the market from Ballyvaghan.

Nowadays, ferns are overlooked more often than they are cultivated, but they continue to amuse passionate pteridologists. As for The Burren's ferns, they flourish today despite past predation.

A casual glance through books about ferns and the journals of natural history societies published during the mania will reveal that several people were active in The Burren collecting ferns, especially those weird yet minor forms loved by gardeners. I have already mentioned Frederick Foot, the geologist who carried out the first accurate geological survey of the barony; he was a very competent botanist and was among the company of fern-gatherers. In fact Foot wrote the first account of The Burren's ferns and specimens of ferns that he pressed and dried are in the Royal Botanic Gardens, Kew, and the National Botanic Gardens, Dublin.[1]

The most prolific collector was P. B. O'Kelly who was a thorough pteridomaniac; having an unequalled knowledge of The Burren and its plants, he was able to exploit all the region's ferns, 'gems of the first water', for a living. *The Gardeners' Chronicle* of 12 January 1884 carried an engraving of a weird form of hart's tongue fern labelled '*Scolopendrium vulgare* var. *cristatum O'Kelly* (Stansfield)'; this is the first published indication of O'Kelly's botanical interests.[2] Charles Druery, President of the British Pteridological Society, noted that he had received the piggyback hart's tongue from one of the leading fern nurseries, Messrs. Stansfield, and that the original had been collected in the 'West of Ireland'. While Druery did not state explicitly that Patrick O'Kelly had found it in The Burren, that may safely be assumed from the name.

I am sure that this extraordinary find stimulated Patrick O'Kelly to look for other mutants and by 1908 when Edward Lowe published *British ferns and where found* he was able to acknowledge O'Kelly as a major contributor and to list over fifty variants which had been gathered in County Clare.[3] Lowe seems also to have been instrumental in persuading O'Kelly to sponsor a bronze medal as the prize for Class Q–'10 wild varieties of Aspleniums (including Ceterach)'–at the Fern Conference and Exhibition held by the Royal Horticultural Society in London during July 1892; while the Clare man is not even mentioned among the exhibitors, Edward Lowe won the O'Kelly medal along with most of the other prizes.[4] A few years earlier, at a meeting of the Belfast Naturalists' Field Club, O'Kelly did exhibit what was described as '...a most beautiful collection of ferns...all his own finds in County Clare.'[5] Once again there can be little doubt that the acquisitive enthusiasm displayed for strange mutants by fern-maniacs persuaded O'Kelly to exploit commercially the botanical riches of The Burren–members of Belfast Field Club were exhorted to write to him if they wanted his special ferns, 'no collection can be complete without them', exclaimed W. H. Phillips in 1890.[6]

Realizing that there was a good living to be gained by selling wild plants, Patrick O'Kelly published a catalogue listing 326 different plants: *A complete list of the rare perennial plants and shrubs of the Burren Mountains of Ballyvaughan, Co. Clare* (see pp. 115-118) was issued for the autumn season of 1893, and inside the author was not adverse to promoting himself, nor to discrete exaggeration:

> These Three Hundred and Twenty-Six rare Flowering Plants, Shrubs and Ferns, are quite hardy, and are real gems of the first water... If any of my friends wish for hardy plants not contained in this Catalogue they will please make their wants known, as I have about Three Thousand species and varieties of hardy Exotic Plants and Shrubs from every country in the whole world. Also 700 distinct varieties of Scolopendrium vulgare, the largest collection of the Hart's Tongue Fern in the United Kingdom...

Seven hundred hart's tongues, and all different! O'Kelly claimed he had collected five hundred–where the other two hundred came from he does not explain! But it is not uncharitable to suppose that they originally were growing in scailps somewhere within the barony of Burren.

Hart's tongue fern (*Phyllitis scolopendrium*) is one of the most familiar, and one of the most elegant Irish ferns. In summer its simple, strap-shaped fronds stand proud in the shelter of the rocks. Usually rooted deep in the scailps, the hart's tongues do not suffer the buffeting of the winds, and the fronds may gently lick the walls of their stony nooks. In exposed sites, or where the fronds poke above

Phyllitis scolopendrium
hart's tongue fern

126

Adiantum capillus-veneris
maidenhair fern

127

the rock-pavement into the bite of the westerlies, their pristine margins and tips soon become tattered and brown.

On the reverse of many fronds are dark brown lines that look like felt–examine these with a hand-lens and you will see that they are composed not of hairs or scales but of tiny stalked capsules, sporangia. Ferns are not flowering plants, so they do not produce pretty blossoms yielding pollen or seeds. Being a relatively primitive group among the vascular plants, ferns propagate by means of a complicated cycle involving microscopic wind-borne spores that are produced in vast quantities by the sporangia. In native Irish ferns, the sporangia are usually formed on the backs of the fronds, either in small spot-like clusters, or in lines as in hart's tongue and species of *Asplenium*. The spores are shed into the wind, and waft away. If a spore lands in a suitable place where there is sufficient light and moisture, it will germinate and grow into a tiny plate-like plantlet (a prothallus), barely visible to the naked eye, that bears the fern's sexual organs. In turn these develop and mature, producing sperm and eggs; the male sperm is stimulated to swim through the film of moisture which coats the minuscule prothallus towards the egg and fertilise it. Fertilization accomplished, the embryo develops, the prothallus withers and the young, new fern grows on by itself. For the cycle to succeed, the delicate prothallus must have a moist habitat and adequate light, conditions that prevail in any Burren scailp, and even inside one cave!

Ferns such as hart's tongues are long-lived perennials. A single plant can grow into a large colonial tuft with several 'crowns', and gardeners exploit this slow, vegetative reproduction, dividing crowns to obtain several plants from one original.

But what about O'Kelly's seven hundred? His claim must have been a trifle exaggerated. It is quite possible, ambling over the pavement, to find hart's tongues that differ in minor ways from their neighbours. I have seen plants with elegant, undulating fronds, but none quite so puckery as the fine cultivar named 'Crispum'. Some have wide fronds, others narrow, and some have fronds that have a forked apex like a fish-tail. But I have not encountered anything approaching the fabulous seven hundred. Nor have I ever seen one like Stansfield's *Scolopendrium vulgare* var. *cristatum O'Kelly* which was fish-tailed and, most remarkably, bore tiny plantlets piggyback where the sporangia should have been. It was thus capable of reproducing by budding new plants on its fronds. Alas this fern–it would nowadays be called *Asplenium scolopendrium* cv. Cristatum O'Kelly (a hefty mouthful)–seems to be extinct not just in The Burren but also in gardens. We may assume safely that only one wild plant ever existed, and that O'Kelly dug it up, and then sold it, or a division from it, so he effectively exterminated it in the wild himself. It is ironic that acquisitive gardeners should be the cause of extinction, but that is a *sine qua non* of horticulture.

For exuberant abundance and variety of ferns there is scarcely a better place than The Burren. Undoubtedly the chief delight is the maidenhair fern, a delight not so much of seeing it for it is not all that unusual, but of seeing it in unexpected places. It is perhaps most easily found about Black Head, in the scailps, and on the shaded north-eastern slopes, rooted in crevices bordering the chert outcroppings above the roadway. But, as I have indicated, it is to be found elsewhere between Poll Salach and the eastern lowlands; the idea that it is restricted to the coastal rim is certainly mistaken.

Maidenhair grows profusely in some most unexpected places. Michael Roberts rescued a plant from an ancient fireplace in Dunguaire Castle at Kinvarra before it was restored as a venue for 'mediaeval' banquets. This species' capacity to tolerate dimly lit habitats is vividly displayed in the show cave at Aillwee. Therein, wherever a light remains lit for most of the opening hours, a green mossiness forms–living plants in an otherwise barren blackness. The mossy growth includes a few species of moss, a liverwort (another primitive plant, closely related to the mosses), a couple of ferns and, according to one of the guides with whom I spoke, clover. The two fern species which I have collected in the cave are hart's tongue–a rather weak specimen–and maidenhair which is exuberant and a pest that must be regularly scraped off the rocks with toothbrushes. The profusion of sporelings on the limestone beside the lights indicates that the maidenhair's spores must be ubiquitous in the cave. But these cannot germinate and initiate the fern's complicated life-cycle in the total absence of light. All green plants must have light to live: remove the source of light and they will die. Thus the small ferns would quickly die if the lights were not turned on for more than a few days, because they depend absolutely on the artificial illumination to allow them to photosynthesise, and thus to grow.

In most of its habitats, *Adiantum capillus-veneris* is rooted deeply, and its jet black stems will be concealed–*dubh chosach* (black foot) is the Irish synonym. At most you see the strange trapezoid pinnae (leaflets) of the fronds delicately embroidering the scailps; or if it is growing on a limestone cliff-face, they will be somewhat battered by the gales, and hanging loosely yet firmly. Along the outer margins of the pinnae may be the dark line of scurfy sporangia. Slight variation occurs in the size and shape of the pinnae–Frederick Foot is credited with the discovery in The Burren of a series of *Adiantum capillus-veneris* cultivars including cv. Incisum and cv. Footii.

The first report of maidenhair fern from Ireland was contained in Edward Lhuyd's letter to Tancred Robinson, published by the Royal Society of London in *Philosophical Transactions* during 1712. Lhuyd had seen 'a great plenty of Adiantum verum…' on the Aran Islands when he stayed there in the summer of 1700.[7] John Keogh provided the earliest record from the mainland of Burren–strangely Caleb Threlkeld did not include it in his flora. Considering that Keogh claimed that basket-loads of the maidenhair fern were brought to Dublin for sale to apothecaries, Dr Threlkeld's silence cannot be explained easily unless the trade sprang up only in the 1730s.

In 1812 'A Gentleman' published *A scientific tourist in Ireland*.[8] The bashful author's identity can be unravelled easily; he was Thomas Walford, a English dilettante who probably never set foot in Ireland, let alone The Burren. Among the colourful list of plants he informed his reader they would find in the hills of Clare were *Asclepias vincetoxicum* (swallowwort), *Ricinus communis* (castor oil!) and *Teucrium chamaepitys* (ground pine), none of which grows wild anywhere in Ireland. He noticed the usual tourist's fare of mountain avens and gentians, and maidenhair fern 'on the rocky mountains of Burrin'. Walford's awful little book is a fine example of abject plagiarism; he copied most of his plant records, mistakes and all, from John Keogh's frequently unreliable herbal.

Thaddeus O'Mahony and Francis Whitla gathered *Adiantum capillus-veneris* on cliffs 'near enough to be washed by sea spray…in rough weather' somewhere in the vicinity of Black Head. O'Mahony was curious about the fern and on consulting 'some old botanical books belonging to Mr. Whitla, I perceive it said that formerly an immense quantity of this fern used to be brought from Burren, for the purpose of making capillare.'[9] As I have mentioned already, Keogh made this claim:

> True MAIDEN HAIR, Hib. *Chossa duh*, La. Adjantum vulgare, seu Capillarus veneris. The leaves are small, round, and serrated, the stalks are black, shining, and slender, near a foot high, it grows on stone walls, and Rocks, the best in this Kingdom, is brought from the rocky mountains of *Burrin*, in the *County* of *Clare*, where it grows plentifully, from thence it is brought in sacks to *Dublin*, and sold there, It is *Pulmonic, Lithontriptic, Emmenagogic, Hepatic, Splenetic, Nephritic, Diuretic, Styptic*, and Deopulative,

it wonderfully helps those, that are afflicted with *Asthmas*, shortness of breath and *Coughs*, occasioning a free expectoration, it is also good against *Jaundice, Diarrhoea, Haemoptysis* and the biting of mad dogs.[10]

Professor Wade mentioned the making of capillare, but dismissed the contribution of the maidenhair fern: 'it never has any of this plant in its composition, being usually made with sugar and water only, and sometimes with the addition of a little orange flower water.'[11]

Many ferns have been endowed with largely imagined virtues. Of the rusty-back 'Spleenwort or Miltwast, [found] in the Openings of Rocks, brought in Quantities out of the Country', Dr Threlkeld reported that 'it is used in Swellings of the Milt and Fluxes of the Belly'.[12] Whence the Dublin market obtained supplies he omitted to record, but there is, and would then have been, no shortage of miltwast in The Burren. Almost any area of pavement, any wall, has colonies of the rusty-back, but it does not enjoy shade, so there is none in the hazel copses, and it does not inhabit wet flushes and turlough brims.

Ceterach officinarum, the rusty-back, in Irish *raithneach rua*, red fern, is a distinctive plant during any season. In winter its fronds are soft, green with a silvery-bronze margin lining the rounded, wave-toothed fronds. On the reverse is a golden-brown felt composed of tiny scales overlapping one another like the scales on an armadillo's hide. In high summer, on the baking pavement, the fronds curl inwards making the plant look more compact. At this season the rusty-back is relatively dormant, having lost much of the water from its tissues, but when The Burren is bathed in rain again, the fronds expand outwards and the fern returns to life. An ability rapidly to take up water is more usually a characteristic of desert plants, but of course in the summer limestone pavement can become parched and, from a plant's point-of-view, desert-like. A rusty-back will tolerate the loss of 98% of the water in it tissues, and it absorbs water again with remarkable rapidity[13]–in a drier clime such a fern might be called a 'resurrection plant'.

Dr Chris Page, author of a modern treatise on ferns in Ireland and Britain, notes that the Irish populations of *Ceterach officinarum* have more noticeably toothed margins to the fronds, and that plants sometimes produce two sets of sporangia on a frond in one year.[14] In Britain the outline of the fronds is smoother, and they are, moreover, shorter and narrower than the fronds of Irish plants. A nineteenth century German botanist, Carl Milde, had noticed that rusty-back ferns existed in these two forms and he named the toothed variant *Ceterach officinarum* var. *crenatum*.

Such variations were a joy to the fern-gatherers at the height of pteridomaia. Patrick O'Kelly was well situated to supply the market with an endless stream of new forms, each one originally a denizen of a crack in The Burren pavement. He displayed a selection of these in Belfast at the Naturalist's Field Club in 1890; there were 'nine most strange and beautiful forms…, [and] one in particular [was] deserving of special notice, *multifido-cristatum*, a perfect gem.'[15] By this time, thanks to O'Kelly, County Clare had yielded no fewer than twenty-one reputedly distinct rusty-backs, and each one was listed by Edward Lowe in *British ferns and where found*:

> The Barony of the Burren, in County Clare, is exceedingly rich in varieties, some very large, and some exceedingly distinct. Mr. P. B. O'Kelly, of Glanarra House, Ballyvaughan, has sent me more than a dozen distinct varieties, and all good characteristic plants.[16]

Lowe then named the Burren rusty-backs: for the sake of history this fern litany is reprinted opposite, although none of the names (apart from *Ceterach officinarum* var. *crenatum*) is retained today, even if similar plants could be wrested from the barony.

Rusty-backs can form a dense capping on walls, and on shattered pavement this species is abundant even when other plants are absent. The fern apparently does not require a moist root-run, but does best in regions where the humidity is high throughout the year and the growing-season is long. Its singular capacity to flourish through sodden winters and scorching summers allows it to colonise even the walls of the green roads.

In contrast, most other ferns that inhabit the Clare-Galway limestone need a continual supply of moisture or some shelter from searing wind. The vertical scailps provide protection but not necessarily a trickle of water, whereas many of the horizontal cracks which develop along the bedding-planes in the limestone ooze throughout the year as water slowly percolates and seeps from the innumerable cracks and underground passages in the hills. The bedding-planes are thus frequented by ferns of less rugged constitution than miltwast, such as the brittle bladder fern, *Cystopteris fragilis*.

Charles Carter was the first to report 'Cistopteris'–he only found a few plants during mid-July 1846 as he walked the 'wretched tract' between Ballyvaghan and Ennistimon.[17] Thaddeus O'Mahony and Francis Whitla gathered brittle bladder

angustatum O'Kelly.	2 x 0¼ inches. Concave
bifidum O'Kelly.	Bifid
crenatum Moore	by far the best forms in the Burren, by Mr. O'Kelly
crenatum-major O'Kelly.	8 x 1¼ inches
crenulare Lowe (*crenatum major* O'Kelly).	2¼ x 0¾ inches. Concave, very pretty.
crispum-major O'Kelly.	10½ x 1¼ inches. A giant
cristatum O'Kelly.	Crested
decorum O'Kelly.	Stiffer texture and rugose. 8 x 1 inches
densum O'Kelly.	3 x 0¾ inches
densum-varians O'Kelly.	4 x 0⅝ inches
giganteum O'Kelly.	7½ x 1 inches
grandiceps O'Kelly.	4 x 0⅜ inches. A fine capitate form
interruptum O'Kelly.	7 x 0½ inches. Lax and interrupted.
lineare O'Kelly.	2½ x 0½ inches. A narrow form and depauperate.
lineare-major O'Kelly.	9 x 0¾ inches. Very lax, stipes long.
majus O'Kelly.	9½ x 1 ⅒ inches. Flat.
multifido-cristatum O'Kelly.	4 x 0 5/10. Multifidly crested
ramosum O'Kelly.	6 x 0 7/10 ...branching in the rachis
subpinnatum O'Kelly.	
superbum O'Kelly.	9 x 1 inches. A fine deeply crenate form.
tenuifolium O'Kelly.	5½ x 0⅜ inches. Slender
truncatum O'Kelly.	2¾ x 0½ inches. Depauperate and truncate
variabile Lowe	also in the Burren by Mr. O'Kelly; ...has a more bushy habit.

O'Kelly's 'varieties' of *Ceterach officinarum*
as listed by E. J. Lowe

Ceterach officinarum: rusty-back fern (above)
Cystopteris fragilis: brittle bladder-fern (right)
Asplenium trichomanes: maidenhair spleenwort (far right)

fern in 1851, and Alexander More noticed it in 1860. Frederick Foot collected specimens at Kilcorney and Black Head, and some from Corrin Hill, west of Ennis (outside The Burren), and grew them together; while in the wild the Corrin Hill plants had long, attenuated fronds, in cultivation these plants were soon indistinguishable.[18]

This delicate, elegant fern does indeed vary considerably depending on its habitat. In shaded places–it does manage to grow in quite dark places such as under rock overhangs–the fronds are bigger than those of plants tightly clustered along seepage-lines on exposed cliffs. The fronds are usually about twenty centimetres long, and the stalk (stipe) is brittle, translucent and pale brownish-green. The pinnae do not overlap and in outline the frond is an elongated oblong, tapering to a point. Each of the pinnae is divided into toothed, or further divided pinnules. The sporangia are borne on the backs of the pinnules.

The brittle bladder-fern (*raithneach bhriosc*) is one of the earliest Burren plants to begin growing. The croziers start uncurling about the end of March and they expand rapidly. The fronds are usually grass-green, but may be darker in very dimly light crevices.

In its habitat preferences *Cystopteris fragilis* parallels the maidenhair fern, but it will not grow so close to the sea, and this tendency, suggests Chris Page, indicates that the brittle bladder fern is intolerant of salt spray. That cannot be said of the sea spleenwort which grows deep in the scailps about Poll Salach and Black Head within splashing distance of the breakers at least during the height of the winter storms. Frederick Foot was most impressed by the luxuriance of this fern in The Burren, and he sent some of the finest specimens to the Botanic Gardens at Glasnevin where David Moore could not distinguish them from a West Indian species so vigorous and large were the fronds; the variant was named *Asplenium marinum* cv. Laxum.[19] It is certainly a wonderful sight in the middle of January, the majestic, dark green fronds of *Asplenium marinum*, dripping wet with rain and spray and just reaching the pavement surface, highlighted by the brief rays of the low sun against the water-black limestone. The fronds are green throughout the winter, deepening in colour as the year progresses for they are apple-green when they first unfurl in the calmer days of early summer.

The spleenworts get their English name from their reputed efficacy in alleviating disorders of the spleen–miltwast (or miltwaste) has the same meaning as milt is an archaic word for spleen. Of this spleenwort, Dr Threlkeld reported that 'it is pectoral, good for Coughs and Consumptions, to help the Stone, Gravel, and Stoppage of Urine'. In a copy of his book, once belonging to Dr Aquilla Smith, someone has inserted the comment that the fern is also helpful in epilepsy 'according to the testimony of some Irish peasants.'[20]

Maidenhair spleenwort is immediately recognized by its linear fronds and its shining, darkest brown stalk along which the tiny oval pinnae are arranged more or less in opposite pairs. The fronds are usually about ten centimetres long, and about a finger-width broad. It is generally stated that there are two subspecies in Ireland and Britain, of which the one named *Asplenium trichomanes* subsp. *quadrivalens* is the most common and the only one definitely growing in The Burren. Its fronds tend to grow vertically and appressed to the rock surface, and they curl sinuously rather than remaining perfectly straight. The pinnae, moreover, are not perfectly symmetrical and lack a stalk. Martin Rickard suggests that this subspecies tends to inhabit wetter places, where there is dripping water perhaps, but in The Burren it is not unusual to see maidenhair spleenwort in the scailps of the pavement expanses as well as on vertical limestone cliffs and man-made walls.

It is just possible, as suggested by O'Mahony and Whitla, that the report of maidenhair ferns being gathering by the sack-load from The Burren, is really a reference to this fern and not to *Adiantum capillus-veneris*. We will never prove it either way. The maidenhair spleenwort is prolific in the barony–'I never saw it in such abundance, or in such luxuriance elsewhere' was O'Mahony's exclamation.[21] Frederick Foot was also impressed by its abundance and its variety; 'some forms have the margins of the pinnae beautifully serrated, and sometimes the sori extend beyond the margin, and round to the front of the pinnae.' He reported that the 'tasselled' variety was not infrequent.[22]

The young geologist was as astute an observer of plants as of rocks and paid particular attention to ferns. He noted all species recorded in the region, including the four true *Asplenium* species–two have already been mentioned, and the others are black spleenwort (*Asplenium adiantum-nigrum*) and wall-rue (*Asplenium ruta-muraria*) The former has winter-green, triangular fronds of triangular pinnae arranged on a black stipe. The wall-rue is the small fern with fan-shaped pinnae that is so familiar as a plant of old mortared walls. 'Those who have only see the wall-rue growing on walls, and covered with the dust of the road,' wrote Foot, 'can form but a poor idea of its luxuriance and great variety of form in its native home in Burren: wherever you turn, it meets your eye; in shady nooks, it attains

Polypodium australe
polypody fern

138

considerable size.'[23] It will grow almost anywhere–even in a minuscule hollow in a limestone slab set in a wall.

Frederick Foot was not the only non-botanist actively collecting ferns in County Clare in the middle decades of the last century. John Kinahan was primarily a zoologist, an expert on bats, yet he was no mean botanist and even proposed a classification system for fern variants that was well before its time. In a paper on bat-hunting he could not help describing the ferns around the mouths of the bats' caves–at Lough Inchiquin one cliff, covered in profusion with ferns, yielded polypody (perhaps *Polypodium australe*) variants 'to which the names "hibernicum", "semilacerum", "pseudo-cambricum", "sinuatum", &c., have been given…'[24] I don't know if any of Kinahan's discoveries was especially notable, nor if any has endured. Incidentally his companion on the bat-hunt was Frederick Foot.

On an erratic boulder a little to the east of the road at Poll Salach there is a veritable rock-garden–rock-roses, stonecrop, blue grass and polypody. The fronds of the polypody (*scim* is its Irish name) would barely cover a fifty-pence piece, so stunted and small is the plant. Yet, on the bridge over the Caher River at Formoyle, on the eastern parapet, the same polypody produces beautiful fronds of the normal healthy size, and on the reverse sides of the pinnae are golden studs of sporangia.

Polypody is a plastic plant, displaying great variation in the size and fertility of its frond; in those habitats where it is restricted and subject to summer drought, the fronds will be small and perhaps never bear sporangia. Plants from such places, transplanted into more fertile, moist soil will soon change and produce large, fertile fronds. The ferns are not genetically predisposed to produce small fronds–the stunted growth is due to the impoverished environment.

However, not all the differences observed between the populations in the wild are caused by different environmental features–some are controlled genetically. Thus, polypody ferns with deeply serrated pinnae will not change to producing fronds with a plain outline when moved to another habitat.

The finest of all the ferns that Patrick O'Kelly wrenched from The Burren is a polypody, still in cultivation and blessed with this name–*Polypodium australe* cv. Semilacerum Falcatum. It is not known precisely whence it came, but as Kinahan and Foot had reported that '…*semilacerum* occurs in great luxuriance on rocks in Clifden demesne, at Inchiquin lake, Corrofin,' that locality may have been

O'Kelly's source.[25] This particular polypody is reckoned among the best cultivars of this genus by present-day fern-fanciers.

Polypody is a plant I have know since the days when I went on excursions with the Fermanagh Field Naturalist's Club, for it was frequently seen in Fermanagh growing on the trunks of oak trees, particularly in the pot-holes of the Cuilcagh foot-hills. In The Burren where mature oaks are singularly lacking, the polypody has reverted to rocks and walls. Nowadays botanists recognize three distinct species, distinguished by their chromosome numbers, and to a less reliable degree by the configuration of the fronds and the shape and disposition of the pinnae. *Polypodium australe* has a much broader frond than the other species, and its sporangia turn amber-yellow.

All three species occur in The Burren, but their separation is usually a matter for experts. In the olden days the niceties of chromosome numbers were unknown, and all polypody ferns were conveniently placed in the one species although the striking variants were separated. Thus Frederick Foot noted that 'Var. β, serratum…is remarkable in having the pinnae deeply serrated. It remains constant under cultivation'. A second variety which 'seems to love a shady place', he called 'Var. γ, Hibernicum' and stated that 'the margins of the pinnules are deeply serrated' implying that it was almost bipinnate–this could even be O'Kelly's cultivar Semilacerum Falcatum for it remains 'constant' in cultivation.[26]

Twenty-four fern species are recorded from the limestone reaches of The Burren, and included is one of the filmy ferns, *Hymenophyllum wilsonii*, which is an unlikely denizen of this calcareous wilderness for it is strictly calcifuge. Wilson's filmy fern thrives on some sandstone boulders and on the trunks of a few trees in Poll an Bhalláin, where doused with rain, it is never in contact with calcareous rocks or lime-rich water. In the hazel copses and woodlands, male ferns and lady ferns abound. In winter these coverts seem to contain nothing but the eternal green carpets of moss, soft and warm, but come high summer, with the leaves on the trees, there are helleborines and ferns rippling across the carpet among the boulders.

At Poll Salach, growing in the grassland on both sides of the road, there is another interesting fern, although one which should be treated with considerably more care and caution than might be imagined. Bracken (*Pteridium aquilinum*) is one of the most successful plants on the globe, a true cosmopolitan growing on all continents and inhabiting many oceanic islands from New Zealand to Newfoundland.[27] One reason for its ubiquity undoubtedly is its armoury of chemical protection, a complicated battery of noxious substances which can kill animals, even human beings, that are unwise enough to eat bracken fronds. Even the spores released in the late summer are now believed to be harmful, causing cancer in the lungs. In olden days such matters were beyond the ken even of botanists, and bracken had many uses; the fronds were employed in dyeing wool green, the ash of bracken was used in soap manufacture and Frederick Foot noticed that the poorer inhabitants of The Burren used bracken as fuel. There is also a midsummer tradition, now extinct, of gathering 'fern seed' and making divinations from the roots of bracken.

The Poll Salach bracken matches a subspecies, *Pteridium aquilinum* subsp. *atlanticum* described in 1990 by Dr Page from limestone grassland in western Scotland. On 1 August 1990 during a brief trip to The Burren, I stopped at Poll Salach–to look at some orchids–and noticed a colony of stunted bracken fronds; I studied these carefully noting that the fronds were silver-haired and unfurling late in the season pinnule by pinnule. A few weeks later I returned to collect some specimens for the scientific record and on a mist-sodden morning it was wonderful to see the rich claret colour of some of the withered fronds.

Bracken tends to be calcifuge but in The Burren colonizes both the distinctly lime-rich soils as at Poll Salach, and also the clods of peat which rest on the limestone rock and are acidic. Webb and Scannell referred to this apparent contradiction, yet it was not until Chris Page's Scottish studies suggested the existence of a bracken variant with different ecological preferences, that an explanation could be attempted. If the Poll Salach bracken is *Pteridium aquilinum* subsp. *atlanticum* it is quite an uncommon plant; elsewhere in The Burren any bracken I examined matched the principal and cosmopolitan subspecies, *Pteridium aquilinum* subsp. *aquilinum* which abounds on the less calcareous peaty soils. It must be added that some botanists do not accept Dr Page's new subspecies and have produced chemical data to support their thesis that it is not worthy of subspecific status–the debate will be a prolonged one.[28]

Thomas Corry's visit to County Clare in July 1879 must have been exhilarating. In the days before electric light and motor cars, botanizing had its own routine and pleasure. All the hours of daylight were cherished and the pace of travel was that of the footfall. In the valley of Glencolumbkille, Corry saw *Cystopteris fragilis* 'showing its dark green fronds. Never shall I forget the appearance of this valley as I saw it about three o'clock in the morning, with a scarlet sun rising in the distance...' One interesting aspect of Corry's account of the visit is his occasional

Equisetum telmateia
greater horsetail
(fertile spike)

reference to ferneries cultivated by local luminaries. Dr W. H. Stacpoole Westropp, the general practitioner in Lisdoonvarna, who entertained Corry and his companions, had a 'pretty fernery, situated by the picturesque villa near the Baths' and had hart's tongues–'for the most part brought from the clefts and fissures of the limestone, both at Pollsallagh and Blackhead'–along with moonwort and exotic species. At Ballinalacken 'a cool fernery, arranged and managed with consummate taste and skill' was, according to Thomas Corry well worth a visit–presumably one of the O'Brien family tended it.[29]

The mediaeval towerhouse at Ballinalacken is one of the most spectacular ruins in the western Burren–strictly it is not within the ancient barony. Perched high above a limestone cliff its position is not just defensive, but to our eyes, 'romantic'. One clear summer days, with the blue sky behind, the tower is majestic; on leaden winter days when sky and rocks and leafless trees all conspire in grey to thwart the sense of distance, the castle is eerie, two upper windows become the ghostly eyes of a bug-eyed owl glowering from a rock. No matter what the colour of the landscape, Ballinalacken is most impressive when approached from the south, down the hill from Lisdoonvarna.

The road winds down the slope from Lisdoonvarna towards the crag on which the towerhouse perches. Not far from the castle the traveller passes from the shale of south Clare on to the limestone; the geological border is not so marked here as it is elsewhere. Along the road verge at about the shale-limestone divide there is a colony of the greater horsetail, a living example of one of the groups of plants that dominated the land vegetation of the Carboniferous Period. At that time, horsetails the size of giant trees throve; the species alive today are much more petite, although the greater horsetail (*Equisetum telmateia*) is the largest of the Irish ones.

The greater horsetail–*feadóg*–is most obvious early in the year, about March. Like asparagus spears, the palely translucent brownish green shoots begin to thrust from the damp ground. The stems are segmented with a collar of long, tapering, red-brown margined teeth at each joint, and tipped with a fine cone composed of the spore-producing sporangia–like ferns the horsetails have no flowers nor seeds. The individual sporangium resembles a small, thick-headed nail, and when ripe it releases a green powder which is composed of innumerable microscopic spores.

The thumb-thick spears rise about thirty centimetres at most; they are rather brittle and many get snapped off before reaching full size. Moreover their only function is to produce spores–they cannot photosynthesise so once the sporangia are ripe they wither away. Following them in April are the wonderful horsetails, green and feathery just like miniature pine trees. These are sterile–they do not produce spores. Like the fertile spikes, they are segmented and at each joint there is a whorl of grooved, green branches. On cool, spring mornings dew-drops of sea-mist condense on the tips of the branches so that the sun, glinting through the droplets, decks each horsetail with points of light.

Glencolumbkille and Turloughmore Mountain

TUSSOCKS OF UNBROKEN GLORY

...lead me then, lead the way.
Reach me a gentian, give me a torch!
let me guide myself with the blue forked torch of
this flower...

D. H. Lawrence, 'Bavarian gentians'

I should repeat that none of the wild species growing on the hills of Burren is unique to the area or confined only to the barony, although the races of some species may be endemic and thus will not be found elsewhere. Likewise, the special character of The Burren's flora is not accounted for by plants of great rarity, even in an Irish context. The region's reputation as a botanical wonderland is gained by inexplicable combinations of plants, the juxtaposing of species which frequent lands within the Arctic Circle and others that are of southern extraction, and by

145

the contradictory occurrence almost at sea-level of plants that are more commonly seen growing high on mountain peaks. Moreover, certain flowers and ferns, which in their other habitats beyond Clare or beyond Ireland are exceedingly rare and fleeting, grow in such profusion in The Burren that it is their principal domain in the British Isles. One indicator of this perplexing state is that none of the wild flowers native in the hills of The Burren is protected by law because none is so scarce within the Republic of Ireland that it requires conservation–two species which occur in the eastern lowlands are listed. The absence of legal prohibition must never be mistaken as an open licence to pick the flowers or remove plants–nothing should done to diminish the populations of any of The Burren's plants.

🌸 There is one plant above every other that exemplifies The Burren–Spring gentian, 'the Gentian of gentians', is abundant from seashore to mountain summit throughout the karst landscape, yet even this gentian is not unique to The Burren.

In Ireland, Spring gentian grows on the three Aran islands and, on the mainland, it ranges northwards from The Burren through County Galway along the eastern shore of Lough Corrib into the southern extremity of County Mayo; on the western side of Lough Corrib its limits are at Gentian Hill, halfway between Salthill and Barna, and thence almost to Oughterard. However, The Burren is headquarters for *Gentiana verna* and the herb is ubiquitous in open habitats where loam has accumulated, being absent only from wet flushes, turlough rims, and those rock-strewn parts where no soil lies near the surface. It grows on stable sand-dunes, as at Fanore and Bishop's Quarter, and in the natural grasslands where

> by the millions…it forms clumps…among the rank herbage of Ladies' Tresses, Ladies' Bedstraw, Lady's Fingers, and the whole botanical department of a lady's plenishing.[1]

Even on the higher slopes Spring gentians flourish in the teeth of the western gales.

For nigh on three and a half centuries '*Alpes Felwort of the spring time*' has been an ineluctable beacon drawing visitors from afar to County Clare. Richard Heaton had seen it 'In the Mountaines betwixt *Gort* and *Galloway*, abundantly' sometime before 1650, and William How had made this fact known to learned men through his pocket-sized *Phytologia Britannica*.[2] Subsequent botanical writers repeated Heaton's locality, although not always with conviction; Dr Jacob Dillenius, who enlarged and edited the third (1724) edition of the Revd John Ray's *Synopsis methodica Stirpium Britannicarum* and became Sherardian Professor

Gentiana verna: Spring gentian

of Botany in the University of Oxford, consigned Heaton's 'Gentianella Alpina verna… [from] the Mountains betwixt *Gort* and *Galloway*' to the *Indiculus plantarum dubiarum* ('list of doubtful plants'). Dr Caleb Threlkeld took up this point but, unable flatly to contradict Dillenius, added only that 'such as go to that Place may inquire for it.'[3]

No-one pursued the floral torch for many decades: at least I cannot discover any definite report about the Irish populations of Spring gentian in eighteenth century botanical writings: Charles Lucas failed to mention the gentian, nor did Dr Patrick Browne record it in his unpublished manuscript flora of Ireland. Almost one hundred and fifty years passed before anyone with botanical leanings is known to have found *Gentiana verna* again in the British Isles; during April 1797 John Binks collected it near Durham in Teesdale. Irish botanists rediscovered the Spring gentian early in the nineteenth century–in 1804 Professor Walter Wade reported that it was

> A very elegant and very scarce perennial, which covers the sterile mountains
> and a few marshy situations near Castle-taylor, County Galway, in the month
> of May…[4]

James Townsend Mackay added to this information in 1806: *Gentiana verna* was

> Plentiful on the estate of Bindon Blood, Esq. near the bay of Galway, on
> a lime-stone gravelly soil [and] abundant near the town of Galway, on a
> calcareous soil in mountainous situations.[5]

At last in 1825, the Spring gentian was confirmed by Mackay as plentiful in '…the
crevices in limestone rocks in the Barony of Burren, and near Galway…'[6]

Between the middle of April and the middle of June each year, The Burren
sward sparkles with the blue and white five-petalled flowers of gentians–'tussocks
of unbroken glory', Reginald Farrer declaimed.[7] In places it is impossible to walk
without treading on these earth-bound stars, so thickly do they grow

Blue–blue–as if the sky let fall
a flower from its own caerulean wall.[8]

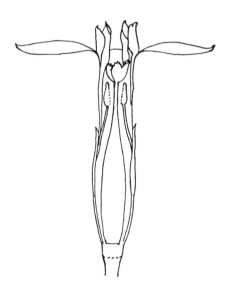

Diagram of Spring gentian flower

At other times, the characteristic rosettes of grass-green leaves have to be searched
for most diligently among the densely packed foliage of other herbs–they do persist
but, out of bloom, the perennial gentians meld into the sward.

A Spring gentian's flower has a tubular, five-ribbed calyx encasing the greenish
basal tube of the corolla that flares into five blue, spreading, ovate petals,

resembling elegant propeller-blades, alternating with five, smaller lobes. The petal margins are minutely ragged because they are toothed–the haphazard teeth are visible with a hand-lens. The erect, intervening lobes are irregularly three- or four-lobed, and the central portion forms into a translucent white streak which leads down to the point where a stamen is attached to the tube. There are five stamens topped with pale yellow anthers held within the tube below the stigma. In the centre of each flower is a single, bottle-shaped, green ovary as long as the calyx; it tapers gradually into the style which is dramatically crowned by a two-lobed, disc-shaped stigma with a minutely fringed rim. The stigmatic disc plugs the mouth of the flower, giving each gentian blossom its striking white 'eye'.

Gentians are pollinated by bees or perhaps butterflies–there is no published information about pollination in Ireland, but in Teesdale bees have been seen visiting the flowers to collect nectar and are believed to pollinate the blossoms. After pollination the stigmatic disc shrivels and the petals close over the mouth, twisting together as they do so. Athena's eyes have closed and the gentians become inconspicuous again; in midsummer, for maybe two months, the spear-shaped fruiting heads will betray the plant to careful observers, but for ten months the rosettes are practically invisible.

Each gentian flower can produce several hundred seeds; these are shed in midsummer but will not germinate until the following spring, or even two years later. Experiments have shown that frosting is necessary for successful germination, as is light–seeds kept warm and covered with soil when sown will not germinate, whereas one quarter of a batch of seeds subjected to a week of spring frost and not covered with soil will produce seedlings.[9] This posess the question: how, in a relatively frost-free habitat such as The Burren, does the Spring gentian reproduce? One answer is that short underground stolons are produced by mature plants and these sprout new rosettes at their tips–thus, in any area, most gentian plants are likely to be offsets from one original parent, and over years the offsets will mature and produce stolons, and so on. By vegetative multiplication the Spring gentian could persist for ever. However, frost is not totally unknown in County Clare, even near the coast, so that germination of seeds is not prevented. Reproduction by seed certainly does occur as indicated by the fact that the colour of Spring gentian flowers is not uniform.

Gentian blue is the blue of the darker part of a clear summer sky at sunset, 'deep, deep, pure blue, the colour which the Greeks gave to the eyes of Athena'.[10] But not all Spring gentians are like Athena's eyes; some are Cambridge blue veering towards turquoise (*Gentiana verna* var. *coelestina*), or ice-blue,[11] and a few even paler, almost white (*Gentiana verna* var. *chionodoxa*). And no matter how dark the petals, the throat is always white. I have seen white gentians several times about Poll Salach, once when I visited with Graham Stuart Thomas, and again some years later in company with other friends. These flowers seemed white on first glance but when carefully compared the corolla was still blue, perhaps even slightly mauve. As for the Cambridge blue gentian, I have also encountered it more than once, and that long after it was first reported as being in cultivation from The Burren; in a few localities pale variants are relatively common, as on one of the grassy slopes on the east side of the Ballyvaghan valley.

Irish gentians differ from those that grow elsewhere in Europe. Dr Trevor Elkington, having studied *Gentiana verna* in much detail, noted that the most marked characteristic of the Irish plants was long calyx teeth, and when he calculated the ratio of total length of the calyx to tooth length, Irish plants were readily distinguished. The shape of the rosette leaves was assessed too, but the races are not so distinctly different. When leaf shape and calyx type are combined, the Irish plants cluster in a separate group apart from the Teesdale population, and those in the Alps and the Pyrenees.[12] Having been completely isolated from other populations of Spring gentians for perhaps eight thousand years, the western Irish *Gentiana verna* has evolved its own particular profile which does allow us to distinguish The Clare–Galway race from those of other regions. In time, after many more thousands of years, if they persist the gentians of The Burren may attain so distinctive a form that botanists working then could describe a new species and call it by a different name.

Similar painstaking measurement by Dr Michael Proctor of leaf and flower samples from the little rock-rose of The Burren, *Helianthemum canum*, and statistical analysis of the data, point to the same conclusion. Irish plants have larger leaves and bear flowers more abundantly than British ones; the differences are maintained when plants from these separate areas are cultivated together under identical conditions. Dr Proctor's data indicated that the Irish race of the hoary rock-rose resembles forms gathered in northern Spain and the Pyrenees, but yet these populations were not identical, and he suggested that Irish plants might deserve separation as an endemic subspecies.[13]

Like Spring gentian, hoary rock-rose is not the most obvious plant when out of flower; it is not quite as invisible, however, as the gentian. The shoots are prostrate,

Helianthemum canum: hoary rock-rose

tightly hugging the contours of the soil or the rocks, and the leaves are small, always less than a centimetre long, with a prominent mid-vein and silvery felted backs. In bloom there is no mistaking a wild rock-rose. The flowers are brilliant yet soft lemon-yellow, the five petals swept backwards and the central brush of stamens forming a inverted cone. Only on warm sunny days do the flowers open fully: when the day is dull and there is a chill wind, the blossoms remain tightly shut. The contrast between the yellow petals and the dark green, slightly glossy, rounded leaves helps to compensate for the tiny size of the individual flowers–each one is little more than a centimetre across. The only wildflower with which a rock-rose can be confused is tormentil (*Potentilla erecta*) but the latter has four petals and finely divided leaves.

The hoary rock-rose occurs principally on the coast from Poll Salach northwards to Black Head; at Poll Salach plants even grow in the natural rock-gardens that sprout on some of the erratic boulders. On Mullach Mór, the upper terraces are also colonized by this species, and it is recorded in an area north of Béal an Chloga. The only other Irish station for *Helianthemum canum* is on Inishmore, where it is restricted to the northern quarter. Together these populations are the largest in western Europe, for while the hoary rock-rose is found in Teesdale and Westmoreland, and in Wales (Gower Peninsula, Anglesey and along the north coast) nowhere is it so abundant. On the European mainland, isolated populations range from northern Spain through southern France and Italy into the Balkans, and there are scattered stations in Morocco and Algeria. *Helianthemum canum* is reported also from Turkey, southern Russia and the Caucasus, and a similar species, generally named *Helianthemum oelandicum*, grows on Oland, in the Baltic Sea off the southeastern coast of Sweden.[14]

The hoary rock-rose is a wild relative of the rock-roses of gardens. Over many centuries, the garden variants have been bred and selected for bigger flowers and different petal colours–nowadays almost every shade from white to darkest crimson is available. The little wild rock-rose of The Burren has a refined charm that outshines its vulgar overblown garden cousins, is easy to propagate from cuttings, enjoys well-drained lime-rich soil, and retains its rock-hugging habit to cascade over stones in a rock-garden. What a pity it is not seen more often even in the gardens of 'alpine' enthusiasts.

In contrast, mountain avens is relatively common in cultivation; I remember it in my grandparents' garden and we had mats of it in the rockery at home. When the conditions suit, *Dryas octopetala* forms dense, evergreen carpets of glossy foliage that keep 'weeds' at bay. Moreover, the white flowers and fluffy fruiting heads add to its value as a garden plant. As with any species, from The Burren or elsewhere, removing plants from the wild to transplant into a garden is reprehensible, and will indubitably fail as established wild plants do not like being disturbed. Mountain avens is widely available from good nurserymen, and can easily be propagated by taking cuttings immediately after the flowers have dropped their petals.

There are few places, even in The Burren, more astonishing than high on the shattered upper slopes of Gleninagh Mountain, on its western side, looking towards Dobhach Bhrainín over the swirling hollow that curls down to Fanore, strewn with fragments of limestone and bedecked with scattered mats of mountain avens. On a warm day, late in May a few years ago, I sat there in a feather-breath of a wind beneath the lark-song and admired the mountain avens, bright white blossoms with glowing golden centres, flowers mimicking the sun and mocking the arid illusion of the grey rockscape. Above the invisible choir of sky-larks spread a pale blue sky, wisped with high, transparent clouds, and far in the distance the darker blue ocean meared with a misty horizon. Over the eastern brow, a little further down the slope where the steep track from Gleninagh North reaches the crest of the pass and you may linger to gaze over Galway Bay, mountain avens

Dryas octopetala: mountain avens

mingle with other flowers in a rich sward and tumble over terraces; so lavish is the carpet that boulders are transformed into green cushions. Frederick Foot marvelled at the mountain avens a century ago:

> a beautiful sight it is in summer, when in full blow, its brilliant white flowers contrasting with the showy blossoms of the Geranium sanguineum.[15]

Dryas octopetala is a member of the rose family (Rosaceae) and is counted by some as a shrub–to be sure it has a woody rootstock and the oldest stems can be well over fifty years old. Long ago, according to Messrs. O'Mahony and Whitla, 'the peasantry [brought] it in loads from the hills and [used] it as fuel',[16] but it is better to think of *Dryas* as an evergreen, perennial herb. The leaves are oval with a sinuously indented and waved margin, like an miniature oak leaf, glistening above and pure white underneath; the individual leaves are about the size of a fingernail. The foliage is crowded on the prostrate stems, overlapping to give almost total cover of the soil, and persists through the winter.

Mountain avens blossoms in May and June, and there is often a second, lesser flush of flowers in August; indeed from April to October it is quite possible to find flowers although at the extremities of the season these are few and far between. The flowers, as the epithet *octopetala* denotes, usually have eight petals, but a considerable proportion have more than eight, and late in the summer the multiplication is more pronounced. Thaddeus O'Mahony and Francis Whitla found 'polypetalous' forms and Frederick Foot wrote that 'in the higher ground, the Dryas is frequently double' but I cannot agree–'double' flowers (that is flowers with more than eight petals) are not uncommon, but no more so on the mountain slopes than on the pavements. Moreover, rarely is a plant consistently 'double' flowered–Dr Keith Lamb, an expert gardener, discovered two 'double' mountain avens in The Burren, near Glencolumbkille, in the late 1980s and one that he propagated from cuttings is remarkable for the extent and constancy of the multiplication of petals.

The flower buds and stems are covered with long glandular hairs–these are usually very dark, almost black, but forms with translucent colourless hairs occur. The hairs exude a sticky fluid, the purpose of which does not seem to have been investigated. In the centre of each bloom there is a circlet of bright yellow stamens–these wither after releasing their pollen–and inside this is a cluster of numerous green carpels each one crowned with an erect style covered with long white feathery hairs. Nectar is secreted by the flowers so *Dryas octopetala* is pollinated by insects such as empid flies (*Empididae*). After pollination the petals also wither and the handsome poached-egg flowers are transformed into a fruiting head, the styles elongate and twist loosely together into a short braided brush. When the carpels are ripe, the styles separate and the characteristic shaggy fruiting head is formed. Those parts of the Burren once cloaked with white flowers are now down-bedecked and the breezes scatter the ripe fruits–they sail by means of their feathery styles.

The individual flowers of *Dryas octopetala* are usually hermaphrodite, with fertile, pollen-filled anthers, and fully formed carpels–these produce seeds after cross-pollination. Sometimes a small proportion of male flowers with moribund carpels are present on individual plants–these cannot produce seed–and I have seen some mats that appear only to have male flowers. Cross-pollination of the hermaphrodite flowers ensures that viable fruits are produced; self-pollination can take place but usually results in a poor crop of seeds. A single *Dryas octopetala* flower can yield at least fifty seeds, and these should germinate in the spring following.[17]

Richard Heaton found mountains avens, growing with gentians; Dr William How reported this discovery:

Teucrium Alpinum Cifti flore. *Alpine Germander with a Cistus flower: In the mountaines betwixt Gort and Galloway.* It makes a pretty shew in the Winter with his rough heads like *Viorna*.[18]

By winter, in The Burren at least, the 'rough heads like *Viorna*' have disintegrated in the equinoctial gales–but the description is apt because *Viorna* is a name for old man's beard, otherwise *Clematis vitalba*, and it has similar fuzzy fruiting heads. Dr Dillenius did not doubt Heaton's finding of this plant, as he had his discovery of the Spring gentian, probably because Edward Lhuyd had brought specimens from County Sligo half a century later.[19]

Outside The Burren *Dryas octopetala* grows on Ben Bulben in County Sligo and at Knockmore in County Fermanagh; there are small populations on other northern mountains, Benevinagh in County Derry, Slieve League in County Donegal and Knockdhu in eastern Antrim, as well as scattered populations through Connemara. Remarkably, there is no sign of *Dryas octopetala* in the Aran Islands–'another fact that admits of no easy explanation'.[20] Mountain avens is recorded in Snowdonia, the English Lake District and the Highlands of Scotland, and thence it circles the globe–Pyrenees, Alps, Apennines, the mountains of Macedonia, through Asia by way of the Caucasus, the Altai, Mongolia, Korea and Japan into North America where it proceeds south along the Rockies into Colorado. Within Arctic and sub-Arctic regions *Dryas octopetala* inhabits Greenland, Spitzbergen, Iceland and the Eurasian mainland from Norway to Kamchatka. Botanists have attempted to segregate the western Europe mountain avens from those of other territories–the Canadian botanist A. E. Porsild named it *Dryas babingtoniana*,[21] and a plethora of names are available for these exotica, but the differences are slight and the populations hardly warrant even subspecific rank.

Frederick Foot recorded that the 'Irish name is *Layheen*'; the modern form is *leaithin*. There is also a report that in Clare it was called wild betony, because the leaves resembled those of betony. Geoffrey Grigson lamented it had not a better name than mountain avens, and while thinking 'white dryas' was better, wanted a name suggestive of 'gold, whiteness, and open sunlight.' I leave the final word to Robert Lloyd Praeger:

> He who has viewed the thousands of acres of the Arctic-alpine plant in full flower on the limestone of the Burren region of Clare, from hill-top down to sea-level, has seen one of the loveliest sights that Ireland has to offer to the botanist.[22]

It is not difficult to envision how Arctic plants–mountains avens, crowberry, bearberry–colonized The Burren. When glaciers descended over north-western Europe, Arctic species retreated in front of the ice into more southern latitudes. Conversely, when the glaciers melted, the cold-adapted plants returned northwards. Thus in the period immediately following the melting of the ice from The Burren, mountain avens and other pioneer species colonized suitable sites. So far, so good. What is much more difficult to explain is the survival of plants of Arctic affinity at sea-level in habitats that cannot be characterised today as having an Arctic climate. Furthermore, given that The Burren was cloaked with open pine forest until perhaps three thousand years ago, how did plants that cannot tolerate competition from other vigorous herbs, let alone shade from pine trees, survive until this time.

The most acceptable explanation is that while a mineral soil covered the rocks in *most* places, and *many parts* of The Burren were wooded until Neolithic times, a state manifest by pollen grains preserved in peat and sediments,[23] on higher, steeper slopes patches of bare limestone and limestone scree were not wooded. These 'refugia' provided habitats for mountain avens and a handful of other species.

When Neolithic tribes felled the trees, they initiated a dramatic ecological transformation–the felling of Amazonian rain-forest is the modern analogue. The thin mineral soil, no longer bound by tree roots and protected by a cover of woodland herbs, was gradually washed away by rain until, as William Trevor graphically described it, 'the very bones of Ireland's landscape [broke] through its skin...'.[24] Vast tracts of rock pavements were laid bare exposing niches resembling those presented by retreating glaciers. The Arctic species which had lingered on exposed screes and hillsides were able to seed into these uncovered habitats and to colonize larger areas of this new limestone 'wilderness'. The eerie corollary is this: the continued survival of carpets of mountain avens, bearberry and crowberry studded with orchids and Spring gentians depends largely on the maintenance of a tree-less landscape, devoid of thick, bushy scrub and barren of loam or deep peat; in short, on the persistence of human interference with the natural progression of the ecosystem. The Burren is an artifice, albeit extraordinarily beautiful, that has arisen by great good chance, phoenix-like, out of mankind's catastrophic meddling with Nature. Its exciting qualities should not be regarded as justification for precipitating similar 'ecological disasters' elsewhere–serendipity is not always so gentle and bountiful.

None of that explains why Arctic plants, tolerant of conditions much more severe than anything experienced in Ireland for at least eight millennia, thrive in

Geranium sanguineum: bloody cranesbill

so mild and equable an environment. Plant and animal species are continually evolving and imperceptibly changing–they must, if individuals are to reproduce successfully and 'hold their own' in their particular habitats. The Burren race of *Dryas octopetala* undoubtedly has changed in subtle ways since it was marooned on the limestone hills thousands of years ago; I suspect that if seedlings from The Burren's populations were transplanted to the north of Spitzbergen, few would survive the first winter. Thus while Burren mountain avens may not look on casual inspection different to the plant of the Arctic, it has surely become adapted to a warmer, softer regime. No-one has done such a transplant experiment–if they do I could, of course, be proved wrong.

The other great botanical treat in The Burren is the spectacle of bloody cranesbill in full blow. While not as widespread as *Dryas octopetala*, with a definite preference for a fair depth of soil and a modicum of shelter, *Geranium sanguineum* is more abundant in the rough flower meadows on north-western Clare than anywhere else in Ireland; indeed in the hinterland of The Burren it is almost entirely wanting, even on limestone soil. Dr Threlkeld had collected bloody cranesbill at Simmonscourt in south Dublin in the 1720s, but no-one reported it from The Burren until Francis Whitla and Thaddeus O'Mahony who recalled that

> …the plant most plentiful, particularly in the southern parts of Burren, when you enter it from the direction of Moher, is the Geranium sanguineum, which, in the neighbourhood of Bealnalack Castle, I have seen spreading over acres of rocky ground.[25]

This is still one of the best places to see the bloody cranesbill.

The adjective 'bloody' is a straight translation of the Latin epithet *sanguineum*, an adjective used for this plant for many centuries, and one that Carl Linnaeus adopted when he devised its current botanical binomial. The native Irish name *crobh dearg*–red bill–is as unimaginative as the others for it harks back to *Geranium*, itself an allusion to the fruit that looks like the prolonged bill of a crane or stork, and to the 'blood-red' flowers. Yet the flowers are not blood-coloured; they are the richest magenta, a colour that is heightened by comparison with the grey limestone. The brilliance of the petals of the bloody cranesbill becomes all the more startling when you gaze into the centre of a flower. Resting on the petals are the stamens, each one crowned with a turquoise blue anther, a perfect combination of colours.

Geranium is a large genus, and there are five other species in The Burren. The flowers possess ten stamens; in some species, including bloody cranesbill, five of these ripen and discharge their pollen as the petals unfurl, followed about a day later by the remaining five anthers. If you look at a newly opened blossom of *Geranium sanguineum* you will notice that there are five turquoise anthers–these are the ones still full of pollen–but look into the same blossom twenty four hours later and they seem to have disappeared because they have in turn ruptured and dispersed their pollen. You can witness the same sequence in herb Robert.

Bloody cranesbill is a perennial herb, but has few basal leaves and so is not obvious in winter when it hibernates as an underground rhizome. The foliage is carried mainly on the flowering stems, the leaves in pairs, each with a long stalk and a deeply cleft leaf-blade which has five or seven principal lobes each one further divided into three; the basal leaves are not so deeply divided as those on the stems. The flowers are held aloft on stalks; the five petals are usually notched at the apex, tapering and fading to white at the base. In autumn the leaves turn scarlet, a fiery colour enlivened by the low sunlight, the translucent lamina glowing as if a flame.

I have walked far in The Burren and glimpsed a myriad cranesbills and most of the plants remain faithful to the general type–there is very little variation in colour of the petals or in the general demeanour of the plants although Dr Peter Yeo notes that *Geranium sanguineum* varies greatly in habit, hairiness and form of the leaves and size of flowers.[26] On Abbey Hill I did notice a plant with much smaller flowers than usual, and elsewhere flowers which tend to be more pink than purple but the difference is only a fractional one. One day maybe I'll find a pure white or a pale pink–they must be there, somewhere.

Thomas Corry sang the praises of *Geranium sanguineum*:

> …the prevailing glory and beauty of these limestone rock gardens is undoubtedly the Bloody Geranium… Dark green leaves, and flowers varying from bloody crimson when they first expand, to deep purple; and in extreme age, before the petals fade and fall off altogether, passing into an intense blue with crimson through it…such are the colour characters of this flower without which these crag lands would appear almost a bare wilderness, but aided by which no more charming prospect of colour could be desired. Lovely, indeed, is the tricolor flag waving on the hills of Clare, formed of the Geranium, Dryad and Gentian.[27]

Corry's red, white and blue tricolor was blowing where Thaddeus O'Mahony had glimpsed masses of bloody cranesbill, beyond Ballinalackan Castle on the coast road between Lisdoonvarna and Ballyvaghan. In the same locality, these botanists and their companions collected saxifrages which they could not definitely identify; Whitla considered one was 'the true Caespitosa' and Corry thought 'a curious form…with the barren shoots terminated in dense rosettes' bore 'a considerable resemblance to *Saxifraga hirta*.'[28] They had stumbled on one of the most tantalizing problems in Irish botany–the mossy saxifrages, a group of plants that acquired a foggy litany of names.

There are three species of saxifrage in The Burren; *Saxifraga tridactylites* (the tiny annual, flowering in early spring), *Saxifraga hypnoides* (a widespread perennial with white flowers, common in the central areas) and *Saxifraga rosacea* (the least common, and most restricted in its distribution, another perennial with white flowers). While it occurs on all the Aran Islands in substantial quantity, *Saxifraga rosacea*, recently dubbed 'Irish saxifrage' (translated into *mórán gaelach*), is much less abundant and moreover confined on the mainland to a narrow strip

Saxifraga rosacea: Irish saxifrage

of the coast between Black Head and Poll Salach. While not considered to be a 'maritime' plant, the Clare habitats are mostly within a few tens of metres of the ocean; elsewhere in Ireland it is both a coastal species and a montane one even growing high in the Galtee Mountains of counties Limerick and Tipperary and MacGillicuddy's Reeks in County Kerry. Despite its recently concocted name, Irish saxifrage is a far-flung plant, occurring in two distinct regions: in north-western Europe *Saxifraga rosacea* is known from Iceland and the Faeroes, Ireland, north Wales (it has not been found there for many decades and may be extinct); in central Europe it ranges from eastern France through Luxembourg and southern Germany eastwards into Czechoslovakia and southern Poland. In Ireland two subspecies are known. *Saxifraga rosacea* subsp. *hartii* is confined to the island of Aranmore off the coast of Donegal. The Burren plant is *Saxifraga rosacea* subsp. *rosacea*, but in nineteenth century accounts it is nameless, or was dubbed *Saxifraga hirta* or *Saxifraga sternbergii*.[29]

Minuartia verna: Spring sandwort

Saxifraga rosacea and *Saxifraga hypnoides* are 'mossy' saxifrages; they form evergreen rosettes of small, deeply segmented leaves, which in the case of *Saxifraga rosacea* are compact, like an elegant rose, and often scarlet not green. *Saxifraga hypnoides*, which occurs in abundance inland in The Burren, also has rosettes but more diffuse ones than those of *Saxifraga rosacea* and hardly ever red. Both species increase vegetatively by producing stolons that develop new rosettes at the tips, and so a plant can establish a considerable colony of offsets. *Saxifraga rosacea* differs from *Saxifraga hypnoides* in that it does not possess prostrate non-flowering shoots. Furthermore the Irish saxifrage has erect flower-buds; in *Saxifraga hypnoides* the buds nod. They also differ in their habitats, as already indicated.

The Burren and Aran Islands populations of *Saxifraga rosacea* can be distinguished from all other populations by the form of their leaves–the tips of the tiny segments are sharply pointed, and the lamina is glabrous.

161

Professor David Webb, the authority on the saxifrages of western Europe, has remarked about the peculiarities of the Irish saxifrage's habitats on The Burren and Aran Islands.[30] On the limestone pavements, the tight cushions are fully exposed to sun and wind, and although rooted in shallow depressions and scailps they never creep into dim recesses and into the deep, more sheltered crevices; one of Robert Welch's classic photographs shows typical hummocks of Irish saxifrage on the exposed lower terrace at Black Head.[31] In its other Irish stations, *Saxifraga rosacea* is generally found on mountain ledges and cliffs, facing north-east or north and often beside streams, where the rosettes are rarely touched by the sun and are constantly splashed by water. The contrast is stark for on the pavements of The Burren in summer the plants are often parched–even by the end of May they can be shrivelled up.

Both saxifrages have five-petalled white flowers about the size of a thumb-nail. Spring sandwort also has a 'mossy' rosette and white, five-petalled flowers but its fine leaves are linear, abut one centimetre long, and the flowers are smaller than those of the two *Saxifraga* species.

Minuartia verna (Spring sandwort; *gaineamhlus earraigh*) belongs to the same family, Caryophyllaceae, as chickweeds, carnations and campions–sea campion (*Silene vulgaris* subsp. *maritima*) is a common and familiar coastal plant, with grey-green leaves and white flowers cupped in a inflated, barrel-shaped calyx. Spring sandwort and sea campion grow side-by-side at Poll Salach, and can easily be identified by leaf and flower size. The sandwort is much smaller in all its parts, more refined and delicate. A perennial herb with a substantial tap-root, *Minuartia verna*, is distinguished from other species of *Minuartia* by the distinctly three-veined, somewhat rigid leaves and the glandular hairs on the flower stalks.

In late May when the gentians and mountain avens are spent, Spring sandwort comes into its own; starry white flowers with bright red anthers, set in mossy, emerald shoots. This is one of the purest of The Burren's plants, and the most widespread, growing not just along the green roads, but on the pavements by the sea at Poll Salach and around Black Head and inland too, although it does not extend far to the east almost being restricted to the hills. *Minuartia verna* also grows on the Aran Islands.

Spring sandwort inhabits sites where the rocks are base rich (limestone and basalt, for example) and even grows on the spoil heaps of old lead-mines. In counties Antrim and Derry, the only other part of Ireland where *Minuartia verna* grows, its habitats are on basalt. John Templeton of Malone, Belfast, discovered Spring sandwort at Magilligan in County Derry in the late 1790s, and Dr Osborne gathered it between Leamaneh and Kilfenora ('Lunenagh Castle and Kilferna, County of Clare') in the early 1830s.[32] Robert Ball later noticed Spring sandwort on the Aran Islands.

The little sandwort is more abundant and widespread in Britain than in Ireland, and extends through Europe into the Caucasus; it is also recorded from North Africa and Siberia. A similar distribution pattern is displayed by dropwort, but in Ireland there are no populations outside The Burren. Moreover, unlike for example hoary rock-rose and Spring gentian, dropwort has a very restricted distribution in Clare and Galway.

Dropwort belongs to the same genus as meadowsweet, but it is a less vigorous perennial with a basal rosette of ground-hugging, finely divided leaves, like elongated parsley, and generally shorter flowering stalk. The rootstock is tuberous, unlike meadowsweet. The leaves are oblong, with up to twenty pairs of leaflets arranged feather-like along a central rachis. The leaflets are finely lobed and both surfaces are rich green–in meadowsweet the leaves are much coarser and frequently white-green below.

The flowers of *Filipendula vulgaris* have spoon-shaped creamy-white petals, sometimes tinted red; the inflorescence is broad, not as elongated as in meadowsweet and the individual petals are substantially larger. Each flower has six petals and sepals, with four to six times as many stamens, and six to twelve hairless and erect carpels arranged like the ruff of an Elizabethan sailor. In its complete demeanour, the inflorescence of dropwort is thicker than that of meadowsweet and seems quite dishevelled, yet the creamy panicles are most attractive and this has been recognized by gardeners who cultivate dropwort and eschew meadowsweet.

Filipendula vulgaris has had a confusingly large number of Latin names–in the early eighteenth century its was called simply *Filipendula*, a name adopted when binomials were invented *Filipendula hexapetala* (referring to it six petals), *Spiraea filipendula*, and *Ulmaria filipendula* are later epithets. The English name, dropwort, suggests an affinity with water dropwort (*Oenanthe crocata*), an extremely poisonous member of the carrot family (Apiaceae) which inhabits stream-banks and lake margins, and which was only recently discovered in The Burren at Aillwee. Dropwort is a member of Rosaceae (the rose family) and is not lethal.

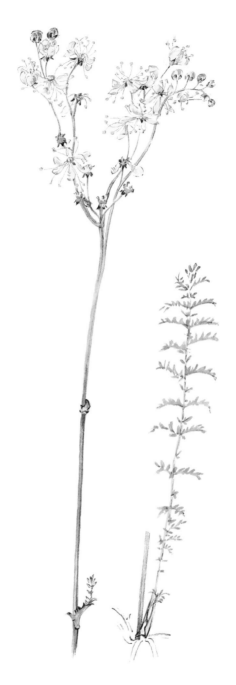

Filipendula vulgaris
dropwort

Ajuga pyramidalis: pyramidal bugle

Remarkably dropwort from The Burren was known to the Revd John Keogh, herbalist and chaplain to Lord Kingston at Mitchelstown, County Cork; in *Botanalogia universalis Hibernica*, published in Cork during 1735, he wrote that

> DROPWORT, Hib. *Lussorynagh*, …grows in Gardens and wild in the *Barony* of *Burrin*, in the *County* of *Clare*, flowering in *June,* and *July*…[33]

Keogh's record was forgotten for more than a century: James Townsend Mackay did not notice dropwort in *Flora Hibernica*, and it remained for Thaddeus O'Mahony and Francis Whitla to claim *Filipendula vulgaris* as a new discovery. Frederick Foot described the dropwort's habitat succinctly, and collected a novel native name for it:

> The Spiraea grows abundantly through [Glencolumbkille] up to the foot of the steep cliff of "Kinallia", or the Eagle's-rock… It grows in the chinks of the rock, among heather and grass, and along the road-side. It is well known to many of the peasantry, the Irish name being *Fillyfindillaun* (I could not ascertain the correct orthography of this word, but this is its pronunciation), and is much used, when boiled in new milk, as a remedy for diseases of the kidneys.[34]

The name 'fillyfindillaun' is puzzling, but Cyril O Ceirin has provided an ingeniously simple explanation, that 'fillyfindillaun' is a local attempt at ancient Latin name, *Filipendula*.[35] The contemporary Irish name is *lus braonach* which closely resembles Keogh's 'lussorynagh'.

John Keogh had already noticed that dropwort was a diuretic, and it is possible that dropwort was exported from The Burren in the eighteenth century; I do not believe Keogh visited the region, although he did report several plants from the area including castor-oil, an astonishing fable which indicates that either he was badly informed or thoroughly gullible.[36]

Dropwort is an oddity. Its habitat encompasses the eastern lowlands, not the western high-ground, and there are few other Burren species with an analogous pattern of distribution. Plants are easily spotted when in bloom or just before the flowers open when the buds are tinged red.

The first inkling of the diminutive bugle, *Adjuga pyramidalis*, as a native plant in Ireland, was David Moore's discovery of just two plants during a hasty visit to the Aran Islands in May 1854 when he also noted *Astragalus danicus*. He suggested it would be found 'on the opposite mainland of Connemara'[37]–and in that prediction he was correct although half a century passed before it was seen there. Strangely Moore did not predict its discovery on The Burren mainland, and yet that was where Frederick Foot found pyramidal bugle in May 1861.

> This rare plant, which occurs on the Isles of Arran [sic.], appears also on the mainland opposite, near Poll Salach… It is apparently confined to a small area along the new coast road. I searched everywhere else in the neighbourhood, along the shore, and on old roads, but without success. This would suggest the idea that possibly the plant flourished on the mainland, as well as on the isles of Arran, before they were separated; that after separation, the plant died out on the mainland in the great struggle for existence, some seeds remaining latent in the ground (there being a small accumulation of clay and gravel here), which were brought to life and light by the turning up of the soil in making the road.[38]

Frederick Foot's allusion to 'the great struggle for existence' suggests that he had read Charles Darwin's shattering book *On the origin of species*, while his idea that work on the new road brought to life seeds long dormant in the soil is also reminiscent of Darwin's studies on the longevity of seeds. It is unlikely that Foot's theory is correct–there is no reason to suppose *Ajuga pyramidalis* ever 'died out' at Poll Salach.

Frederick Foot's annotated field-map for the western coast of Clare bears an inscription at the precise locality that he found the bugle,[39] and in the same locality I saw my first plant in 1987. In mid-May 1991 pyramidal bugle flowered abundantly at Poll Salach especially near the sea where plants must have been doused by salt-water during the ferocious storms of the previous January. Did their bath induce them to bloom?

Pyramidal bugle was thought to be one of Ireland's rarer plants, but in recent years it had 'turned up' in unexpected places. In Connemara, there is a suggestion that it is spreading, and in May 1983 Paul Murphy, a young student from the National Botanic Gardens, Glasnevin, photographed it on Rathlin Island, off the north Ulster coast where subsequent investigations revealed a substantial colony.

Like some orchids, *Ajuga pyramidalis* has a tendency to 'disappear'–or to be more exact, plants persist as inconspicuous rosettes, and bloom only very occasionally. Dr Ralph Forbes has used the opportunities afforded by annual field-trips with extra-mural students from The Queen's University, Belfast, to study in detail populations of pyramidal bugle at Poll Salach. Meticulously they mapped every rosette in a precisely marked series of four plots, and every year checked the state of the rosettes in each area. For seven years, Dr Forbes' parties measured and marked, and their study suggests that *Ajuga pyramidalis* at Poll Salach is a perennial, and not a monocarpic biennial as stated in many standard floras. Plants in the study plots blossomed only when rosettes had reached a critical diameter–about seven centimetres, the length of a finger. The other startling conclusion was that at Poll Salach there were hundreds of pyramidal bugles concealed among other herbs–the randomly sited plots, each covering one square metre, contained between thirty-five and fifty rosettes, but only a small proportion flowered in any one season, and the number of flower spikes varied substantially from year to year.[40]

Ajuga pyramidalis has persisted at Poll Salach for over one century, and undoubtedly for very much longer. Its erratic, unpredictable flowering makes it elusive, as I know very well having searched for it on many occasions without success. The Queen's University students have elegantly demonstrated that the species-rich sward at Poll Salach contains hundreds of bugles and Ralph Forbes has argued that, given adequate seed production every year, *Ajuga pyramidalis* will survive where Frederick Foot first found it.

To find *Ajuga pyramidalis* at Poll Salach, you will need acute eyes, and a fair amount of luck. The tell-tale sign is the stubby inflorescence which should be

Solidago virgaurea
golden rod

well developed by the middle of May, but being only about five centimetres tall–shorter than the diameter of the whole plant–can still be inconspicuous among the other herbs. However the hairy bracts, arranged in tiers, are rich blue-purple during the short flowering season; they are much longer than the small blue flowers. After pollination the concealed flowers wither, and the bracts rapidly lose the purple tints, changing to a pallid green, and thereby once again the bugle slides into obscurity among the rapidly growing scabious and hawkweeds.

And now a mystery–the hybrid bugle (*Ajuga* x *hampeana*), reputedly the progeny of a cross between the common (*Ajuga reptans*) and the pyramidal (*Ajuga pyramidalis*), is persistently reported from The Burren. Patrick O'Kelly believed he had found such a plant and he sent a clutch of herbarium specimens to George Claridge Druce at Oxford, and to other botanists. Miss Maura Scannell studied herbarium specimens sent by O'Kelly to the Revd William Bentley[41] and wrote at length confirming O'Kelly's hybrid. I remain sceptical, and my scruples are reinforced by a letter to Dr Druce from P. B. O'Kelly, attached to one specimen of the supposed hybrid now in the Fielding-Druce Herbarium (University of Oxford).

> Dear Sir
> I herewith enclose you a specimen plant of my new Ajuga Hybrida O'Kelly from Ballyreen Mountain. It grows about 1000 feet above sea level on the ledge of a cliff and about an Irish Mile high upon the Mountain from where Ajuga pyramidalis grows which is only 60 or 70 ft above sealevel. This new Ajuga is a splendid flowering plant. It flowers in April on up to the first week in May. I think it is a distinct species. It grows most luxuriant in the open air. It grows about twice the size of the Ajuga reptans. If you like to change the name you can do so & with pleasure.
>
> Yours truly
> P. B. O'Kelly
>
> July 26 1909.
>
> PS You need not return the Plant as I have two or thee more of them. And a few I left behind in the Habitat.[42]

Five days later O'Kelly sent four plants of a 'new orchis and one of my Ajuga. The only one in fruit. It is a strong grower & the flower spike is most elegant & all the leaves very hairy & in the young state almost woolly.'[43] His bugle was cultivated for many years in Oxfordshire gardens, but what was it?

O'Kelly's description of the site, an Irish mile away and higher in the hills, can only refer to the townland of Ballynahown, between Oughtdarra and Knockauns Mountain, a spectacular locality of sheer ivy-encrusted cliffs and wedge-tombs overlooked by the crumbling walls of Cathair Dhúin. In May 1991 with Paul Carter, I walked to the edge of the cliffs overlooking Ballyryan and Poll Salach. We meandered on to Cathair Dhúin, now carpeted with mossy saxifrage, and returned over lawns of bird's foot trefoil and mountain avens to the green road, but we saw no sign of bugles, pyramidal, hybrid or common.

I believe the hybrid bugle is a phantom, wishful thinking on O'Kelly's and Druce's parts, one more puzzle in The Burren's quiver-full. O'Kelly collected plants in flower about one month before there is any sign of *Ajuga pyramidalis* in bloom. He described it as twice the size of common bugle, yet pyramidal bugle is a dwarf compared with *Ajuga reptans*. And crucially, I have never seen *Ajuga reptans* in any locality near Poll Salach, so how could a hybrid arise?

From the cliff edge at Ballynahown the view southwards is breath-taking. In the far distance the dark ramparts of the Cliffs of Moher form the horizon. Ballinalackan Castle stands four-square on its bluff, and between the fortress and my perch spreads a mosaic of fields, with grazing cattle and sheep, and hazel scrub dotted with the hawthorn and blackthorn. To the west, the three Aran islands slumber in the ocean and in between are the grey pavements and grassy moraines of Poll Salach. Here it was that Frederick Foot heard the wind make music.

> The rocks...are Limestone varying in texture from compact to finely crystalline & in colour dark blue, dull blue or pale grey, thick bedded, thin & often flaggy & then weathering out into loose, flaggy fragments which often shake with the wind and ring when struck with a hammer forming cliffs & terraces & traversed by numerous joints...which cut up the surface of the beds into fissures of various depths, abounding in vegetation.[44]

He inked in the terraces and cliffs, boulder fields and the new line of roads, and wrote *Ajuga pyramidalis* on his field map.

Solidago virgaurea is too abundant about Poll Salach to have been worthy of a special annotation of Foot's maps, but he did notice it in print—valerian and hemp agrimony and golden-rod were 'very characteristic plants...everywhere to be met with in abundance.'[45] Charles Lucas was the first to publish a record of 'Virgaurea' in The Burren, including it among the 'great variety of the Capillary herbs' that the limestone hills yielded.[46]

Geoffrey Grigson draws together some interesting facts about golden rod which may serve to explain Lucas' mention of it. *Solidago virgaurea* was highly regarded as a wound-herb 'used inwardly or outwardly': '...since there were stabbings and thrustings enough in Tudor London, such herbs were expensive and in demand.' The same holds true for eighteenth-century Dublin. When golden rod was discovered in Hampstead the price in London herb-market slumped, and John Gerard railed that no-one would pay half-a-crown for a hundredweight of it.[47] Dr Threlkeld noted two variants in Ireland, including the lesser golden-rod–a montane, dwarfed variant–which William Sherard found in the 1690s, but made no remarks to indicate rarity or cost. Instead he picked up another use for golden rod: he quoted a passage in Latin about *Solidago virgaurea* as an ingredient of snuff, and concluded thus

> I leave the Observation untranslated, looking upon common snuffing to be the meanest Way of Debauchery, hurting the Eyes and Ears, and shocking the Senses, stuffing the Stomach and Lungs, and most practised by the most unpolite of Men, as in the *Highlands*, &c.[48]

Solidago is a large genus belonging to the daisy family (Asteraceae); over one hundred species are named in North America and a few of these are familiar as garden flowers. *Solidago virgaurea* is widespread in Ireland and Britain, and is also recorded from Asia, the European mainland and North America; it is immensely variable, sometime dwarfed, sometimes with branched flowering heads, and sometimes glabrous. The Burren golden rod is a diminutive, early blooming variant which may well deserve a name to itself. The archetypal Irish golden-rod is a leafy stemmed, herbaceous perennial, reaching above half a metre in height, and its peak flowering season is late summer. At Poll Salach *Solidago virgaurea* rarely grows more than fifteen centimetres in height and begins to blossom in late May, reaching full bloom in June and July, depending on the season. The leaves are dark green, and the flowering stems do not branch. Otherwise the Poll Salach golden-rod is identical with the common form. The flower heads have about ten bright yellow ray florets and about the same number of yellow disc florets. The dwarf golden-rod is not confined to Poll Salach, and is frequent throughout the western hills and in the eastern lowlands.

When this variant is brought into cultivation, it remains small and flowers in early summer.[49] Thus the dwarf stature and early flowering are characteristics that are genetically controlled. Dwarf plants are also known from montane habitats throughout the British Isles, and have been called *Solidago virgaurea* var. *cambrensis*, a name that could encompass The Burren plants too.

Some folk, having seen the dwarf golden-rod, pale blue Spring gentians and double-flowered mountain avens blooming in The Burren, will take up the challenge of growing some of these plants in their gardens. Let me echo Reginald Farrer and repeat what he wrote about the Spring gentian: 'The plant may be raised by cuttings struck in sand, or raised from seeds; it is exceedingly unsatisfactory and odious to collect' it from wild habitats. This applies also to every other plant in The Burren.

Abbey of St Maria de Petra Fertilis, Corcomroe

A PROVOCATION OF ORCHIDS

… In coupling people a steady help
Are scraps of apples and powdered herbs
The purple orchid and cowslip plant
The knotted figwort, the shepherd's purse
Kid's desire and also rib-wort,
The yellow cummin with its magic for lust,
Leaves that are burned in secrecy -
And more of this kind 'tisn't right to teach…

Brian Merriman: 'The Midnight Court'[1]

A unique cluster of botanical carvings in an ancient abbey, and a gallery of twentieth-century flower paintings on the walls of a secluded hotel are among the little-told treasures of The Burren.

The mediaeval sculptures adorn the chancel and a side chapel of Corcomroe Abbey which lies snugly in the shelter of Abbey Hill, east of the hamlet of Béal an Chloga (Bell Harbour) between Ballyvaghan and Kinvarra. The abbey's setting

173

is sublime, encircled by hills and set among strip-fields whose boundaries are perhaps as ancient as the church itself. Spleenworts, pellitory-of-the-wall (*Parietaria judaica*), pennywort (*Umbilicus rupestris*) with its succulent rounded leaves, and poppies inhabit the walls and windowsills of the unroofed nave and transept. Jackdaws claim possession in raucous monotone chants that sound through the empty architraves. The fossil-speckled limestone blocks of the abbey's masonry are splashed with white, grey and orange lichens. Eccentric rock dragons slide silently down the quoinstones of the presbytery, clawing at the string course. While wind and rain and careless men have whittled the abbey to a ruin, the capitals of the columns at the entrance to the chancel, out of reach and out of sight to most who visit this ancient sanctuary, are still almost intact and adorned with stone-grey flowers and poppy fruits.

Like other Cistercian foundations Corcomroe Abbey was dedicated to the Blessed Virgin, *Sancta Maria de Petra Fertilis*, Our Lady of the Fertile Rocks. Perhaps mindful of this, an anonymous master-mason carved floral ornaments, completing his work about 1210[2] so that these are the earliest botanical carvings in western Europe, pre-dating by a century many more elaborate ones in English and French cathedrals. The plants sculpted for Corcomroe were not native species, but medicinal herbs and flowers associated with the Virgin, foxgloves (which do not grow on the limestone hills) and lily-of-the-valley, a wonderful miniature frieze of poppy fruits and flowers whose bells bear some resemblance to henbane.[3] When finished the botanical carvings were probably painted, as were the heads guarding the transept chapel and the geometrical mouldings of the chancel's ceiling ribs, but the colours have long since been eroded away. Be that as it may, protected under the stone arches of the crossing, the carvings are almost as crisp today as they were when the mason set down his mallet and chisel almost eight hundred years ago.

Local tradition in The Burren related that there were five masons employed on the Abbey, and that when they had completed the wonderful carvings in the chancel, Conchobar na Siudhaineach, King of Thomond, put them to death to stop them building any other masterpiece.

The unique stone-flowers of Corcomroe have twentieth century counterparts in Ballyvaghan valley on the western side of Moneen Mountain–a series of wall-paintings by Raymond Piper who is an artist and craftsman the equal of the Cistercians' master-mason.[4] Moreover, Raymond is one of The Burren's great champions, and his special delights are its orchids. During 1960 he travelled through Munster preparing a sequence of distinctive and intimate pencil-sketches for Richard

Hayward's *Munster and the city of Cork*, including a suite of The Burren's wildflowers: mountain avens, twayblade, gentian, wild strawberry and, somehow or other, a waif piece of St Dabeoc's heath.[5] In 1968 Raymond visited the Burren again and painted some of the native flowers in oil on prepared boards for Edgar Taylor and Alan McCorkindale.[6] To see Piper's orchids take the road south from Ballyvaghan towards Lisdoonvarna, and just before the tortuous climb of Corkscrew Hill, turn down the short drive to Gregan's Castle Hotel. Raymond was one of the first guests to stay there–indeed it was not completed when he was working on the orchid portraits. Originally the boards clad the walls but when extensive renovations were carried out in the late 1970s by Moira and Peter Hayden, the painted panels were removed. Framed and protected under glass, they now hang as pictures in the hotel's sitting-room.

Each orchid is depicted larger than life. Accompanying a cluster of the Spring gentian is an anthology of the Burren's orchids, frog (*Coeloglossum viride*), bee (*Ophrys apifera*) and fly orchids (*Ophrys insectifera*), Autumn Lady's tresses (*Spiranthes spiralis*), fragrant (*Gymnadenia conopsea*) and pyramidal orchids (*Anacamptis pyramidalis*), helleborine (*Epipactis helleborine*) and O'Kelly's spotted orchid (*Dactylorhiza fuchsii* f. *okellyi*). One large panel, besides the gentian, has portraits of early purple orchid (*Orchis mascula*) and red helleborine (*Epipactis atrorubens*) with the Irish (or dense-flowered) orchid (*Neotinea maculata* var. *straminea*). This incomparable set of paintings is an exquisite introduction to the orchid flora of the limestone hills.

Orchids are most enthralling. Like tulips which provoked a disastrous mania ending in financial ruin for many Dutch 'investors' during several decades of the seventeenth century, orchids have animated acquisitive gardeners, making some go crazy. Orchidmania was at its frenzied height during the late 1800s. Tropical species, stripped from their native habitats by professional collectors, were sold at London auctions for fantastic prices and ended their days as dying baubles in fashionable conservatories and drawing-rooms. Less exuberant, puny species such as those native in Ireland and Britain were also in demand–gardeners frantically following the vogue for 'wild gardens' sought them for planting in meads and rock-gardens. To satisfy this craving, orchids were dug up and exported even from The Burren; a bee orchid cost two shillings and sixpence in 1909, but the price fell to one shilling in the 1930s.

The popularity and mystique of orchids are more ancient than that of almost every other flower, undoubtedly pre-dating the earliest botanical tomes of classical

Greece. The herb-women of Thessalia collected orchid tubers to make into love potions; fondly they believed that an infusion of the roots in goat's milk would inflame the passions of their menfolk! This lore has much to do with the appearance of the egg-shaped, paired tubers of some European orchids, one plump and white being the new year's growth, the second tuber shrivelled and dark is the old one of the previous year. The underground tubers looked like a pair of testicles and so these attractive plants received their name–although few people today realize the hidden message, that seemingly inoffensive word *orchid* comes from the ancient Greek word for testicle, ορχισ.

The aphrodisiac property of orchids was believed for centuries. Caleb Threlkeld was restrained when recording the superstition; of salep '…deemed to be the dry'd Root of some sort of *Orchis*', demurely he made note only that it was 'in great Vogue…to restore a decayed Constitution, to provoke natural Vigours, to help Sterility, and facilitate the birth, made like *Chocolate*.'[7] In fact this lore was repeated in herbal after herbal–the gullible Mitchelstown cleric John Keogh gave it full rein–

> …the Decoction of the roots drank in *Goats-milk*, mightily provokes *Venery*, helps *Conception*, and strengthens the Genital parts, the said roots are *Analeptic*, good for them that are in a *Consumption*, or a *Hectic fever*. they also stop the *flux* of the *belly*, being applyed outwardly, they dissolve humours, mundifie rotten *Ulcers* and *fistulas*, it is reported that if Men, eat the greatest roots, they shall Beget Sons, if Women, the smallest roots, they shall bring forth daughters.[8]

The power of orchid tubers as a lusty stimulant was accepted by Irish herb-gatherers and that belief persisted into this century. In a way it still survives in the florists' trade–orchids are popular for bouquets and button-holes. Nor was the sexual pun in the orchid's name lost on earthy Irish peasants, for the native name for some orchids is *magairlín*, and that has the same dual application as in ancient Greece! *Magairlín mór*, large orchid (testicle) is the early marsh-orchid: *magairlín glas*, green orchid, has been concocted by some wit for what is also called in English dense-flowered orchid: *magairlín na mbeach*, orchid (testicle) of the bee needs no further glossing, while *magairlín meidhreach* is the early purple orchid.

Brian Merriman, a native Clare poet, introduced the lore of the orchid into his famous epic-poem 'Cúirt an Mhean-Oíche' ('The Midnight Court'). A lady lamenting her unmarried state muses that '…Only by withered and devilish herbs' is she likely yet to find herself a handsome fellow. 'And I shall prepare the very same means', she says, for

...Is daingean an cúnamh dúbailt daoine
Greamanna d'úlla agus púdar luibheanna:
An maigairlín meidhreach, meill na mbuailte,
An tathaigín taibhseach, toill na dtuarta,
Mealladh na minseach, cloi na mbonnsach,
An comáinín buí'san draíocht chun drúise,
Duilliúr dóite ar nós gur rún é,
Is tuille den tsort nár chóir a mhúineadh...[9]

Leaving aside sexual folklore, orchids display a multitude of fascinating floral forms, their beautifully coloured, sometimes scented blooms seem so exotic. They bewilder botanists. They are enmeshed in astonishing biological symbiosis whereby the life-cycles of fungi and animals coalesce with those of the plants. These traits are particularly evident in tropical species that grow as epiphytes on trees in the rain forests, but the native Irish species are as intriguing and as beautiful, even though they have small flowers and do not cascade from trees. And the orchids that sprout from The Burren's pastures and pavements are as pregnant with mysteries. Well might we reckon them provocative, still.

The succession of orchids that marches through The Burren's year is heralded by the early purple orchid, *Orchis mascula* (see plate, p. 185). The spikes begin to show in April and by the middle of May they are in full blow, spires of rich crimson through paler lavender to pure white. The inflorescences on stout stems rise from rosettes of blunt-tipped leaves that are usually spattered with dark purple-black spots–these marks have given rise to a legend that this plant grew at the foot of The Cross and that its spots are a memory of the blood of Christ which fell onto the leaves. An occasional purple blossomed plant, and those that have pure white flowers, do not have spotted leaves.

The early purple orchid has large flowers, each one subtended by coloured bracts. The lip (labellum) of the flower has three lobes and can be more than one centimetre long and as broad; it is shaded paler at the base and dotted with dark purple spots. The straight spur is as long as the ovary and stout, projecting backwards horizontally.

It is contradictory to write about *white* early purple orchids but they do exist, appearing occasionally yet with unusual frequency in The Burren; I know one plant well, perched on a ledge in Caherbullog townland, surrounded by a carpet of crowberry and whortleberry, and with many purple companions nearby. A small colony of whites also thrives on the verges of a by-road at Lough Gealáin.

Frederick Foot obliquely noted the white variant: 'they are all liable to flower white in the high ground', he remarked referring to early purple, spotted and pyramidal orchids.[10] P. B. O'Kelly listed 'Orchid mascula alba, white flower' in his 1892 catalogue *A complete list of the rare perennial plants & shrubs of the Burren Mountains of Ballyvaughan, Co. Clare*–I do not know of any other published record of white-flowered plants before Professor Webb's and Miss Scannell's note in *Flora of Connemara and The Burren*.[11]

The early purple orchid is not the only spring-blooming orchid, but the other is not nearly as conspicuous, although its makes up for its invisibility by being one of The Burren's most interesting inhabitants.

In May 1864, at Castle Taylor, a few kilometres west of Ardrahan–outside The Burren as I have defined it–Miss Frances More gathered flowering stems of a 'very ugly' orchid.[12] She pressed them and quickly despatched several examples to Dublin thereby providing the first record of a species for which the Clare and Galway limestones quickly became famous. She picked this 'pretty little plant'[13]–opinions about its beauty were completely contradictory!–in a rocky field called the 'Hunting Course', west of the Castle Taylor Nut-wood.

Frances' brother, Alexander Goodman More, was a well-regarded naturalist who shortly thereafter collaborated with David Moore, director of the Royal Dublin Society's Botanical Gardens at Glasnevin, to publish *Contributions towards a Cybele Hibernica, being outlines of the geographical distribution of plants in Ireland*. For six years (1881-1887) he was curator of the Natural History Museum in Dublin. After Alexander's death on 22 March 1895, Charles Moffat edited More's letters and published one of those eulogistic books favoured by our Victorian predecessors, *Life and letters of Alexander Goodman More*. So reverential a biography would be unacceptable today.

In *Life and letters of A. G. More...* the story unfolds of that spring in 1864 when 'as a health restorative', More was invited to stay at Castle Taylor:[14] 'Towards the end of February...his sister and he crossed over to Ireland, making his fifth visit to that country and to Castle Taylor.' Alexander's health did improve: 'We have killed lots of wood cock, and I have had shot at twelve Wild Swans here.' The blood-letting was ameliorated by searches for rare moths and by observing the flowers–blue grass spikes were one inch tall on 13 March, and on 8 April the anthers emerged.

Frances and Alexander botanized the Hunting Course beyond the Nut-wood and found 'among the symptoms of the spring' immature spikes of 'an inconspicuous but evidently unfamiliar orchidaceous plant.' Leaving his sister at Castle Taylor with instructions to keep watch over this strange plant, A. G. More travelled to Dublin to propose co-operation on an Irish flora to David Moore.

> The curious orchid now came into flower, and "my sister, following up the clue after I had left Castle Taylor, collected and dried several specimens, remarking that the little orchis was something she had never seen before." [Moore] was not yet quite ready to start for Mayo, when he received one of these specimens and noticed its resemblance to Reichenbach's figure of Tinea (or Neotinea) intacta, a plant of Southern Europe and Northern Africa. But the identification was not to be fixed in a day…
>
> Dr. Moore…continued to look into the question of the orchid, and after careful research concluded that it could be none other than Neotinea intacta. On June 15th, while still in "some little doubt about the identical species", Dr. Moore wrote a letter to "congratulate Miss More on adding a new plant to the Irish flora"; and about the same time he forwarded one of her specimens to Dr. Reichenbach, by whom its identification as "indeed Neotinea intacta" was confirmed.[15] The addition of this species to the British flora was announced by Dr. Moore at the next meeting of the Royal Irish Academy, on the 17th of June.[16]

Alexander More undoubtedly considered this new orchid a fascinating addition to the flora of Ireland, and its appearance at Castle Taylor growing with such 'alpine' plants as Spring gentians and mountain avens merely enhanced its fascination. Here was a truly provoking plant.

Further work indicated that the ugly orchid, variously named *Neotinea intacta* and *Habernaria intacta*, grew in western Connemara, the Corrib-Mask basin and The Burren whence it was first reported–from Glenquin–by Thomas Corry in 1880. *Neotinea maculata* is the correct botanical name for the orchid which has since been found in Cork, Limerick, Roscommon, Mayo and Offaly, and most recently in Donegal and Fermanagh. This species has not been collected in Britain yet it turned up on the Isle of Man in the 1960s–I understand it has not been seen there in recent years. *Neotinea maculata* (see plate, p. 196) grows on continental Europe from France to Greece, and is also reported from Madeira, the Canary Islands, Cyprus, western Asia and north Africa. In other words, its Irish populations are, by many kilometres, the most northern.

Robert Lloyd Praeger succinctly noted the significance of the occurrence of this orchid in The Burren; it contributed to the 'startling mixture' of plants, a tapestry not found elsewhere in the British Isles or Europe.

The cracks which are filled with the delicate green foam of *Adiantum* are set in *Arctostaphylos* and *Gentiana verna*; *Neotinea intacta*, far from its Mediterranean home, sends up its flower-spikes through carpets of *Dryas*...[17]

This same commingling of 'arctic', 'alpine' and 'Mediterranean' plants provoked the German botanist Otto Drude to write about 'so perverse a distribution and mixture of relict stations'.[18]

Like other native orchids, *Neotinea maculata* possesses a pair of egg-shaped underground tubers from which leaves are produced in October forming a rosette which remains compact and inconspicuous through the winter. Two variants are known and easily distinguished; one, the original described by René Desfontaines, has spotted leaves, while the other is spotless, immaculate. In April the inflorescence begins to elongate rising from the centre of the leaf-rosette and by mid-May the dense-flowered orchid joins the blooming mosaic of gentians, mountain avens, primroses and early purple orchids. The flowers are small, hooded, neither colourful nor spectacular; they are clustered, as one vernacular name suggests, in a dense, compact group at the apex of the stem. The Burren plants usually have sepals and petals that are uniformly pallid green or creamy-green (some writers have described them as primrose-yellow, or straw-coloured). Growing alongside, but much less frequent, are plants with faintly spotted leaves; these also have pink-tinged flowers–when the two are seen side-by-side, the difference in hue is quite clear. The variety gathered at Castle Taylor by Frances and Alexander More was the pinkish one with spotted leaves. More and Henry Levinge[19] separately had noticed the colour variants but the 'straw-coloured' *Neotinea maculata* var. *straminea* was only adequately described and named in 1934 by the English botanist Herbert Pugsley using Burren specimens.[20]

Soon after the orchid's discovery in the early 1860s, botanists began to ponder the significance of its occurrence in a place far removed from its centre of distribution around the Mediterranean Sea. A. G. More accepted it simply as one of the congregation of 'southern plants' known from Ireland but not Britain, although he was unable to say 'with which group the *Neotinea* should be associated'.[21] He suggested that *Arbutus unedo* (strawberry tree) was the closest analogue. In *Cybele Hibernica*, David Moore and A. G. More placed *Neotinea* in the 'Hibernian type',[22] but elsewhere assigned it, with *Asplenium acutum,* to a group of species which they labelled 'Azorean'[23]–dense-flowered orchid is not recorded in the Azores. Towards the end of his life More returned to the view that 'this Mediterranean Orchis [is] a species as eminently southern as is the

Arbutus.[24] The apparent confusion, or rather the inability of botanists to find an exact 'pigeon-hole' for *Neotinea maculata* does not reflect anything other than the inanity of our desire to dispose everything into neat categories.

Neotinea is remarkable because it is found both in western Ireland, almost entirely on soils derived directly from Carboniferous limestone, and in regions bordering the Mediterranean Sea. Its distribution pattern is disjunct–not continuous–and unlike that of any other Irish native species except, as A. G. More noticed, *Arbutus unedo*. Why? That question still cannot be answered satisfactorily. In part it can be claimed that the mild, equable climate of western Ireland is congenial for the orchid, permitting its survival.

We must also remember that orchids have extraordinary life-cycles, intimately associated with fungi and insects; they do not thrive in solitary isolation, insulated from the changes that have moulded the flora and fauna of the entire hemisphere during the past fifteen millennia. The symbiotic fungi and the pollinating insects must also inhabit *the same* territory throughout *the same* period otherwise the orchid will disappear simply because it cannot thrive and reproduce. Fifteen thousand years ago, when severe tundra conditions prevailed in The Burren, it is more than unlikely–I would argue that it is impossible–that *Neotinea maculata* and its symbionts were established here. They must have migrated into Ireland since the end of the last glaciation. The quest to explain adequately how such an invasion took place, and when, is a unfinished enterprise that obsesses Ireland's botanists and geographers.

The isolation of such species as *Neotinea maculata* in Ireland, far from their main centres of distribution in southern latitudes, suggests, as Professor Webb has affirmed, 'no ordinary history'.[25] Be that as it may, most Irish native plants have mundane, explicable histories, and the other orchids of The Burren pose no geographical conundrums for botanists. For taxonomists, on the other hand, they may precipitate an endless procession of sleepless nights!

In stark contrast to the early purple orchid which cannot be mistaken for any other species, the spotted orchids present botanical nightmares that wise folk avoid–more provocation. Many reams of paper have been absorbed in discussing variation within and between populations of spotted orchids, and while one botanist will aver that he had 'sorted out' these orchids, another will produce a different thesis, and so the argument revolves eternally. The name changes imposed during the last century are an additional source of confusion to both amateur and professional botanists. Patrick O'Kelly knew them as members of the genus *Orchis*; in standard botanical texts for the mid-1900s they were assigned to *Dactylorchis*, but now they are placed in *Dactylorhiza*.

At the start of this century the spotted orchids were usually given the name *Orchis maculata*, but George Claridge Druce of Oxford, having studied the plants growing in Britain and Ireland, and compared their characters with those in the early scientific descriptions in works by such botanists as Carl Linnaeus, realized that two separable entities bore the same botanical name. Thereafter he described *Orchis fuchsii* and within it placed all spotted orchids with solid stems and prominently, almost equally tri-lobed labella. *Orchis maculata*, while also possessing a solid stem, was distinguished by Druce as those plants with a minute central labellum lobe between two large lateral lobes. There are other distinguishing characters, and the two plants occupied contrasting habitats; *Orchis maculata* grows in acid peatland, while *Orchis fuchsii* is found on base-rich soils such as those derived from limestone. But, this simple segregation of two species is not so marked as suggested on paper because of the immense range of intermediate forms growing in intermediate habitats.

As early as the 1890s Patrick O'Kelly listed 'Orchis maculata alba' in his catalogue–a single plant cost six pence, or one dozen five shillings.[26] He reported the white variety around Lough Ghort Baoithín ('Gortbweeheen Lake'), west of Turlough, in June 1902 growing with fragrant orchids, twayblades, and lesser butterfly orchids, and *Neotinea maculata*.[27] Not content with the name *Orchis maculata* var. *alba*, O'Kelly started to call his variant *Orchis immaculata*, but so far as is known he never published that name even in one of his catalogues.

But nothing in this story is simple. Mr George Claridge Druce visited County Clare for a few days during June 1909, and met O'Kelly who pointed out the white-blossomed spotted orchid. It was 'in the immature condition', not yet in flower. Some weeks later Patrick O'Kelly sent fresh specimens, in full flower, to Oxford for Druce to study. This satisfied Druce that O'Kelly's Burren plant was 'a variety or sub-species' distinguished by its 'unspotted and narrower leaves and pure white flowers'. Crucially, Druce noted that the mid-lobe of the labellum was 'longer and as broad as the lateral'–the original pressed specimens in Druce's herbarium at the University of Oxford, demonstrate this proportionality well.[28] He wrote to Patrick O'Kelly presumably thanking him for the specimens and suggesting that the new variety might bear the epithet *o'kellyi*. To this letter, P. B. O'Kelly responded.

Dear Sir

I am in receipt of your letter concerning my new orchis. Please attach my
name to it. I appreciate it very much. I have one plant of Orchis pyramidalis
variety Flore Albo, Pure White, which I collected about ten years ago in
a field near Ballyvaughan. I am leaving home tomorrow for Killarney. If
I meet with anything strange there I'll send them to you.

Yours truly

July 19. 1909   P B O'Kelly[29]

Thus G. C. Druce made available for white-flowered forms of spotted orchids the
label var. *o'kellyi*. That epithet being valid must be attached to this variety even
when its specific name changes–thus when renamed *Dactylorhiza fuchsii*, it is still
var. *o'kellyi*. At one time, it was suggested that this plant should be treated as a
species in its own right, as *Orchis o'kellyi* but, given the intractable complexity of
this group of plants, few botanists accept that extreme view today.[30] Similarly few
believe O'Kelly's plant is sufficiently distinct to warrant the rank of subspecies.
For my own part, I don't think it should even be regarded as a botanical variety,
and that it would be best classified as a forma, as *Dactylorhiza fuchsii* f. *okellyi* (see
plate, p. 192) (current rules of nomenclature oblige us to remove the apostrophe).

Patrick O'Kelly deserves the tribute, even the restless immortality of a subspecific
variant. He assuredly furthered the study of orchids in The Burren through his
collecting, although this has to be counterpoised by his exploitation of the same
orchids for profit. By the end of the first decade of the present century, most of
The Burren species had been reported, and Druce had named *Orchis o'kellyi*.
However there are still surprises–in 1980 Mary-Angela Keane found the greater
butterfly orchid near Mullach Mór, confirming its presence in The Burren, for
while Mrs. Jessie O'Callaghan had collected it in woods near Ballyvaghan in 1912,
her discovery had not been published and remained in some doubt.[31]

Between late May and late July every quarter of limestone pavement, every
pocket of drift or peaty loam, has its compliment of orchids. Some areas are better
than others for particular species, and when one learns the orchids' habitat
requirements it is possible to predict the species in each place. Thus in hazel copses
it is most probable that helleborines will be found, while on dunes pyramidal
orchids are assured; red helleborines are rarely found except on the most shattered
pavement, a habitat eschewed by almost every other species except the occasional
bee orchid.

The Burren is one of the best places in Ireland to study orchids; twenty-two species are known to grow in the region, along with a handful of enigmatic variants. While none of the eighteenth-century visitors recorded these plants, O'Mahony and Whitla were impressed; indeed the first flower they noticed in their paper was a species of helleborine 'evidently differing from any of those described in our Flora...the flower of a deep purple'. They could not identify and name the helleborine with certainty, so Thaddeus O'Mahony spoke out at the meeting of the Dublin Natural History Society and asked that

> some one of our eminent botanists–and I am happy to say we can boast of many such in Dublin–will examine the plant and ascertain its true specific designation.[32]

Evidently this did not prove too taxing and this particular unnamed orchid was soon known to be *Epipactis atrorubens* (*cuaichín dearg*) (see plate, p. 188).

At the best of times helleborines–not to be confused with the completely unrelated hellebores–are difficult plants to name because within any particular region forms may persist that differ slightly from members of the same species in other places. This tendency has led to a proliferation of specific names. The genetic variability is compounded by environmental plasticity–small differences in the habitat can affect the orchids, altering their appearance. However, *Epipactis atrorubens* growing on the shattered pavement of County Clare is not likely to be confused with other helleborines.

At their finest the red helleborines have deep claret coloured flowers; the three sepals are almost identical in shape, size and colour, and closely resemble the two lateral petals, whereas the lip (labellum) is shorter than the petals and sepals. The pear-shaped, ribbed ovary is covered with minute whitish hairs. Each flowering stem has at least five leaves arranged in opposite ranks, and eight or more individual flowers–small, weak plants may have fewer flowers and likewise vigorous plants can have many more. The height of the orchid will depend on where it is growing–some inhabit wind-swept sites and can become battered and stunted.

Red helleborines blossom in the middle of summer, and are easy to spot in the right place. A ramble over bare pavement, its surface shattered into fragments not plane, solid rock, should yield some of these orchids. I have seen them on the summits of Cappanawalla and Dobhach Bhrainín, about Ballyryan and bordering the trail to Tobar MacDuach. Thaddeus O'Mahony described the typical habitat of the red helleborine as being '...among stones than can be separated

Orchis mascula
early purple orchid

without much difficulty, and…when removed, rattle over each other with a peculiar metallic kind of ringing sound…'[33]

Epipactis atrorubens is abundant in The Burren and is restricted in Ireland to the Carboniferous limestones of Clare and Galway. The seventeenth-century record from Roscrea must be regarded as an historical curiosity as it has not been seen in Tipperary since the Revd Richard Heaton's time.

In the hazel woods at Tobar MacDuach there grows a quite different helleborine, usually green flowered and much taller than the plants of the pavements, and with leaves spirally arrayed along the stem. This stately orchid crowds every footfall within the wood, and it is the archetypal species of the genus. The flowers are not as colourful as those of *Epipactis atrorubens*, yet their intricacies and the subtleties are as entrancing. Some plants have such a fine cloak of hairs on the stems and ovaries that they seem dusted with a grey felt, and some have flowers that are red, not green.

Epipactis helleborine (*ealabairín*) is in flower in late summer, and is pollinated by wasps of various species–I have seen what were almost certainly common wasps (*Vespula vulgaris*) on the plants along the roadside in Knockans Lower townland, and it is well-recorded that helleborines are frequently and persistently visited by wasps.[34] At Tobar MacDuach, in September, helleborine spikes swarmed with small, black insects resembling miniature wasps. The flowers are 'classic' examples of blossoms adapted for pollination by wasps–they are nodding, 'dirty red' or pinkish, secrete nectar and bloom late in the summer when the worker-wasps are swarming. Wasps are red-blind, so reddish flowers will appear very dark to them, and they are also attracted by particular scents.

Helleborines can also be self-pollinated, a fact that complicates their already remarkably plastic nature and contributes to the bewilderment of taxonomists. A third species, the marsh helleborine, is also recorded in The Burren, but it is by far the least abundant. As its name suggest, *Epipactis palustris* grows in fens and marshes which are uncommon anyway in karst, and has brownish or purple-green sepals and white and purple petals.

Scents and colours are lures, signalling that a flower is in bloom and that a reward is available to a beneficial visitor. An insect following these signals will receive that reward, usually a sugary secretion, nectar, and as long as the reward is available, insects will come again and again to this source of food. Some insects–bees, for example–take their reward as pollen, a rich source of protein, but many others, including wasps, cannot use pollen. Thus pollination of a flower by an insect is a balanced relationship. If the plant fails to produce nectar or pollen, insects will stop visiting it and pollination will not be effected; that plant may wither without setting seed and its survival could be jeopardized.

Scents and colours are among the most difficult characters to describe; we rarely agree about perfumes or the exact description of a particular colour. *Gymnadenia conopsea* (*lus taghla*) (see plate, p. 193) has vanilla-perfumed flowers—at least that is the best simile I can produce, and Thomas Corry also thought so. Others assert that the scent resembles cloves or rubber[35] which reminds me of the equation of old socks or fine old hock for the perfume of the California tree poppy—an aroma is as much in the mind, as beauty is in the eye of a beholder. Be that as it may, Thaddeus O'Mahony and Francis Whitla were ecstatic—when they walked through The Burren in 1851 'the very air was laden with [the] delicious perfume'[36] of the fragrant orchid which has to be a slight exaggeration, to be polite. Although its flowers are fragrant there are few occasions, and few places nowadays, where fragrant orchids are so plentiful that they could perfume Atlantic breezes.

Flowers and insects often have evolved in tandem, so that many flowers are successfully pollinated only by one group of insects—in particular instances by only one species. The fragrant orchid lures butterflies and moths by its fragrance, whether vanilla or cloves or rubber; it offers nectar as the reward. The nectar is secreted into the long spur that projects behind the individual flower, and only a long-tongued insect can get at this food. As an insect prods the orchid flower with its long proboscis, two sacs of pollen (the pollinia) become attached by a quick-setting glue to the proboscis and stay firmly attached when that butterfly or moth moves on to another orchid. As the insect probes for more nectar, the pollinia are transferred to the stigma of the next flower.

The spur of the fragrant orchid is straight, slender and twice the length of the ovary. The buds are dark red tinted with crimson, and as the flowers expand the colour lightens to a rich pink—the 'wings' (the lateral petals) extend horizontally. The lip (labellum) has three more or less equal lobes. O'Mahony and Whitla reported a white-blossomed fragrant orchid, not an uncommon thing—I have seen several, and also a strange flesh-pink variant on a road verge at Caherbullog.

The Burren populations of the fragrant orchid represent a subspecies named *Gymnadenia conopsea* subsp. *densiflora*, distinguished from the type subspecies by bright rose-red or magenta flowers smelling, some say, of cloves.

Epipactis atrorubens: red helleborine

Epipactis helleborine: helleborine

🌸 Similar to *Gymnadenia,* but differing in certain critical characters especially in presenting paired pollinia on a single viscidium, is the pyramidal orchid, *Anacamptis pyramidalis, magairlín na stuaice* (see plate, p. 193). If you want to compare their fragrances, *Anacamptis* is said to have a foxy aroma.[37] The flowering times are different by a few weeks, pyramidal orchid being the later of the two coming to its prime usually in mid-July.

In general orchid species can be distinguished by the size, shape and colour of their inflorescences. Fragrant orchid has an elongated, cylindrical spike, while pyramidal orchid had a short and, in its early stages, conical inflorescence. The flowers of *Anacamptis* tend to be a purer pink than those of *Gymnadenia* but I do not think this is a reliable difference.

Both species inhabit every county in Ireland, yet like many other plants they are, at least to the casual eye, more abundant in The Burren, and certainly easier to find. Pyramidal orchids swarm in the dunes at Fanore peeping from the marram grass, and along road verges wherever there is a rich, well-drained loam. One of the strangest orchids ever found in The Burren was a 'double-flowered' pyramidal orchid, spotted on the sand-dunes at Bishop's Quarter in 1861 by the young son of Dr O'Brien of Ennis when he and his father were botanizing with Frederick Foot. The party found two plants that first day and, according to Foot, he later saw four more. A plant was sent to David Moore, director of the Glasnevin Botanic Gardens, and the oddity grew there for several years.[38]

The 'foxy' fragrance of *Anacamptis pyramidalis* attracts moths and butterflies. There is no free-flowing nectar but the thickened walls of the spur contain a liquid which is collected by the insects. In probing the flowers for this, the moths and butterflies detach the paired pollinia which coil around the proboscis, and when later visiting another flower these are transferred to the stigma.

All Irish orchids reproduce by seed–in general their tubers or rhizomes are not reproductive organs but allow individual plants to survive from year to year. Orchid seeds are minute, little more than a few undifferentiated cells. When such a tiny seed germinates the embryonic seedling must quickly form an intimate association with a fungus because it is incapable of surviving alone, and for several years the new orchid may not even produce green leaves. *Anacamptis* takes four years to sprout its first leaves and seven years elapse before any flower spike appears. This extraordinary, prolonged life-cycle is not unique and I shall return to the topic when describing Lady's tresses.

Pyramidal orchid ranges through southern Europe towards the Caucasus; it is abundant in the Mediterranean region, and does not extend north of Denmark. Other orchids have a more northerly distribution with colonies in Iceland, Scandinavia and northern Asia inside the Arctic Circle. *Listera ovata* displays this pattern, and it is reported as far east as the Himalayas and Lake Baikal in Siberia.

There is nothing immediately spectacular about twayblade, *Listera ovata* (see plate, p. 197), but it is one of the easiest orchids to find and to identify. The two prominently veined, pleated leaves clasping the base of the flowering stem like miniature saucers are most distinctive–even when not in blossom, there is no other plant native in The Burren that can be mistaken for a twayblade. The English name, invented by Henry Lyte in the sixteenth century, alludes to the two leaves, as does the Irish synonym *dédhuilleog*–sweethearts is more romantic version.[39]

Twayblade is frequent in Ireland, and I knew it well as a boy in Fermanagh. The other native species, *Listera cordata*, is smaller, more delicate and more than inconspicuous growing concealed in the heather on peaty soil–I once found it in Fermanagh too, among ling on the plateau near Lough Navar. Twayblade will grow in acid, peaty habitats, but tends to be more abundant where the soil contains some lime, and in The Burren, as in Fermanagh, it is common in the grasslands.

The flower spike can appear in late spring and it is not unusual to find *Listera ovata* in bloom at the end of May–the flowering season can be prolonged, with a peak in June, and in some years plants with fresh flowers are seen as late as September. The spikes are up to twenty centimetres tall and have numerous small greenish, hooded flowers. The most obvious part of the individual blossom is a forked, bright yellow-green labellum, projecting stiffly forward below the hood of petals and sepals, and then abruptly turned downwards. The forked lip, occasionally with two lateral lobes near the base, resembles a tiny manikin, although the Elizabethan herbalist, John Gerard, likened the flowers to 'a gnat, or a little gosling newly hatched'.[40]

Twayblade is pollinated by small insects. The mechanism is so finely modulated that large insects, such as honey bees, are too clumsy to effect pollination. Small flies and beetles crawl up the lip, following a trail of nectar, until they touch the rostellum to which the pollinia are attached. Even the gentlest touch on the rostellum causes an explosion–a liquid, which is a quick-setting glue, is squirted on to the insect and the pollinia are cemented fast to it. Frightened by the explosion, but bearing its load of pollinia, the startled insect departs and visits another flower, where unwittingly, but very precisely, it deposits the pollinia on the stigma if it

Dactylorhiza fuchsii f. *okellyi*
O'Kelly's orchid

Dactylorhiza fuchsii
spotted orchid

Gymnadenia conopsea
fragrant orchid

Anacamptis pyramidalis
pyramidal orchid

is receptive.[41] Last May I watched a group of ants crawling about twayblade flowers presumably collecting nectar and most had tripped the mechanism; they were wandering about the twayblade stems with pollinia attached to their heads, a comical sight, little black ants with huge yellow horns. Ants are not listed as pollinators of *Listera ovata*, although given the relative size of the flowers they may well serve this function.

Listera ovata can increase vegetatively, so it is not entirely dependent on seeds. However most plants in The Burren have swollen ovaries and seed production must be abundant; pollination therefore is frequently successful. The remarkable explosive mechanism, the 'super-glue', and the exactly aligned parts of its intricate flowers are the results of a delicately honed evolutionary process that ensures cross-fertilization.

The orchid year closes in September with the sweetly perfumed blossoms of Autumn Lady's tresses. Yet *Spiranthes spiralis* (see plate, p. 197) is not an orchid that splashes colour through The Burren. Autumn Lady's tresses is a tiny, inconspicuous plant; when not in flower it is impossible to find as all that appears above ground is a rosette, about the same size a thumb-print, hidden among the annoyingly similar rosettes of cat's-paw, Spring gentian and a myriad others; when in flower the tresses are more eye-catching although the spikes are still not obvious being about a finger-length tall and grey-green, and among the rank grasses and herbs of late summer never easy to find. The individual flowers of *Spiranthes spiralis* are less than half a centimetre long, beautifully fluted and of most subtle colouring, white and green, yet what is most wonderful is their arrangement–the flowers form a single row that spirals up the stem. Each plant produces a solitary inflorescence of not more than twenty flowers. The sweet perfume of this little orchid is only released during the day when the humble-bees that are its pollinators are flying. To savour the fragrance, you must, appropriately, prostrate yourself before the plant.

A diligent search–on hands and knees–during August and September at Poll Salach, about halfway between the road and the storm beach should yield a few Lady's tresses. I am also familiar with colonies along the shore of Lough Gealáin beyond the chert dyke. There are numberless other populations and all that is required to find them is good eye-sight and 'noses to the ground'. Frederick Foot noted that *Spiranthes spiralis* was by no means common in The Burren–he saw it at Black Head and Kinvarra.[42] Professor Webb and Miss Scannell suggest that this is an under-recorded species because of 'its irregularity of flowering' and because it is rarely in flower before the end of August.[43] Certainly flowering is unpredictable; after a warm, dry summer Lady's tresses can blossom as early as the first week in August, but if there is cool, damp weather, the flower spikes may still be seen in mid-September.

Dr Terence Wells published a fascinating account of Autumn Lady's tresses growing wild in a Bedfordshire nature reserve, and in particular discussed the reputation of populations to fluctuate dramatically from year to year. His study contradicted the general view–Dr Wells showed that the colonies are remarkably stable.[44]

Spiranthes spiralis is a very slow-growing orchid with an extended life-cycle. The minute seeds germinate but do not immediately yield a new plant; in fact eight years must elapse after germination before the first root tuber is produced. During these years the orchid exists underground as a leafless mycorrhizome, a strange symbiotic amalgam of a fungus and an orchid seedling. Another three years pass before the tuber sends out its first green leaf. A couple more years elapse before the young leafy plant has developed sufficiently to bloom. Thus, like a human child, one Autumn lady's tresses has to be not less than thirteen years old before it can reproduce sexually.

Although mature and capable of flowering, individual *Spiranthes spiralis* may remain dormant during an occasional year, persisting merely as a root tuber without green leaves or an inflorescence. The reasons for this are not understood, but Dr Wells discovered that a year's dormancy does not prevent the orchid blooming during the following year.[45] *Spiranthes spiralis* is a perplexing plant. It can also reproduce vegetatively by forming lateral buds that will develop into a tuber and ultimately yield a new plant–small colonies can form in this manner.

'Lady's tresses' alludes to the resemblance of the spirally arranged flowers to braided hair, to Our Lady's hair, or as it is in Irish, *cúilín Muire*, Mary's hair.

John Gerard, the famous Elizabethan herbalist, has the final word about orchids and ladies; noting that Lady's tresses was sometimes called sweet cullions, he continued:

> ...but euery countrey hath a seuerall name; for some call them Sweet Ballocks, sweet Cods, sweet Cullions, and Stander-grasse...in Latine *Testiculus Odoratus:* in English, Sweet smelling Testicles or stones, not of the sweetnesse of the roots, but of the floures.[46]

I have not written about bee or frog or fly or butterfly orchids; they also occur

Neotinea maculata
dense-flowered orchid

Spiranthes spiralis
Autumn Lady's tresses

Listera ovata
twayblade

in The Burren. Nor have I chronicled in detail the varieties (or perhaps subspecies) of the marsh and the spotted orchids; a library of books could be written about them. I conclude by suggesting that you wander the pavements and green roads, and take time to admire the great congregation of twayblades, helleborines, orchids of all sorts.

> We found it in his Beauty, when the Wheat was almost Ripe in plenty enough: I have seen more Sorts of this large Family, but these…I am certain of. They are reckoned Provocative…[47]

Tau stone, Kilnaboy

CARNIVORES AND PARASITES

And dearer the wind in its crying,
And the secrets the wet hills hold,
Than the goldenest place they could find you
In the heart of a country of gold.

Seamus O'Sullivan: 'Lullaby'

Plants have adopted many different strategies for survival. As in the animal
kingdom there are carnivores and parasites. Carnivorous plants are sustained
by absorbing essential nutrients derived from animal flesh but to do this they have
first to catch their prey. As for parasites, among the flowering plants there are as
many as three thousand species which have forsaken, wholly or in part, a life of
photosynthetic rectitude and steal their food from other plants; species that have
become total parasites may even have lost their then useless green pigments.

The Burren is not in any sense a particular haven for carnivorous and parasitic
flowering plants, although in certain areas plants with these propensities do
abound, and can perhaps be more easily seen than elsewhere, but only because
they are herbs among equals.

199

Orobanche alba
red broomrape

Euphrasia salisburgensis: Irish eyebright (upper left)
Euphrasia sp.: eyebright (upper right)
Thymus praecox: thyme

Frederick Foot drew attention to some of the parasitic denizens; he wrote of broomrape that 'this curious parasite is very abundant on the hills S. and E. of Ballyvaughan…it seems to be always parasitical on the roots' of thyme. As for the eyebrights, he exclaimed–

> If anyone should ask, why do you mention a very common plant as the humble *Eye-bright?*–my answer is, "Go to Burren and tell me if you ever saw it growing so luxuriantly at such elevations, and of such a size as it does here."[1]

It is unfortunate that studies by botanists and historians sometimes necessitate a change of name for a familiar plant, and more unfortunate when the change leads to a confusion. In the 1790s, John Templeton who lived at Cranmore in Malone, a short distance from the centre of Belfast, gathered a broomrape on the slopes of Cave Hill, the mountain that dominates the city's skyline. He sent drawings and specimens to Sir James Edward Smith, founder of the Linnean Society in London, who named the species *Orobanche rubra*. Smith's epithet was descriptive for the vast majority of the spears of this strange plant seen in Ireland are tinged brownish red. Many decades later, as a result of studies on the genus, it was realized that the same species had been named by the German botanist Carl Willdenow, who chose to call it *Orobanche alba*. As the first published Latin name must be kept as the one universal name for a species, Smith's *Orobanche rubra* has been sunk, and Willdenow's name takes precedence.

But no matter how deeply we believe we have buried old names, there is no way to expunge them from the older literature. Thus *Orobanche rubra* runs like a thread through nineteenth century accounts of visits to The Burren. Francis Whitla was the first to make it known that the parasite grew in Clare; his almost casual remark at a meeting of the Dublin Natural History Society on 10 March 1851 included the observation that it was a parasite on thyme.[2] Four months later, Whitla and O'Mahony visited The Burren and studied *Orobanche* in some detail; they gathered specimens, pressed and dried them, and showed them to members of the Dublin Natural History Society in June 1852:

> This Orobanche rubra which you have before you, gentlemen, we found among limestone rocks in the mountains above Ballyvaghan, a village where I may remark, *en passant*, the naturalist may be sure of sufficiently good accommodation. In every instance, and we examined the point most carefully, we found it parasitical on the *Thymus Serpyllum*.[3]

Thaddeus O'Mahony assured the society that the question of the broomrape's parasitic habit could be considered 'definitely settled'.

Red broomrape looks like a red fleshy orchid, but it is not an orchid; broomrapes belong to a family of parasites, Orobanchaceae, that is more akin to the figworts (Scrophulariaceae). *Orobanche alba* lacks green leaves, just a few red scale-like ones on the lower part of the stem. The scented flowers are in a terminal cluster, at first tightly packed, but as the plant grows taller, they become more irregularly spaced; they are the same colour as the stem. The calyx is inflated, slightly paler, pinkish-brown, and covered with short hairs. The five petals are fused into a tubular corolla which has a three-lobed lower lip hooded by the upper lip which has two lobes. The four stamens are included inside the corolla, as is the red style.

The individual plants of red broomrape are annuals, and may be up to thirty centimetres tall; while they do grow as solitary, isolated spires, it is more usual to see clusters. Invariably they are surrounded by a mat of aromatic, purple-blossomed thyme (*Thymus praecox*). Below ground, in the soil, the roots of thyme will have become fused to the haustoria of the broomrape; haustoria are specialized organs that act as bridges between the parasite and its host. Through an haustorium sap from thyme is transported into the broomrape, and many complex metabolic reactions also occur therein, including the alteration of nutritious components in the host's sap—the sugars and amino acids—into forms that the parasite can use.[4]

The Burren is one of the principal haunts in Ireland and Britain for *Orobanche alba*[5]–it occurs always on basic rocks near the coast, in Donegal, Derry and Antrim, and in Britain is restricted to Cornwall, the Pennines and western Scotland. Two other broomrapes grow in The Burren, but neither is as abundant as the red broomrape. The second native species is the ivy broomrape (*Orobanche hederae*), a taller, more floriferous plant with a paler demeanour and a yellow stigma–it is a parasite of ivy, and has been gathered near Corrofin, but surprisingly, nowhere else, although ivy is ubiquitous. The third broomrape is an introduced species, *Orobanche minor*, that parasitizes members of the pea family (Fabaceae; Leguminosae) including the clovers.

The eyebrights are not holoparasites–plants totally dependent on a host–but having green leaves, they can produce at least some of their own nutrients by photosynthesis and so are classified as hemiparasites. As well as being part-

Pedicularis sylvatica: lousewort

time scroungers, eyebrights are promiscuous forming hybrids some of which are fertile and can multiply promiscuously too. This proclivity to interbreed causes taxonomists, let alone amateur botanists, endless difficulties of identification, and it is wisest, unless you are determined to pursue eyebrights to the bitter end, to look upon them as an almost intractable group defying simple classification.

That does not mean it is impossible to segregate a few easy ones, and fortunately the one species which is as quintessential of The Burren limestones as mountain avens and Spring gentians, has had the decency to maintain two good characters for its identification, and moreover the decency to produce only sterile hybrids. (Lest any botanist should wince at my turn of phrase, I hasten to add that, of course, *Euphrasia salisburgensis* has not adopted these traits deliberately; the characteristics evolved through natural selection.)

Euphrasia salisburgensis–the Latin epithet signifies a denizen of Salzburg in Austria–is a small, bushy plant, which is usually copper-coloured all over, not bright grass-green. The tiny leaves are deeply toothed and narrow, much longer than they are broad, appearing quite jagged. Flowers are borne at the tips of the

Rhinanthus minor: yellow rattle

branchlets in the latter part of the summer. The individual bloom is about the same size as the leaves, and pure white, with a three-lobed lower lip and a short upper one which is two-lobed. But, as all flora-writers caution us, if in doubt look through a hand-lens at one of the heart-shaped fruits–if the plant is *Euphrasia salisburgensis* there will be no hairs on the upper margin.

Irish eyebright is easy to find in August–it is frequent in such places as Poll Salach–and like red broomrape is a parasite of thyme (a common plant, widespread and abundant, well able to survive the onslaughts of the parasites). Outside The Burren, *Euphrasia salisburgensis* is rare although it ranges along the west coast from County Limerick to County Donegal, and always occurs on calcareous soils. There are no indubitable records of this species in Britain, so the nearest colonies are in France whence Irish eyebright ranges northwards into southern Sweden. The Irish plants differ from those in European populations sufficiently for at least one botanist to distinguish them as members of an endemic subspecies *Euphrasia salisburgensis* subsp. *hibernica*.[6] The vernacular names, Irish eyebright and its Irish synonym *glanrosc gaelach*, both of recent derivation, have already taken this into account.

As Frederick Foot remarked, eyebrights abound in The Burren. Given the intimidating complexity of this genus, it would be brave to try to name each and every one. In any case Nature merely begs that we look upon its works and marvel; we don't have to fit all plants into precisely limited species labelled with Latin names.

🌸 *Euphrasia* (eyebright), *Pedicularis* (lousewort) and *Rhinanthus* (yellow rattle) belong to the figwort family (Scrophulariaceae) which also includes such native herbs as foxglove and speedwell, and the exotic fairy foxglove (*Erinus alpinus*, see pp. 249–250) and monkeyflower. Lousewort and yellow rattle are hemiparasites like eyebright; foxglove, speedwell and the alien species are not parasites.

Lousewort (*Pedicularis sylvatica*) and red rattle (*Pedicularis palustris*) are both frequent in The Burren. Red rattle is an annual herb of wet ground, marshes and lough margins, so in the western highground of Burren it is not abundant. Lousewort is a perennial, abundant in the region, growing in drier sites, on hummocks of peaty soil. The two species are quickly distinguished by looking at the lobes on the inflated calyx–in lousewort the calyx has four lobes, whereas red rattle has just two.

Lousewort (in Irish *lus na ghiolla*) is a conspicuous plant in the summer sward. Its flowers are rich crimson, in clusters, and the calyx may also be coloured; white blossomed plants, without any red tints, arise infrequently. The corolla has an upper hood and three lower lobes; the hood conceals four stamens and the style just emerges beyond the rim of the hood. In lousewort, the corolla has small teeth only near the hood rim, and this may also serve to distinguish it from its fellow–in red rattle there is a second pair of teeth half-way along the margin of the hood. Both species have small leaves that are finely divided and almost fern-like, and often tinged with reddish-purple.

Thomas Corry had good reason to remember the leaves of lousewort and red rattle for during a walk from Lisdoonvarna to Ballinalacken, he 'met with one of those extirpators of the rare plants with which this county abounds.' This particular person was not removing maidenhair ferns, which was a profitable source of income last century, but

> …had been reaping gain by collecting the leaves of the Red Rattle (*Pedicularis palustris*), before the plant comes into flower, and palming them off upon the innocent credulity of the visitors to the Spas as the rare "Monks'-hoof" fern…[7]

Corry added, wryly, that this name was 'evidently one of his own invention.'

🌿 Lousewort is an antique name, supposedly indicative of the plant's use as a
repellent against lice. Yellow rattle is explanatory too–the flowers are yellow,
and the plant rattles! Walk through any area of The Burren where there is a rich
sward of herbs–even along the roadside–in late summer and the seed-heads of
Rhinanthus minor (yellow rattle, *gliográn*) will rustle as your feet brush past them.

Rhinanthus is a close relative of *Pedicularis*, and differs most noticeably in its
yellow flowers. Like the red rattle, yellow rattle is an annual herb with small opposite
leaves which are toothed but not divided and fern-like. The flowers are borne in
groups at the tips of the shoots in early summer, and each blossom has a striking,
inflated calyx which is flattened laterally. From the narrow mouth of this emerges
the bright yellow corolla, hooded and lobed in a similar fashion to *Pedicularis*.
Once the flowers have been pollinated, the corolla withers and the calyx swells
and eventually dries; inside is a flattened capsule containing a few flattened black
seeds which, when ripe, cause yellow rattle to rattle.

Yellow rattle exhibits a fair amount of variation and at least two subspecies are
reputed to grow in The Burren. Moreover, some plants in the region, possessing
short and narrow leaves, bear considerable resemblance to a race of *Rhinanthus
minor* which inhabits the chalk-lands of southern England and is segregated into
a separate subspecies (*Rhinanthus minor* subsp. *calcareus*). No-one has yet had the
temerity to say that the race from the limestone pastures of Clare is the same as
the English one.[8]

🌿 A parasitic plant draws all or some of its food from another green plant. A
carnivorous plant gains some of its nutrients by exploiting animals. Such
plants cannot obtain their entire requirement from animals, so they do have green
leaves and can by photosynthesis combine carbon dioxide with water to produce
sugars that are energy sources, and to build proteins and cellulose. But green plants
also need other substances–nitrates, phosphates, mineral salts, are basic
requirements–and many of these chemicals are absorbed directly from the soil.
However in certain habitats, the soil is a very poor source of nitrates, phosphates
and mineral salts, and carnivorous species overcome any deficiency by extracting
these substances from the decaying tissues of trapped animals.

The raised bogs of central Ireland are good examples of habitats where nitrates,
in particular, are unavailable to plants, and carnivorous species frequent these
areas–sundews, bladderworts and introduced pitcher plants (*Sarracenia purpurea*)
are all carnivores. Our three native species of butterwort are carnivores too,

Pinguicula vulgaris
common butterwort

Drosera rotundifolia: sundew (left) *Pinguicula lusitanica:* pale butterwort (right)

although they do not usually grow in the central peatlands; all three are found in The Burren.

Butterworts have a rosette of soft leaves studded with microscopic glands which secrete enzymes and a viscous sticky fluid that coats the leaves and makes them glisten. Insects are attracted to the leaves, perhaps deluded that they are coated with nectar, and if they land on the leaves they are held by the sticky secretion. As they struggle to get free, their movement stimulates the leaf margins slowly to curl inwards, so that the animal is eventually engulfed. Death is slow, but not pointless, for the enzymes break down the soft tissues within their bodies, and the butterwort absorbs the nutritious soup that flows.

The effect of the enzymes has been known for hundreds of years–*Pinguicula* leaves curdle milk, a process akin to the digestion of the insects. The English name butterwort alludes to this property.

Pinguicula vulgaris, common butterwort (*bodán meascáin*), is frequent throughout The Burren, often growing in unexpected sites. It occurs in quantity, for example, alongside the steep track leading from Gleninagh up the northern side of Cappanawalla in places which are quite dry in summer. Any site where springs flow almost continuously, coating rocks with water, will have a colony of butterworts–the northern slopes of The Burren hills between Gleninagh and Black Head are typical. There is also a colony in a damp flush on Mullach Mór, whence came a plant with extraordinary eight-petalled flowers.

I have noticed that there is variation in the size of the white patch in the throat of the violet flowers of common butterworts, but I have never seen any plants with entirely white blossoms. The individual bloom is composed of three equal lower petals that do not overlap and two much shorter upper ones fused into a short tube which is extended backwards into a slightly curved spur. The flowers are produced singly atop translucent green stems which can be about ten centimetres tall; these rise from the centre of the rosette of yellow-green leaves.

Frederick Foot reported common butterwort from The Burren, and he also noted that the smaller, grey-leaved *Pinguicula lusitanica* grew in a marsh near Lisdoonvarna. While that site is outside The Burren proper, the pale butterwort (*leith uisce beag*) grows on Black Head and near Lough Bunny, well within the barony of Burren.

The clamber up the grey brow of Black Head is not arduous, perhaps for the unfit a bit of a puff, and the reward is a magnificent panorama. Perched on the main terrace about two hundred metres above South Sound is the stone fort of Cathair Dhúin Irghuis, a masterpiece of dry-stone walling, and while modest in scale as awesome as the great monuments of other countries. On a mist-less day the unimpeded prospect from the Cliffs of Moher sweeps over the whale-backed Aran Islands towards Errisbeg and the ramparts of the Twelve Bens, and then curls towards Galway city and returns to the limestone slopes of Burren. No traffic on the Atlantic is out of sight–watchmen here must have seen many a curragh and galleon, and could have watched Christopher Columbus sail by.

The cathair is backed by limestone terraces that ooze water into fens where a marvellous mixture of plants grow. There is water in the air too–mist condenses on leaf tips and soft rain washes in from the ocean so rarely do the plants have to survive droughts. *Sphagnum subnitens*, one of the mosses which contribute to the production of peat, thrives hereabouts forming hummocks that in turn provide habitats for carnivores. Among the sphagnum-moss I found the pale butterwort; its rosettes are composed of neatly arranged grey leaves shot with green and blood-red veins, looking almost more animal than vegetable. This diminutive butterwort is not easy to see–the plants are smaller than a fifty-pence piece–yet the pale pink and white and lemon-throated flowers sparkle in the sunlight.

I have tramped to Cathair Dhúin Irghuis several times. In June 1990, I admired again the stonework, wondering what the builders made of the landscape and its flora and fauna. The breeze was cool, invigorating. I walked towards the cliffs of Murroughkilly beyond the cathair. Did the folk who made the fort ever stop to admire Spring gentians? Were they scolded by peregrine falcons?

The cliffs face west and are the first to receive any showers of rain; towards their base there are springs. Dobhach Bhrainín, the summit that falls into Galway Bay at Black Head, acts like a gigantic sponge–it is not soft, but it is porous and those springs hardly ever cease to ooze water. Hummocks of peaty soil have formed on the terrace at the foot of the cliffs and are always wet, if not sodden; because the soil lies on top of the rock the hummocks are leached and acidic, making ideal habitats for another Burren carnivore.

Sundews are alluring plants. There are three species in Ireland, but only one has been found on The Burren hills to date–*Drosera rotundifolia* (round-leaved sundew, *drúchtín móna*). Each plant is a compact rosette of spoon-shaped leaves studded with a battery of lethal, glistening, scarlet pin heads. The 'pins' are glandular hairs which secrete a sticky mucilage that serves as a lure and a trap. Flies that land on the leaves are held fast in the syrupy fluid, and they instinctively struggle to get away. Slowly the whole leaf reacts; it begins to curl and the red hairs gradually concentrate about the trapped fly. Eventually the insect, if it is small, is smothered and dies–larger ones may succumb to the stress caused by the struggle to break free. Enzymes secreted by the glandular hairs then break down the soft tissues of the victim and the sundew absorbs the released nutrients.

Drosera rotundifolia was not recorded from the western Burren before I found it in the summer of 1990.

A third species of butterwort grows in The Burren in the soft muddy flushes below spring-lines near Ballyvaghan. This plant has to rank as one of the most spectacular wildflowers of The Burren, although I strongly recommend that anyone wishing to see it should head south, take the ferry across the Shannon from Kilrush to Tarbert, and explore the mountains of County Kerry where the same butterwort abounds, even growing along the roadsides. *Pinguicula grandiflora*, known in Irish as *leith uisce*, is often called the Kerry butterwort because that county is its principal haunt in Ireland. The two colonies in The Burren are the most northerly ones in the species' entire range, and the plant's survival in one of them must be viewed with considerable concern following agricultural improvements in fields immediately adjoining. A third colony, the one first recorded for County Clare, is not far from the spa in Lisdoonvarna but it is on the shale, and so is really outside my domain.

In 1903 Professor Ambrose Birmingham, a distinguished anatomist and registrar of Cecilia Street School of Medicine, was staying at Lisdoonvarna; near the spa he found a plant that he did not recognize so he sent a specimen to Robert Lloyd Praeger who was immediately able to identify it as the large-flowered butterwort, *Pinguicula grandiflora*. When Praeger reported the Lisdoonvarna colony in a note in *The Irish Naturalist*,[9] he was cautious about its status, and for many years botanists held a nagging doubt that the butterwort might have escaped from a garden at the top of the cliff on which Birmingham had found it growing. However, in 1949, Professor John Heslop-Harrison discovered an extensive colony of the same butterwort on the slopes of Cappanawalla, overlooking Ballyvaghan,[10] and the original misgivings about the plant's claim to be a true native of Clare evaporated. In 1983 Dr Cilian Roden succeeding in confirming a suspicion he had about some butterworts on the slopes of Moneen Mountain on the opposite side of Ballyvaghan valley—he had seen them first in 1974 but none was blooming so he was unable to be certain that this was a third Clare colony.[11]

Words are inadequate to describe the fragile flowers of this lovely plant. They are much larger than those of the common butterwort, frequently not less than three centimetres across. The lobes overlap, indeed fuse for part of their length, so that the lower lip is almost entire, undulating, with delicate venation patterns and small hairs. The colour is a rich blue-purple, fading only slightly into the throat when first open; but the whole flower will gradually fade to slate-blue as it ages. The spur is curved and its tip is minutely but distinctly forked. The leaves tend to be broader than those of the common butterwort, but it is most unwise to attempt to name non-flowering rosettes—size is not a reliable character.

In 1956, Professor David Webb collected at Ballyvaghan a plant of *Pinguicula grandiflora* 'with very pale, almost white flowers' and sent it to Jurg Steiger; nothing more is recorded about this plant, although for several years around 1970, 'a small

Pinguicula grandiflora
greater butterwort

213

proportion of the plants in the [Ballyvaghan] station had flowers of a very pale lilac colour'. These seem to have disappeared; searches in 1974 and 1975 failed.[12]

The flourishing colony on Moneen Mountain was uniform in colour when I visited it in 1989. That same year, there was a solitary plant with white flowers in the companion colony on Cappanawalla. I photographed it, and so did John and Sue Leonard. The flowers, at first sight, were entirely white, without any purple or pink marks or tints, however in 1990 the same plant blossomed profusely and I noticed that the very young bud, just as it begins to rise above the rosette, had a light pink flush although the blush fades and is not apparent in the fully open flowers. Despite the local cattle which roam freely in this flush, drinking from the little pools, the white butterwort thrives. In the late spring of 1991, *Pinguicula grandiflora* f. *chionopetra*[13] bloomed again. It should survive.

The white butterwort is not a novelty; there are late nineteenth-century published accounts of such variants from County Kerry, but none in more recent decades. The earliest, by Veronica (a nom-de-plume used by Frederick Burbidge, curator of Trinity College Botanic Garden, Dublin), dates from 1886:

> As peculiar to Ireland, or nearly so, we have Trichomanes radicans [Killarney fern], Polypodium vulgare var. semilacerum (= P. hibernicum), Pinguicula vulgaris var. grandiflora, in white, rosy lavender and dark violet forms.[14]

In 1916 Reginald Scully recorded white butterworts from several sites in County Kerry:[15]

> Colour variants are very rarely met with in this plant; forms with pure white flowers are, however, occasionally seen and have been gathered in the Gap of Dunloe by *Lady Godfrey* and on the east side of Caragh Lake by *Capt. Creaghe-Haward*, while pale lilac forms have been sent to the writer by Mrs. Jenner from the Gap of Dunloe...

A search of European literature indicates that no entirely white variant has been described hitherto from Spain or France where *Pinguicula grandiflora* is also native. The white flowered plant from The Burren is the only one known at present although it is quite likely that it may be found again in County Kerry whence it was reported before 1903.

Poll Salach

A WEALTH OF HEATHER

A wealth of heather glimmering far and wide,
Pink spray, and crimson tuft, and waxen bell;
A thousand spears of yellow asphodel
Guarding each hollow where marsh mosses hide…[1]

The Burren is limestone. Consequently its soils should contain large amounts of the principal component of limestone, calcium carbonate, a substance that is inimical to many plants. Gardeners know this well; there is no point trying to grow most species of *Rhododendron* and *Camellia*, for example, if the garden soil is a heavy, alkaline clay. Given that limestone is the bed-rock, and the soils are calcareous, it is reasonable to conclude that all the native Burren plants are tolerant of calcium carbonate–they are calcicoles, dwellers in lime.

This is not true. Vast areas of The Burren are cloaked with bell heather and ling, with bearberry and crowberry, plants that are known not to thrive in soils containing lime. These are essentially calcifuge species, ones that literally flee from lime, the opposites of the calcicoles.

Across Galway Bay in Connemara the bed-rocks are schists and granites that contain no trace of calcium carbonate and, moreover, are impervious to water. On the slopes of the Twelve Bens, and in the lowlands around, are wildernesses of peat colonized by a profusion of calcifuge plants–heathers, cotton-grasses, sundews and bog asphodel. The Connemara boglands are indeed famous as the habitats of rare heaths, especially Dorset heath (*Erica ciliaris*) and Mackay's heath (*Erica mackaiana*), and the loughs that wallow among the knolls and in the blanket of peat are colonized by pipewort (*Eriocaulon aquatica*), water lobelia (*Lobelia dortmanna*) and naiad (*Naias flexilis*) which also are intolerant of lime. Calcicoles

215

do not thrive on the Connemara mountains–there are no Spring gentians, no shrubby cinquefoils, no yellow worts growing on the bogs.

How is it that heathers with a suite of other calcifuge species can cohabit with Spring gentians, shrubby cinquefoils and yellow worts in The Burren?

Limestone is a soluble, porous rock, and because the hills and lowlands of The Burren are crisscrossed by scailps and tunnelled with subterranean channels, any rain that falls will quickly drain away underground–within a few seconds most water has run off The Burren's surface[2] and gone beyond the reach of plant roots.

A peat hummock on limestone

Thus, a pocket or hummock of soil lying on the surface of the limestone rapidly sheds rainwater, and because the underlying rock is usually almost flat, no standing pools of lime-enriched water remain to be soaked back up into the soil. Over time, all the lime and other soluble mineral salts in these soil hummocks are washed out by rainwater which, by virtue of the small quantities of carbon dioxide absorbed as it fell through the air, is weakly acidic–this not only accelerates the solution of any lime in the soil but also tends to make the hummock acidic too. The outcome of this process–leaching–is that accumulations of soil lying on top of limestone can, given time, become lime-free and acidic. Of course the thin layer of soil immediately adjacent to the rock may retain some lime simply because it is in direct contact with limestone, but the raised, central part of a pocket or hummock of soil remains acidic. Leaching of soil and the concomitant increase in acidity are accelerated by plants that colonize the soil; heathers, for example, are known to enhance acidification because their litter contains high concentrations of acids.[3]

There is only one way by which the process of leaching and acidification can be reversed or halted. Calcium carbonate leached from the soil by rain must be replaced. In The Burren such a process occurs naturally when turloughs flood, because the ground-water contains dissolved limestone. Thus the soils surrounding turloughs, at least below the winter high-water mark, should not become leached or acidic as long as the water-levels continue to rise and fall.

The progression from lime-rich to acid soil is reflected in the plant communities. Where the soil retains calcium carbonate–for example on the stable dunes at Fanore–the flora is distinctly calcicolous, but the peaty hummocks sitting on the rock often have heathers and other calcifuge species. And not only are the flowering plants and ferns susceptible to the acidity of the soil; Ivimey-Cook and Proctor noted that in Burren heathlands dominated by *Calluna* and *Erica* calcifuge mosses replaced calcicole ones.

Annual plants including the rue-leaved saxifrage behave as pioneer species, capable of exploiting shallow soil whether on a wall or in a solution cup. Plants like these contribute to the cycle of soil development and erosion that indubitably characterises the pavements. They assist the process of soil accumulation, and once a patch of vegetation is established, leaching of that soil leads to its gradual acidification, allowing new species, less tolerant of calcium carbonate to invade. In the vanguard for the calcifuge transplantation, is another pioneer, bitter-vetch.

Bitter-vetch (*Lathyrus montanus*), according to standard texts such as *Flora of the British Isles*,[4] is a plant of woods, thickets and hedge banks in hilly country, and Professor Webb and Miss Scannell, among others, assert that it tends to be calcifuge. *Lathyrus montanus* is abundant in The Burren, where in early summer the multi-coloured flowers peeping from weather-beaten bushes of heather are a joyful sight. Bitter-vetch inhabits soil hummocks that have not yet been monopolized by heather, and because it is a perennial with a persistent, tuberous rootstock, doubtless the vetch continues to thrive as the hummock soil becomes more acidic and other acid-loving plants invade.

The stems of *Lathyrus montanus* are annual, rising each spring from the root tubers. The leaves are alternately arranged along the stems which are prominently winged. Each leaf has from two to four pairs of leaflets, but there is no tendril so the stems require support from surrounding shrubs–they cannot cling and climb

Lathyrus montanus
bitter-vetch

like the garden pea. At the base of the leaf, where the leaf stalk and the stem join, are two arrow-shaped, toothed stipules. As many as six flowers cluster in a stalked raceme like those of sweet-pea, which is also a member of the genus *Lathyrus*; they have a prominent standard whose colour is hard to describe, partly because it changes dramatically as the individual bloom ages. At first the standard and wings are plain crimson; this slowly transmutes into blue and green. When the flower withers, the pod, containing about half a dozen seeds, elongates.

In bygone days, at least in the Outer Hebrides and north of Scotland, bitter-vetch was harvested for food. The tubers are edible, fresh and raw–John Gerard affirmed that they taste like chestnuts–and according to Scottish sources they were used not only to 'flavour' whisky but also when steeped in water and fermented to make a liquor called cairm.[5] The peas, no doubt, may also be eaten. The Irish–indeed Gaelic–name *corra meille* conveys that this is a honey-sweet plant, not a bitter one. Dr Patrick Browne, who lived at Rushbrook in County Mayo, a little north of the limestone country around Lough Corrib, listed bitter vetch, 'carmel carra millish', as growing 'in campis sub ericosis satis communis' and noted that 'radicus tuberosae gratae dulcrius'.[6]

Like bitter-vetch, standard texts about the floras of Britain and Ireland state that *Hypericum pulchrum*, slender St John's wort, is an inhabitant of 'dry woods and rough grassy places on non-calcareous soils';[7] its general ecological propensities suggest that it is calcifuge and especially intolerant of lime-rich clay. Yet *Hypericum pulchrum* is one of the most widespread plants in The Burren, frequenting patches of soil on limestone pavement, rough pasturelands and roadside verges. Its abundance here and on the Aran Islands suggested to Professor Webb and Miss Scannell that the Clare race is an ecotype which has evolved some tolerance for calcareous habitats.[8]

Dr Richard Ivimey-Cook and Professor Michael Proctor showed that an association characterized by *Dryas octopetala* and *Hypericum pulchrum* (Asperuleto-Dryadetum) was the 'commonest limestone grassland community',[9] but they did not argue that slender St John's wort was a calcicole species, rather they noted that it was one of a group of species, typical of leached, organic soils, that become progressively more prominent in plant communities as leaching enhanced the acidity of the soil. The presence of *Hypericum pulchrum* is therefore not surprising–habitats dominated by the *Dryas octopetala–Hypericum pulchrum* association are not underlain by calcareous clay but a peaty soil derived largely from the debris of the plants themselves. Another important aspect of this *Dryas–Hypericum* community is the fact that it is grazed but never mown and rarely manured–in other words this is the type of community which develops in undisturbed places where traditional grazing regimes have been maintained for ages.

Hypericum pulchrum is an herbaceous perennial, with erect, leafy stems. The stalkless, stem-clasping leaves are arranged in opposite pairs; their blades are about the length of a fingernail, heart-shaped, and dotted with tiny glands that look like pin-pricks. Bright yellow flowers, similar in size to those of buttercups, grouped in a branched cluster atop the stem open in June and July; the five petals are often tinted with red and with a hand-lens you should see a row of black glands around the margins. The glands on the sepal margins are also black and have minute stalks. There is a brush of stamens in the centre arranged into five bundles, each with ten or more stamens. The fruit is a capsule, straw-coloured when ripe, not a black berry as in tutsan (*Hypericum androsaemum*) which is a shrubby species often seen in scailps.

There is a respectable congregation of saints in a Gaelic litany of Ireland's flora: *cruach Phádraig* is great plantain (*Plantago major*) and Patrick's only authentic flower; *liach Bhride*, Brigid's spoon, is a native synonym for the broad-leaved pondweed (*Potamogeton natans*); golden samphire (*Inula crithmoides*), known as *ailleann Pheadair*, has some unfathomed link with St Peter while Autumn Lady's tresses is but one of many flowers named for Mary, *cúilín Muire*; Columbcille has to his name a handful of plants of which *lus Cholm Cille*, yellow pimpernel (*Lysimachia nemorum*) is possibly the most familiar.

It seems hardly necessary then that St John's worts should also become associated with Columbcille, but this group of herbs were held in such high esteem that the Blessed Virgin is invoked too. There is an antique tradition about Columbcille walking around with a plant stuffed under his arm, in honour of John the Baptist (a dubious honour I would have thought), and Gaelic names for this wort are *achlasan Choluimchille* (for which the unlovely translation is armpit package of Columbcille) and *sean Columcille* (charm of Columbcille). The Virgin's associations are not explained; *lus na Maighdine Muire*, herb of the Virgin Mary, is now reserved to *Hypericum perforatum*. Another name, *beathnua baineann*, is a simple translation of slender St John's wort.[10]

Hypericum pulchrum is not confined to organic soils colonized by mountain avens; it is also a common associate of cat's paw and hawkweed (*Antennaria dioica–Hieracium pilosella* Nodum) as long as the soils do not contain high proportions of clay from glacial drift. Moreover it frequents the limestone heaths wherein *Calluna vulgaris* and *Erica cinerea* are prominent and the community characterized by the presence of mountain avens and *Arctostaphylos uva-ursi*; again the soils are leached and peaty, so they are acidic not alkaline.

From the bridge beside St Patrick's Roman Catholic Church at Fanore, a road heads eastwards into the centre of the barony following the course of the Caher River into a steep-sided defile known as Khyber Pass–there are two Khyber Passes in The Burren, and this is not the genuine one. At the seaward entrance of the pass, on its northern side, is a cliff of glacial till cloaked in a few places with juniper, and the river here burbles over a bed of white-crusted stones–until about 1870 the track used to be on the northern bank of the river traversing the esker crest. The road enters Formoyle townland and, as the valley broadens, crosses the river and winds among hazel scrub on the northern side, past small farms, little fields and ruined chapels. Soon the road forks, the southerly way dipping towards the river, crossing it again by a bridge wreathed with polypody and rusty-back ferns, before the green road that leads up to the flat tableland of Sliabh Eilbhe. Keeping track with the river for a short distance, this south road then twists and begins climbing the broad northern flank of that mountain. Eventually it meets the boundary of Eilbhe's shale cap, traces it for a kilometre or so and finally winds down the slope joining the main Ballyvaghan to Lisdoonvarna road near Toomaghera.

Between the fern-bridge in the dip at the fork, and the rush-lined shale boundary, now helpfully (but needlessly) also marked by ranked forests of Sitka spruce, the green road traverses limestone terraces which yield many of the most interesting Burren plants. At one spot beside the road, in the townland of Caherbullog, a cascade of evergreen shrubs hugs the natural steps. In late spring, as the gentians and mountain avens are blooming, this mat sprouts small clusters of hanging flowers, tiny urns, red-rimmed, shading to coral pink or white: in May 1991 the Caherbullog plants were astonishingly floriferous, a joy to behold even on a miserably wet day. By autumn there are round, glossy red berries among the jade-green leaves. This is *lus na stalóg*, bearberry, *Arctostaphylos uva-ursi*, sometimes also called cranberry although that name is more usually given to plants of another genus, *Vaccinium*. Bearberry has a dry, tasteless fruit; cranberries and bilberries (or fraughans) have juicy ones much used in sweets and pies.

Bearberry is a prostrate shrub, typical of terrain that is acid and snow-bound in winter–high mountains and Arctic peat moors–not of warm, limestone terraces

Narthecium ossifragum
bog asphodel

Hypericum pulchrum
slender St John's wort

Arctostaphylos uva-ursi: bearberry *Empetrum nigrum*: crowberry (lower right)

although it does frequent heathland overlying limestone in mountain areas. While its principal habitats encircle the globe in the Arctic and sub-Arctic latitudes, in warmer zones bearberry has refuges in the Pyrenees, Himalayas and Rocky Mountains. As might be anticipated, in Ireland bearberry grows on the higher slopes from Connemara northwards into Achill Island and Donegal, but its haunts are far between. Yet the western hills of The Burren are one of the species' Irish strongholds: here *Arctostaphylos uva-ursi* grows on the highest summits (320 metres, 1046 feet asl) and also descends almost to sea-level on the shaded north-eastern brow of Black Head.

This lovely relative of the strawberry tree (*Arbutus unedo*) and the Californian manzanita is one of the enigmas of The Burren. Bearberry's ecological leanings suggest that it should not colonize bare limestone pavements, but it does with such exuberance that in places thick carpets of long, flexible stems are woven with mountain avens. When *Dryas* and *Arctostaphylos* entwine, as in Caherbullog and on the mountains overlooking Gleninagh, herbs and even mosses are almost entirely excluded.

In the early 1860s Frederick Foot recorded the extent of *Arctostaphylos uva-ursi* with commendable accuracy, noting the remarkable fact that it does not venture on to the peatlands overlying the shale; to this day there are no reports of bearberry from the shale cap of Sliabh Eilbhe which meres upon Caherbullog. At the beginning of the last century Walter Wade reported that bearberry 'spreads to a vast degree on the limestone rocks on the Burren mountains…where it is called *Burren myrtle*'[11] but the earliest report, hidden away in his massive tome *Archaeologia Britannica*, is that of Edward Lhuyd, the Welsh virtuoso who toured Ireland at the close of the seventeenth century:

> Lusradh na geire bornigh bear whortle berries, viz. Radix Idaea putata, sive uva ursi… I observ'd this plant to be so called in the County of Clare.[12]

There are many names for what the early botanists, Wade included, called 'red trailing *Arbutus*'. Karl Sprengel, an eminent Prussian botanist, removed bearberry from the genus *Arbutus*–its fruits are quite different–in the early 1800s and placed it within Michel Adanson's genus *Arctostaphylos*. Thus bearberry's two Latin names–all botanical names are treated as if they are Latin–combine in an elegant piece of tautology for they are synonymous: *arctos* and *ursus* are, respectively, Greek and Latin for a bear, and *staphyle* and *uva* similarly signify a bunch of grapes.

Crowberry is not related to bearberry, but it does look like a prostrate member of the heather family. The creeping stems are arrayed with spindle-shaped leaves. Tiny green flowers appear in early spring, from March into April, male and female borne on separate plants. The little black berries that follow are rich in Vitamin C but poor eating and sparsely produced in The Burren; they are ripe by September and disappear quickly, presumably harvested by small mammals and birds, but a grouse would have poor pickings here. The seeds of crowberry can lie dormant in the soil for at least four years before germinating, and it has been shown that they do not germinate until they have been subjected to cold winter temperatures. Crowberry spreads most effectively by vegetative means; the shoots will root wherever they touch soil so that in any area all the plants of *Empetrum nigrum* may belong to the same clone, and to one sex.

In some areas of The Burren, including Caherbullog and Black Head, crowberry and bearberry grow together, often colonizing the same peaty hummock and tumbling together into the crevices. Like *Arctostaphylos uva-ursi*, *Empetrum nigrum* displays, throughout its range in the northern hemisphere, a marked preference for peaty, acid soils, and it is frequently associated with *Calluna vulgaris*. It might be classified as a calcifuge species, but it is not restricted to lime-free habitats as The Burren populations demonstrate with startling clarity. To underscore that point, crowberry grows on peatlands near the Cliffs of Moher, but is most prolific in The Burren hills; it does not extend into the eastern, low-lying areas, nor has it colonized the extensive peaty moors overlying the shales on Sliabh Eilbhe. Ivimey-Cook and Proctor defined one vegetation community that is characterized by crowberry and red helleborine (*Epipactis atrorubens*), and which in certain exposed sites, on shattered limestone pavement, contained a mixture of mountain avens, crowberry and blue grass (*Sesleria albicans*). Such a community is distinctly calcicole.

Crowberry displays a preference for cool, moist habitats and is unable to withstand exposure to dry winds;[13] it is unlikely to experience such conditions in The Burren for the winds that sough through the stone walls and rattle the rocks on the pavements are laden with moisture. *Empetrum* is intolerant also of shade and of long-lying snow–neither of these factors will mar life on The Burren hills. *Empetrum nigrum* encircles the globe in northern latitudes from Iceland and Ireland eastwards through Russia to Kamchatka, island-hopping across the Bering Straits into Alaska and thence southwards into northern California, skipping central Canada but extending eastwards into Quebec and the maritime provinces.

Crowberry got its name, it is said, because the berry made poor food, fit only for crows or crakes (one alternative name is crakeberry); in Irish it is *lus na feannóige*–plant of the hooded crow. Threlkeld recorded other names for the berries including, from County Wicklow, 'brallan duh' (breallán dubh) which literally is black blunderer; one can but wonder how that arose. In the same entry in *Synopsis stirpium Hibernicarum*, the ever-observant doctor reported that 'some use the ling instead of Hops, and is said to give no ungrateful Taste to the Ale.'[14] Scottish children are said to relish these, but too many will give you a headache. Boil crowberries in alum and you can dye cloth a dark black-purple.[15]

Ling is the plant more commonly called heather or by Irish speakers, *fraoch*. It is abundant throughout The Burren, growing anywhere that a clod of earth has accumulated on or between the limestone rocks. The swirling terraces of the hillside are often accentuated by dark eddies of ling.

Most heather enthusiasts will be surprised to hear the advice that if you wish to see ling in all its glory go to The Burren, but that is good advice. On the slopes of Black Head ling blooms in all shades from white to purple. At Poll Salach in the close-cropped turf are curls of *Calluna*, prostrate among the grasses and rosettes of devil's bit and cat's-paw, even creeping out to touch limestone. Where dark bands of chert crisscross the pavement, heathers march along these dykes–some fine examples can be traced eastwards from the shore of Lough Gealáin. There is plenty of ling around the turloughs, although not below the general winter water-mark because it would be swamped then with lime-choked water. The only other places where heathers do not flourish are in dimly lit recesses of the hazel copses and woodlands.

Calluna-dominated communities in The Burren represent the final product of the interaction of the processes of leaching and the succession of species, according to Ivimey-Cook and Proctor. Ling itself has a startling capacity to modify soil especially by facilitating the transition to highly acid conditions. Various elegant studies have been carried out which suggest that the litter accumulating naturally under a heather bush makes soil more acidic.[16] Under the plant the soil pH will be very low (highly acidic), and this rises steeply towards the the soil-rock interface where the pH will be higher (alkaline). *Calluna* roots are concentrated in the upper few centimetres of a soil hummock so that even the thinnest patch of peaty soil can support a shrub of ling. Once established, the heather generates more peaty soil by shedding its leaves and flowers.

The pedantic explanation of a progression from a lime-rich soil to a dense stand of heather does not diminish the wonder that I experience as I walk on the September pavements and inhale the honey-aroma of heather in full bloom, or in the winter as I stumble through the knee-high thickets that conceal dangerous ankle-traps. There is no corner of the wild Burren pavement that is out-of-bounds to a heath, be it ling or bell heather.

What I have written about *Calluna vulgaris* can be repeated with equal validity to *Erica cinerea*,[17] bell heather, the only representative of *Erica* in The Burren proper. Cross-leaved heath (*Erica tetralix*) has not been collected within the limestone domain, because there is no pocket of permanently sodden peat therein; it does inhabit boggy ground on Sliabh Eilbhe and southwards, and also a few areas of wet peat in the eastern lowlands about Rinroe, to the north of Corrofin and outside The Burren as I define it.

Bell heather is not as abundant as ling, yet the two are inseparable companions throughout the region, and where ling is tall, bell heather is tall: where one is prostrate, the other keeps it company. A low-growing, sward-hugging habit can be an artefact resulting from close grazing by cattle and goats, or even pruning by the gales which batter the rockscape, but in *Erica cinerea* the habit appears to be fixed genetically, for when bell heather plants, prostrate in their wild haunts,

Erica cinerea: bell heather (left) *Calluna vulgaris:* ling

are grown in sheltered gardens away from wind and beasts, they remain prostrate. If the decumbent habit was not an inherited character, plants removed from a windy place, or protected from grazing, should become tall and bushy. I proved this when I gathered a few cuttings from a royal-purple bell heather that I noticed crawling onto the pavement from a tussock at Poll Salach; the slips rooted easily and now the mature plants are cascading down the sides of a trough in Dublin, unwilling to grow upright.

I fancy that flowers on Burren bell heather (*fraoch cloigíneach*) are a brighter, richer red than those which grow in Connemara. Certainly there are scattered plants with blood red, not crimson-purple bells around Lough Gealáin, and I know well a patch on the slope above Gleninagh Castle with dusky red blossom.

A pathway which passes by that particular heather leads into the sheltered valley of Gleninagh on the southern side of Cappanawalla. Its beginning is not marked, but it starts beside one of the small North Gleninagh farms and corkscrews to a wayside cairn and my dusky heather, and on up the northern flank of the hill to a dip in the summit table-land. Carry straight on, descending into the pasture of the glen and you will eventually come to the green road that traverses the lower glen. But that is a dull walk, and I prefer to strike off left or right, across the pavement and terraces, gradually ascending on to the summits. If you veer to the left (to the south east), Cappanawalla will become your chessboard as you tread between the crisscrossing scailps. Turn to the right, westwards, and the various summits of Gleninagh Mountain and Dobhach Bhrainin (320 metres asl.) lie ahead, and in their lap a vortex of limestone. This is the kingdom of eight-petalled dryades, of juniper and flycatchers and bone-breakers, a strange stone world, searing with a bright heat on calm, sunny days, and searing with sharp rain when one of the four winds of heaven is at play.

On a hot, still and sunny afternoon on Dobhach Bhrainin I saw '…a thousand spears of yellow asphodel guarding each hollow where marsh mosses hide'.[18] *Flora of The Burren and Connemara*, indicates that bog asphodel occurs on peatlands in southern Clare with many other plants typical of wet, acidic habitats. The Burren, however, is not notable, for extensive peat deposits yet as we have seen its flora is not exclusively composed of calcicole plants; calcifuge species such as ling, bell heather and even bog cotton abound because they can colonize the small hummocks of peat that rest on the limestone rocks. Plants characteristic of the wettest parts of raised bogs–for example cross-leaved heath–are absent from this region, or at least have not hitherto been reported. The bog asphodel, *Narthecium ossifragum*, was included among the absentees.

Bog asphodel is a member of the lily family (Liliaceae). The sword-shaped leaves, often curving like a crescent, are arranged in a fan; the blades are ribbed and the apex is pointed. The golden yellow flowers have six petals–the outer side of each one is green. Arranged opposite the petals are six stamens with vivid red anthers and densely hairy filaments. The ovary is in the centre and after fertilization it swells to form a capsule containing numerous seeds–as the capsule ripens it turns to coral red. The seed of bog asphodel is strange; it looks like a miniature fishing float with a central seed-body and long tapering tails above and below.

My first sighting of bog asphodel was on 1 August 1987 near the summit of the ridge at about 270 metres (almost 900 feet) above sea level, in a damp, peaty area facing north-west. There were only about one hundred flowering spikes in the colony but they were sufficient to stop my trek towards the summit. I photographed the asphodels, and carefully removed one flowering stem as a voucher specimen to be dried and pressed and then preserved for posterity in the herbarium at the National Botanic Gardens, Dublin. I gathered that solitary voucher with some misgivings because I did not want to deplete the colony, but I was sure no-one had reported this bog-plant from the top of these limestone mountains before, and the voucher was necessary proof of this contradiction. My qualms were mollified on the succeeding three days, for I encountered other populations on the north-eastern slopes and summit plateau of Cappanawalla, and on the northern slopes of Gleninagh Mountain. At all the sites the bright yellow spears were accompanied by purple ling, bell heather and purple moor-grass. These were substantial colonies, much more extensive than my first find on Dobhach Bhrainin, so there were a thousand spears of yellow asphodel in the barony, and the species was not endangered by my gathering for the scientific record.

The presence of *Narthecium* on the hills of The Burren is surprising, but when the peculiarities of the Burren flora are considered, especially the extensive covering of heathers, its occurrence becomes less perplexing. Bog asphodel has a relatively wide tolerance of soil acidity from very acidic (pH 3.6) to almost neutral (pH 6.5)–a similar range is characteristic of *Calluna*–but it abhors calcareous habitats. Moreover, Dr R. J. Summerfield, an authority on the ecology of *Narthecium*, noted that bog asphodel tends to inhabit sites where water is moving through the soil; the peat hummocks, overlying the Burren limestone, provide such conditions albeit briefly as rain water rather than ground water percolates through them.[19]

What is most unexpected about the bog asphodel colonies in The Burren is the absence of earlier reports. It is not an abundant plant, but it is certainly not rare–anyone walking during the summer on the high plateaux of The Burren is likely to encounter it in blossom. Perhaps the silence of earlier botanists is explained by remarking that the bright yellow flower-spikes of bog asphodel can be mistaken, at a distance, for those of lady's bedstraw or golden rod; even at close range, to the short-sighted, there is a confusing similarity between the inflorescences of bog asphodel and the diminutive golden rod of The Burren.

However that may be, I am sure that the silence is due to the fact that botanists tend to avoid The Burren in the 'close-season' for the blooming gentians. Perhaps if they do frequent the region out-of-season they stay in the lowlands, and never see the eddying rocks and the kingdom of dryades from the vantage point of Dobhach Bhrainin. This must also be the charitable explanation for another lapse;

no-one has reported round-leaved sundew before from on the western slopes of Black Head, where it grows with *Narthecium ossifragum*–but that is another story, told elsewhere.

And why is bog asphodel named the bone-breaker–*ossifragum*? In the olden days folk believed that cattle eating this relative of the iris would suffer fractures. In Donegal its names include cruppany grass, from giving sheep a stiffness of the bones, whereas the standard Irish name is *sciollam na mona*, bog squill. While thought to be poisonous, there is no modern evidence to confirm bog asphodel's deadly reputation. No matter how much it may be reviled or feared, *Narthecium ossifragum* is a most admirable plant, with red anthers, golden petals green on the outside, and as the fruits ripen they are transformed into coral spears, fit to guard 'each hollow where marsh mosses hide…'

Black Head

STONY SEABOARD

Stony seaboard, far and foreign,
Stony hills poured over space,
Stony landscape of The Burren,
Stones in every fertile place,
Little fields with boulders dotted,
Grey-stone shoulders saffron-spotted,
Stone-walled cabins thatched with reeds,
Where a Stone Age people breeds,
The last of Europe's stone age race.

John Betjeman: 'Ireland with Emily'

Late one evening when hints of sunset were in the western sky, in autumn about the time of the solstice, I was driving south along the coast road from Black Head heading for Doolin. The Aran Islands were placid whales aslumber in a grey sea. I had passed through the long village of Fanore and the road was rising to crest the ridge from Knockauns Mountain. Something in the sea caught my attention and I stopped. A school of six dolphins broke the surface, leaping playfully through the gentle swell. They were travelling south too, out of Galway Bay, heaven knows where, and appeared to engage me in a race. Such fleeting moments on serene evenings are immensely re-assuring; perhaps the world may be alright.

Halfway between Fanore and Doolin is Poll Salach, an intriguing site for plants, and a place where frequently I linger. The limestone terraces slip beneath

231

the waves and where the rock has resisted attempts to remove it, there are cliffs, nothing like the Cliffs of Moher whose distinctive tower-crested extremity can be seen to the southwest, but still forceful testimony to the power of the ocean.

Standing on the cliff at Poll Salach I listen as a flight of sixteen oyster-catchers screams past in irregular formation, their calls a descant above the tympany beat of the sea in the scailps of the cliff, a drum-roll that rose and fell in concert with the Atlantic swell. The water was grey, streaked with foam. Six more oyster-catchers swept past, silent this flight, flashes of white eclipsed in black. The sky was grey too, foreboding rain, but the three islands were still clearly visible on the horizon.

Many's the day peering westwards will reveal no sign of the Aran islands nor of dolphins and oyster-catchers; on such days sea and sky meld indivisibly in a haze of sea-mist or rain. And there are days when the westerly gales impel the ocean to assault the land, crashing angry breakers headlong against the limestone terraces and cliffs with such fury that it is unwise to approach the edge–in the winter storms of 1991 such was the power of the furious ocean that the water moved huge boulders several metres across the pavement. Plumes of water-smoke may rise high about the coastal fields as the rocks resist and the sea foams. When the storms have ceased battering the land, and the rain has raced away eastwards, less comforting sights can mar that sense of well-being. A dead pilot whale washed ashore on the orange sands at Fanore, a flotilla of rubbish ranging from broken toys and light bulbs to beams of timber and refuse bags filled with putrid offal. The whale will decay and its flesh will melt back into the ecosystem, but the oil, the plastic and the bottles will not disappear so congenially. The coast of The Burren is not immune to the carelessness of mankind.

The coastal zone, from the lowest watermark to the precipices a few tens of metres inland which are sprayed by the salt-mist thrown skywards by the thundering waves, has it own distinctive flora and fauna. Study of the submarine plants–the seaweeds–is a specialized subject on which I am not competent to discourse, yet it may be remarked that the seaweed flora of portions of The Burren coast–the Finavarra peninsula, for example, and its north shore, the Flaggy Shore[1]–is well recorded and of considerable interest. Fragments of it can be glimpsed and admired when there are very low tides, and the rock pools, especially about Poll Salach are accessible on foot–but remember, please, that the rocks can be slippery and you must never approach them when the sea is rough for fear of being swept off by freak waves.

Under the waves there is teeming life, and the marine plants and animals, each in their own zone, work with the water to hasten the disappearance of the

Calystegia soldanella: sea bindweed

limestone. The territories of the seaweeds and marine beasts are displayed most vividly at Poll Salach where the blue-black mussels cling to the rocks further from the high-water mark than the lawn of pale grey acorn barnacles. Here too spiny, jet-purple sea-urchins, *Paracentrotus lividus,* inhabit the permanent rock-pools. Each urchin has it own perfect cup in the rock, a natural bullaun, and the colonies have sculpted a honeycomb city in the pools. Vacant cups may be occupied by the brown soft-bodied sea anemones–very occasionally by a pale, whitish-grey one. The pools look as if they are filled with the finest chocolates, each one arrayed in its own compartment. Acorn barnacles and mussels, whelks and hermit crabs vie for whatever space remains, and the beautiful pink-purple, crunchy feathers of *Corallina officinalis,* a red seaweed whose fronds are impregnated with limestone, cover the pool-sides. Old discarded shells have a crust of lavender *Lithophyllum incrustans.* Small tufts of glistening brown seaweed (*Bifurcaria bifurcata*) colonize any pieces of rock that may be left unoccupied by barnacles, and squelch underfoot.

The orange sands at Fanore are bisected by a reef of black limestone that gleams like a dark mirror after it has been washed by rain or the receding tide-water. Gulls rise and hover in the west wind, flapping their wings lazily just to stay in one place above the white breakers; those scarlet-legged oyster-catchers often flicker over the reef. This is a beach for combing on hands and knees, for along the thin line that describes the limit of the last wave, even among the bottles and plastic pellets, you will certainly find seeds that are not the offspring of Irish plants. On almost every visit I have gathered this flotsam from the Americas and have even sown them and raised their seedlings into fine plants. Perfectly round, dun-coloured, with a linear scar around a third of its circumference–that is a sea-pea, *Lathyrus japonicus* subsp. *maritimus*, a congener of the garden sweet pea and bitter vetch. The creamy-gold seed with two flat faces, a rounded back and a circular scar somewhat offset at its bottom is a morning glory or a sea bindweed. Fanore has yielded these and others including the rock-hard pale grey nickar nut, the true sea-bean which looks like a flattened pebble but is shining chestnut brown and floats, and the black banded, rich brown horse-eye bean! These latter seeds, and some others, are from tropical beach plants, and they have floated to Fanore on the currents that sweep across the Atlantic from west to east, driven by the earth's rotation and the winds. The sea-peas, morning glory and the other tiny seeds also came from America, but not from tropical parts. They are invaders, and if all the circumstances are right they might one day germinate, establish and form a new colony on The Burren coast.[2]

The dunes which back the beach at Fanore are cloaked with tough, wiry marram grass; the gales comb it against the sand like locks of silver hair. Among the tufts of grass, which stabilize the sand dunes, several other plants find refuge from the west winds–sea spurge (*Euphorbia paralias*) and sea holly (*Eryngium maritimum*), for example. Thomas Dineley seems to have heard about this in the late 1600s, for in his diary he recorded that 'The barony of Burren is famous for curative herbs, the best in Ireland and equal to the best in England. Here are Eringo roots in great quantity.'[3] Dr Threlkeld informs us that Eringo is of 'use against a *Winchester* goose'–whatever that may be![4]

Where the Caher River disgorges, on both sides there are patches of a plant with kidney-shaped bright green, somewhat succulent leaves. It creeps through the dune sand, sending out 'runners', so that each of the patches, representing a single plant, may cover several square metres. In June and July, among the leaves, beautiful pink flowers appear; these are identical with the bindweed, and indeed this plant is called sea bindweed (*Calystegia soldanella*; in Irish *plúr an phrionsa*).

At Fanore, I have never found seeds on the sea-bindweed plants, and I believe the patches may represent just a single clone. As the plants are genetically identical they cannot cross-pollinate each other and so at Fanore the bindweed reproduces only by means of its 'runners'. Thus any seeds of the sea-bindweed that might be identified among the flotsam at the high-water mark must have come from elsewhere–and the only possible origin is North America.

Many coastal plants, including almost all that flourish closest to the high tide mark, produce fruits and seeds that are tolerant of immersion in salt water–if the seeds could not survive this, the species would in all probability disappear from this habitat. The fruits or seeds may also have the ability to float in sea-water for quite substantial periods. *Calystegia* seeds have a very hard, almost porcelain-like seed coat which is water-tight; salt water is not absorbed by the seed and therefore cannot kill the embryo within, and the seed is buoyant. If you crawl along the tide line, you can find other seeds, many of which not only float but also remain viable.

In the late autumn the harvest of these seeds is richest, and includes the corky coated fruits of samphire, tiny jet seeds like little beads which I have not yet identified, and many others. There should be the fruits (achenes) of some of the coastal daisies–*Aster tripolium*, for example, and scentless mayweed (*Tripleurospermum maritimum* subsp. *maritimum*). The mayweed, with white and gold flower-heads like those of the ox-eye daisy, occurs in drifts above the tide-line at Bishop's Quarter and among the pebbles at Poll Salach. Its achenes, unlike many members of the daisy family (Asteraceae), do not have a feathery pappus to act as a parachute aiding their dispersal by wind–they are distributed by water and can float for at least half a day, a sufficient time for the inshore currents to move them along a beach. Scentless mayweed colonizes a zone that is usually beyond the reach of the daily high tide–it may be washed by storm tides, but it certainly does not court a twice-daily bath in brine.

In contrast, the sea aster (*luibh bhléine*) will tolerate a twice-a-day dip in the sea. There are clumps of this aster in the sheltered harbour at Ballyvaghan, on the rocks by the pier, which are submerged every high tide, yet they flower wonderfully in the summer. Along the Poll Salach cliff edge, sea asters are abundant but well out of reach of the tides–here they are showered with spray from the waves that thunder against the rocks. *Aster tripolium* is a widespread plant of salt marshes and rocky habitats, ranging along most of the European coast, and also inland around salt-pans as far east as the shores of the Caspian Sea and Lake Baikal in central Asia. Remarkably, sea aster is not recorded from Iceland and the Faeroe Islands.

Scentless mayweed and sea aster are short-lived perennial herbs. The foliage of the aster is unremarkable–crisply fleshy, hairless, paddle-shaped and pale green

Aster tripolium: sea aster

with a prominent paler mid-rib. *Aster* gave its name to the Asteraceae (also known as Compositae), the family which includes the common daisy and the scentless mayweed. All members of the Asteraceae possess a 'flower' that is in fact a compound head–a capitulum composed of numerous tiny florets–the number varies from species to species, and genus to genus. In *Aster tripolium* there are two different kinds of florets making up the capitulum. In the centre, making up the disc, are tubby, bright yellow tubular florets formed from five fused petals which surround the club-shaped style that bears a glob of lemon-yellow pollen as it emerges from the opening tube. The outer florets have a different structure; they function as female flowers but each one looks like a single petal–five lavender petals are fused into a strap-shaped 'ray'. Ray florets have styles but no stamens. Each head has perhaps eighteen ray and a dozen disc florets and they begin to unfurl about the beginning of July. On the Aran Islands some of the sea aster plants have white rays, but I have not seen such a variant on The Burren shores.

Each floret is capable of producing a single seed which is contained within a fruit–because it is single-seeded and because the outer coat does not rupture to release the seed, this type of fruit is called an achene. The achene of *Aster tripolium*

236

Crithmum maritimum: samphire

does have a pappus of feathery hairs almost twice as long as the achene and this means the fruits can be dispersed by wind. The achenes will also float for several days, so sea aster can be distributed to new habitats by ocean currents too.

As I have mentioned, another seed frequently picked out of the tide-line debris is that of samphire. In experiments carried out early this century, Robert Lloyd Praeger found that samphire fruits stayed afloat for five months[5]–not a record, by any means, as the fruits of a closely related plant, fine-leaved water dropwort (*Oenanthe aquatica*), floated more than fifteen months.

At Poll Salach on the storm beach, that accumulation of hefty rounded rocks which the Atlantic waves carried out of reach, there are clumps of samphire, with fleshy green leaves like translucent deer's antlers, each one divided into many points; the branches are slightly ridged but generally rounded in cross-section. This is a member of the carrot family, Apiaceae (or Umbelliferae), which characteristically has umbrella-like inflorescences composed of many small flowers. In the samphire the individual flowers are yellow-green, and by September the swelling fruits may begin to take on a dark red glow–some fruiting heads merely darken to an olive green. This sturdy herb grows generally within the zone immediately above the high-tide mark, but at Poll Salach there are thriving plants on the precipices on the landward side of the road, well away from the beach, but near enough to the ocean for a guaranteed shower of salt-water in the winter storms.

Samphire is perennial, the stems and leaves wither away in late autumn leaving only the root-stock beneath the soil surface. By mid-summer the fresh green of the foliage stands out against the grey rock, and the samphire plants will reach perhaps twenty-five centimetres in height where they are established in a sheltered spot. The Irish name for *Crithmum maritimum* is *craobhraic* from *craobh* meaning a branch, hence a branchy plant (creevereegh is a partly Anglicized version from Donegal). Samphire is from the French, *herbe de Saint Pierre*, St Peter's herb, making an oblique connection both to the meaning of the name Peter—rock—and to the saint's connection with fishing; this is a seaside plant that can grow from seaside rocks. In olden days, samphire (of various genera) was gathered in May when the leaves were fresh and soft and pickled for eating as a salad and as a cure for ailments of the bladder and kidneys. Dr Threlkeld, apart from delivering one of his succinct sermons—on the pre-eminence of St Peter—noted that pickled samphire strengthened the stomach, 'procuring Appetite, and removing all Obstructions…' He did not, however, say it was harvested in Ireland. John Keogh, on the other hand, wrote deliberately about the plant's habitat '…on rock by the Sea side very plentifully in the Isles of Aaron, and in the west of the county of *Clare*.[6] Whence he received that information, we cannot tell, but it is the earliest localized report for Irish colonies of *Crithmum maritimum*.

Where samphire grows, sea lavender will probably also thrive. This is true at Poll Salach. Where the spray washes continually in the stormiest weather, there is a zone occupied by sea lavender, sea aster and thrift, intermingling with sea campion and sea plantain, samphire and sea milkwort. The sea lavender on this particular part of The Burren coast is a diminutive one, less than a finger-length tall, even when the plants are hiding in the lea of the few rocks that project above the general level of the ground. The spoon-shaped leaves are grey-green (in Irish it is called *lus liath na Boirne*, the grey-green plant of The Burren), forming a small erect rosette in the centre of which are the diagnostic branched inflorescences. The flowers are tiny, five-petalled and lavender, and each is enclosed by a flimsy white petticoat of the calyx.

There are clumps of dwarf sea lavender on the cliffs on the eastern side of the road too, rooted in the cracks and demonstrating that the salt spray from the ocean influence the vegetation on these precipices. Samphire and scurvy-grass keep it company.

Another taller species of sea lavender, *Limonium humile*, with a lax flower-spike, inhabits much more sheltered coastal sites east of Black Head–I have seen it on the muddy, rocky flats backing The Rine at Ballyvaghan and at Bishops Quarter, at Finavarra and Newquay.

Sea lavenders have a particularly complicated nomenclatural history. Many people, gardeners especially, still call them *Statice*, although the native species are all placed now in *Limonium*. The dwarf Burren plants form a 'very famous' population, one that has perplexed many botanists, and an indication of that is the plethora of names applied to it since the early 1850s. For a time it was identified as *Statice occidentalis*, and then as *Limonium binervosum*. Now it rejoices in the name *Limonium recurvum* subsp. *transwallianum*, yet that is only the latest attempt. Such a delightfully delicate plant does not deserve so long and cumbersome a Latin name–but the perversities of botanical nomenclature take no account of stature.[7]

Limonium is notoriously complicated–the various wild populations do not fit neatly into that set of precisely separated 'pigeon-holes' which botanists know as species. Not only will the sea lavenders alter their habit when transplanted to a different habitat, demonstrating that they are especially plastic in their response to environmental conditions, but the different species possess few 'good' characters which can be used to distinguish one from another, and there are often intermediates linking what appear to be distinct species into a continuum. Complicating matters even more is the biology of these plants–they can set seed apomictically–without fertilization preceded by pollination–and so populations may not vary much within themselves but differ markedly from even nearby populations. To 'sort out' intractable groups such as sea lavenders, botanists often resort to cultivation experiments; by growing plants from different populations in the same soil at the same time and in one garden (or glasshouse), environmental factors can be controlled and differences caused by the plants' plastic responses to their native environments are eliminated. The true morphologic patterns within and between populations are then discernable. Experiments of this nature are characteristic of twentieth century botany–remarkably, however, the dwarf sea lavender from Clare and the Aran Islands was subjected to such experiments almost one an a half centuries ago!

'*Statice occidentalis*' from 'rocks by the road-side south of Black Head' had been cultivated last century in the Botanic Gardens at Glasnevin. David Moore must

Limonium recurvum subsp. *transwallianum:* sea lavender

have collected it in 1852 during a visit to the region, although he does not state explicitly anywhere that he did. On 24 August 1853, according to an annotated drawing in the Department of Botany, Natural History Museum, London, there was a plant from Clare growing in Glasnevin.[8] A. G. More saw the same plant in 1854: 'some green tufts caught the eye, and these turned out to be samphire; close by, [sea lavender], quite recently added to the Irish flora, and new to me.'[9] The plant in Glasnevin did not survive for long–Moore and More commented on its hardiness in *Cybele Hibernica:*

> The form found in [The Burren and Aran] differs remarkably in appearance
> from the ordinary state of the species as found on the east coast, being

Armeria maritima: thrift

only about half the size, with a less branched panicle and it does not survive the ordinary winter at Glasnevin when planted in open ground.[10]

Professor Herbert Baker of the University of Leeds was the first to apply modern techniques to the Irish west coast sea lavenders–he collected plants in The Burren and elsewhere, and concluded that the 'conventional classificatory treatment accorded to sexual species cannot be applied satisfactorily...' to the Irish plants which he placed with the *Limonium binervosum* complex. Moreover, he suggested that these plants were relatively recent immigrants, their seeds perhaps distributed by wind, on birds' feathers or in sea currents. Such a thesis was, he believed, adequate as an explanation both of the fragmented distribution pattern and of the apparent morphological differences between the several isolated populations.[11]

Sea lavender is a member of the Plumbaginaceae, a family which includes thrift, and familiar garden plants such as *Ceratostigma* and *Plumbago* (cape jasmine). Certain members of the family reproduce asexually–by apomixis, for example, as in Burren sea lavender–whereas others have evolved a complicated method of ensuring that cross-pollination takes place. The pin- and thrum-eyed system of primroses is analogous with the dimorphic adaptations in the Plumbaginaceae. In thrift (and also some sea lavenders), the stigma is covered with either small regularly arranged papillae, or an irregular pattern of stumpy warts (cob stigma). The pollen grains are also different–the flowers with papillate stigmas produce pollen which will only successfully pollinate the plants with cob stigmas, whereas the pollen from cob stigma thrift pollinates only plants with papillate stigma.[12]

Thrift is undoubtedly the most familiar of all seaside plants and it too seems to thrive particularly well on rocks. The cushions of flat rosettes of dark green, short, linear leaves are easily recognized when there are no flowers, and because of this habit it has long been called Lady's Cushion. Sea-pink is its other familiar name. In Ireland it has been called sea turf, while the native names include *rabhan* and *nóinín chladaich* meaning beach daisy.

There are drifts of sea-pinks at Black Head, along the roadside in the lea of the rock walls. On the windswept pavement by the lighthouse thrift marks and at the same time conceals the lines of the scailps. The cushions are dull when out of bloom, but when the button-heads on tall stems appear in the summer, the cushions seem to dance in the sea breeze. Each compact head is composed of a cluster of perhaps twenty individual flowers, each with a trumpet-shaped calyx composed of five fused sepals with five hairy ribs and a pleated mouth. The five pink petals are not joined except at the base. There are five stamens arranged opposite the petals, and five styles.

In The Burren thrift grows only along the sea coast, but despite its names, sea pink is not confined to maritime regions. I have seen *Armeria maritima* near the summits of mountains in Donegal, on the magnificent cone of Errigal and its neighbour Muckish, and small cuttings from Errigal plants flourished in my garden for many years. The flowers were rather pallid, washed-out pink, not as vivid as the bright pinks of most of the coastal plants. The colour of the corolla does vary within and between populations–deep rose-pink to almost white can be seen between Black Head and Doolin. And thrift flourishes as vigorously on the shale cliffs of south Clare.

Castle Taylor, Ardrahan

DOWN THE BOHREENS FUCHSIA-HIGH

Has it held the warm June weather?
Draining shallow sea-pools dry,
Where we bicycled together
Down the bohreens fuchsia-high.
Till there rose, abrupt and lonely,
A ruined abbey, chancel only,
Lichen-crusted, time befriended,
Soared the arches, splayed and splendid
Romanesque against the sky.

John Betjeman: 'Ireland with Emily'

The wild plants of Ireland are a strange assortment nowadays; there are species, including mountain avens, which undoubtedly have been here since the end of the last glacial epoch, and there are others that, it can be said with equal certitude, reached the island in much more recent times with the assistance of mankind. The interlopers cohabit with native 'original' species as if they always had,

243

Mycelis muralis: wall lettuce

competing for space within the landscape, and even producing hybrids that never could have arisen without the help of the human race.

For thousands of years gardening in various forms has been a necessary occupation, and in its most basic form was little more than the sowing of some grain seeds in a newly cleared piece of land. Much later gardeners began to grow plants for their curative properties; there is every likelihood that the Cistercian monks who lived at Corcomroe had a vegetable garden, one for medicinal herbs somewhere in the abbey precincts, and fields of corn; they may even have had orchards and a vineyard. Eventually, gardens were planted containing nothing but beautiful, exotic flowers of no value except as ornaments. At all stages in our horticultural progress, new plants were imported into Ireland, and with the desired plants came weeds. One result of all this activity is that mankind has unintentionally modified the wild flora of Ireland, and it is often difficult to tell whether a plant came here by wholly natural means, or whether it came as a deliberate or accidental import.[1]

The Burren contains over six hundred different flowering plants and ferns.[2] None of the ferns is an alien species. Of the flowering plants, a considerable

Cuscuta epithymum: dodder

proportion are believed to be, or are known to be exotic. In a few instances the evidence one way or the other is tantalizingly sparse and all we can do is make an educated guess about a plant's status.

Wall lettuce is one of the many enigmas of The Burren. Professor David Webb has pointed out that *Mycelis muralis* was not reported as an inhabitant of The Burren until 1939. Noting that Robert Lloyd Praeger believed wall lettuce to be an alien, Professor Webb concluded:

> I am certain that it has been widespread in the district since 1941 at latest, and still believe it may be native, but the silence of earlier writers is certainly suspicious.[3]

Mycelis muralis is one of the most common plants in The Burren, abundant on the open pavement, rooted in the scailps, anywhere a modicum of shelter and soil persists. This relative of the daisy is beautiful, especially when its leaves and tall stem is rich crimson, as is usually the case–pallid plants without any crimson flushing seldom occur. Wall lettuce is a biennial; in the summer the flowering shoots rise from a rosette of leaves that formed the previous autumn. When in bloom, the stems can be one metre or more tall, branching near the top into a bushy panicle of flowering heads. Each little head usually has five yellow florets, and each of these has a single, strap-shaped 'petal' which actually represent five fused petals. The contrast between the claret stems and the lemon-yellow flowers is alluring.

But is wall lettuce an original denizen of The Burren, a true native that arrived without any human intervention? Professor Webb has changed his opinion slightly; he hesitates no longer and affirms this plant is an alien.[4] If he is correct, *Mycelis muralis* must have been imported–by chance, perhaps–around 1930 and spread with considerable rapidity through the region. Unless evidence is discovered which demonstrates beyond doubt that wall lettuce was in The Burren before the 1930s, but so commonplace that no-one thought it worth mentioning, it is wisest to accept this considered opinion.

The case of dodder is almost as intractable. *Cuscuta epithymum* is a full parasite, which clings to thyme, bird's foot trefoil, squinancywort and bedstraw, and like the red broomrape derives its nutrients entirely from the green hosts. The haustoria are not formed on the roots below the soil surface but on the stems–they can be seen with the naked eye as pads closely pressed to the stems of the host plant. Dodder is a strange plant, resembling a tangle of fishing-line with clusters of whitish flowers strung at intervals along it; sometimes the thread-like stems are pink, sometimes they are a pallid yellow.

Dodder was discovered on the Aran Islands in 1890. In 1909 George Claridge Druce collected it 'about a mile south of Black Head', and in succeeding decades Arthur Stelfox and Dr Patrick O'Connor gathered specimens on the sand-dunes at Fanore where it may be seen to this day; David Webb published the first record of it.[5] Druce's locality was perhaps on the northern side of the esker that juts across Murroogh and is the bastion against which the Fanore dunes nestle. Dr Gerry Doyle found *Cuscuta epithymum* during 1990 in the eastern Burren not far from Lough Bunny, a new record for the area.

Is this species of dodder native? The silence of such botanists as Henry Chichester Hart who visited its Aran stations many years before 1890, is suspicious, and again suggests that this is an introduced plant. Nowhere in Ireland can dodder be said without doubt to be a native, yet it is most unlikely that a parasite was deliberately planted, certainly not where it is growing today. Accidental introduction with crop seeds is a possibility, and the other possibility remains, that it may be truly native. We will probably never solve this riddle.[6]

Dodder and wall lettuce are not the only species that perplex botanists. The remarkable wild onion, *Allium babingtonii*, that grows on the Aran Islands and around Galway Bay is closely allied to *Allium ampeloprasum*, a species native in southern Europe. At least one critical botanist, Professor William T. Stearn, is convinced that the Irish plants represent a race of *A. ampeloprasum* that evolved here following the species' introduction perhaps two thousand years ago; certain minor characters serve to distinguish the Irish populations from their parental stock. However, others disagree, questioning why a 'distinctive cultivar should have been dispersed only along the extreme Atlantic fringe of the British Isles, entirely in regions of relatively primitive agriculture, and yet never to have been cultivated there within the last 150 years.'[7]

This stately onion, with clusters of bulbils replacing most of the lavender flowers is an occasional plant in The Burren, around the harbour in Ballyvaghan, for example. To see it in its prime it is necessary to go to the Aran Islands, where it is still used as a substitute for garlic—it may not be deliberately cultivated on the islands today but the islanders do not weed it out or discourage it.

There cannot be arguments about *Fuchsia magellanica*. It is not a native Irish species, and was brought here as a garden plant.

How many different *Fuchsia* species, or cultivars are 'wild' in Ireland today? There are two distinct 'races' in hedgerows about The Burren, and indeed, throughout the west of Ireland, and they can be recognized immediately by the shape of the unopened buds. The predominant one has fat buds, the lower portion being distinctly bulbous, almost as broad as long—they can be 'popped' by pressing them between one's fingers. The buds of the less common *Fuchsia* cannot be 'popped' sonorously for they are limp and slender with a long, narrow profile. The hue of the sepals which form the buds also differs; the fat buds are bright, scarlet-red, while the slender ones are dusky.[8]

Names have been given to the fat and the slender, but there is no certainty that they are correct. *Fuchsia magellanica* var. *gracilis* is used for the race with the slender buds, and *F. magellanica* cv. Riccartonii for the plump. My opinion is that the latter is indeed correct, that fat-budded plants throughout Ireland have descended from plantings of a cultivar which was produced in Scotland in the middle of the last century. As for the name *F. magellanica* var. *gracilis*, it is perhaps

Fuchsia magellanica: fuchsia

not valid, and I think it would be better to regard the slender-budded plants simply as *Fuchsia magellanica*.

This shrub is now firmly established in the Irish countryside and innumerable visitors, unaware of its history, are deluded into thinking it is indigenous. John Betjeman's 'fuchsia-high' bohreens on the road to Drumacoo Church, with its 'fantastic mausoleum',[9] are repeated throughout the western seaboard, yet these scarlet-ribboned lanes could not have existed without the acquisitive gardeners who cossetted exotic plants and pioneered their cultivation out-of-doors. Some of the cherished exotics 'jumped the garden wall', escaped into the countryside, and become naturalized, 'more Irish than the Irish'. *Fuchsia* is not, however, really a wild plant, for it cannot spread far without human assistance. Seed is set infrequently, and seedlings are exceptionally rare–indeed there is no incontrovertible evidence of *Fuchsia magellanica* spreading by seed anywhere in Ireland except (perhaps) on the Aran Islands. So *Fuchsia* is not really a 'garden escape'; gardeners helped it over the garden fence.

There are several true garden escapees in The Burren. A pale, double-flowered columbine (*Aquilegia vulgaris*) is established on the green road east of Black Head–wild columbine is usually blue and never double-flowered. The plant known as Montbretia, a hybrid (*Crocosmia* x *crocosmiiflora*) which arose in France last century between two South African species of *Crocosmia*, infests road verges about Doolin and Ballyvaghan, to mention but two localities. The spectacle of the orange flowers in the ditches rivals the scarlet and purple droplets of *Fuchsia*. *Cotoneaster integrifolia*, a native of the Himalayas, has been known on the summit above Black Head for at least forty years, and also grows in other, quite isolated spots as at the old lead mine above Carron and on a rough track leading from Fanore to Sliabh Eilbhe. Birds love the berries and must have distributed the *Cotoneaster* to these out-of-the-way habitats.

Take the road that runs along the coast from Ballyvaghan towards Black Head. For a while you meander along the shore and then through thickets of hazel and holly. About three kilometres from Ballyvaghan pier, on the south side of the road is Tobar Chornáin, a fresh-water spring covered by a stone-built 'Gothic' well-house; the pinnacles on this folly mean that today the well is known as The Pinnacle Well.

Growing on the outside of the well-house, rooted in the mortar, are many plants of fairy foxglove, a small herb which is native in the European mountains. *Erinus alpinus* has been established on the Pinnacle Well for several decades, and is also now on rocks and pavement around, although it does not appear to have spread far from this particular site. A few years ago, Clare County Council workmen repointed the well-house and local people feared that the fairy foxgloves were doomed, but this resilient herb has slowly yet surely recolonized the mortar. Gardeners know *Erinus* well, and many an old garden contains clumps growing in similar places, rooted in the mortar of brick and stone walls. It might be classed as a weed in some gardens, for it seeds about with impunity.

A green road curls around the brow of Black Head tracing one of the natural terraces high above the modern road and the lighthouse. Fairy foxgloves are also established on the cliffs thereabouts–they were first spotted over fifty years ago at this locality by Mrs. Verschoyle. How they got there, who brought them there, are unanswerable questions.

Erinus alpinus: fairy foxglove

I might add, not to illuminate the riddle, that Patrick O'Kelly offered fairy foxgloves for sale in the mid-1890s–a single plant cost seven pence, or a dozen for five shillings, more than he charged for the same quantities of Spring gentians! That does not mean he sowed seeds of it at Black Head, but we do know that at least one person grew *Erinus alpinus* in Clare a century ago.

Portal dolmen, Poulnabrone

BEHOLD THE EARTH APPARELLED
WITH PLANTS

*For if delight may provoke mens labor, what greater delight is there than to behold the
earth apparelled with plants, as with a robe of embroidered worke, set with Orient
pearles, and garnished with great diversitie of rare and costly iewels?*

John Gerard: *The Herball or Generall Historie of plantes.* 1597[1]

I have visited The Burren when Spring gentians are in bloom, at Christmastide
when the pyramids of holly glitter with hoarfrost, during the autumnal equinox
as the wind begins to remove the leaves from the trees, and in high summer when
the pageant of flowers is at its grandest. John Gerard's 'earth apparelled' with plants
like pearls and costly jewels is an apt metaphor for The Burren in summer.

Each season, every month, is as exciting and interesting as the month and the
season past, and each promises rewarding times to come. Yet there is a prevailing
notion, even among botanists, that May is the *only* month during which flowers
blossom on the limestone hills of Clare, that there is nothing, *absolutely nothing*,
to see in The Burren for eleven months of the year. This myth undoubtedly arises
from the singular, hypnotic elan of the Spring gentian, and The Burren is
thereby ill-served.

The Burren blazes with colour in summer: to be sure the Spring gentians–true
to their name–have furled their blue petals and become invisible, but other

plants are blooming in their stead. My notebooks are filled by memoranda of summers past, of shimmering hazes patterned with small fields, of harebells and purple loosestrife, roses red and white, of bees murmuring on the field scabious and a young fox bouncing through long grass, of a quiet sanctuary with its bubbling stream and the fresh smell of water-mint, of cool hazel copses full of green ferns and golden poppies, and under skylark descants, softly carolled "Wo-coo... Wo-coo..." floating over thistledown and turlough.

Frederick Foot spent most of 1861 walking the limestone pavements and vividly declaimed the red and white and blue of the season of gentians; he may be forgiven for omitting to sing the praises of the other colours for after all he was studying the grey rocks. Thomas Corry spent only a few days in the area during July and was charmed, so much so that he exclaimed

> The fields appeared one blaze of flowers, some cornfields especially reminding me, by the brilliancy and varied hues of their colouring, of Gustave Doré's admirable picture entitled "The Prairie"; one especially so, a field of golden wheat, amid which rose one blaze of silk and scarlet flame, due to the splendid flowers of the Corn Poppy. Along with these were mingled the light blue heads of the Field Scabious.[2]

Corn fields are part of the bygone days, the history of The Burren. Nowadays the small, stone-walled fields have been merged with their neighbours into large, uniform pastures empty of wild flowers. The few little meadows that have survived are usually maintained as hay-fields, cut during late summer in the old manner, the golden hay stacked in ricks; cowslips, orchids and field scabious thrive in them, and should survive as long as the pasture is not ploughed, fertilized and sown with modern grass cultivars. While corn fields have been replaced by emerald greensward, the flowers that Thomas Corry and Frederick Foot saw still abound on the green roads, in the verges of by-roads, and throughout the broad expanses of natural herb-field and rough mountainy grazing on the patches of good soil on gentler slopes.

Many of the finest and best of The Burren's flora can only be spied by trudging–which sounds like drudgery, but never is–along the old trackways and getting into places where the most recent bipedal visitors are likely to have been skylarks. Yet the verges of the tarmacadamed highways are still bedecked with lots of interesting plants in summer–even from a motor car, and especially from a bicycle, there are countless possibilities of seeing a surprising array of plants.

One of the finest views in the eastern quarter of The Burren is from Carcair na gCléireach (Corker Pass, correctly Pass of the clerks) that links Beal an Chloga and Corcomroe with the main Kinvarra road. Where a green road meets the main road, there is a easterly prospect of the southern shore of Galway Bay from Oranmore over Kinvarra, a pattern of islands in a maze of bays. Drumlins are crisscrossed with hedges and walls, and the little fields sometimes have hay-ricks. The bays hold sparkling blue water.

Stranding proud above the hum-drum greenery of hedges which by July are drab except for flowering brambles, are spikes of blue about as thick as a thumb and as long. They do not hide, and will tantalize as you speed past in a car. Taking time to stop, and a closer look, the blue candles are composed of perhaps forty small pea flowers, each a wonderful blue with tints of purple especially on the inner face of the standard (upper) petal.

Vicia cracca, tufted vetch, is a member of the pea and bean family (Fabaceae or Leguminosae), a relative of clovers and bird's-foot trefoil, but differs most noticeably in having an elongated inflorescence, and tendrils at the tips of the leaves. The leaves are not trifoliate, but spleenwort-like, with opposite pairs (usually six to a dozen) of small leaflets, each narrowly elliptical and perhaps one and a half centimetres long; the leaflets nearest the base of each leaf are the longest. Where the terminal leaflet should be is a branching set of watch-spring tendrils that will coil tightly around any twigs or stems that they touch, so enabling vetch to climb through blackthorn and bramble and to flaunt those blue flowers at passers-by. Like all leguminous plants, the fruits are pods, like those of bird's-foot trefoil and garden peas. *Vicia cracca* is named *peasair na luch*, mouse pea; I suppose the tiny seeds–the pods contain up to half a dozen–just the right size of a pea for a wood mouse's lunch.

Tufted vetch is a common perennial on calcareous soils and is a familiar species throughout Ireland, in hedgerows and grassy places; it ranges throughout temperate parts of Europe and Asia from the Atlantic seaboard to the Pacific.

In the verges of the green road is a haze of lavender and claret during July and August: wild marjoram (*Origanum vulgare*) in blossom shaded from white–there is an 'albino' clump on the New Line–to dark burgundy with purple undertones. Marjoram flowers are enhanced by contrast with grey walls and green foliage, and that combination of colours ensures this plant is conspicuous. Plants with deep green leaves tend to have dark red calyx segments complementing a paler corolla, while the clumps with pale pink flowers usually have light green leaves.

Vicia cracca: tufted vetch

Marjoram, like wild thyme (*Thymus praecox*), is a member of the dead nettle family (Lamiaceae) and both are characteristic plants of well-drained lime-rich soils. They are not confined to The Burren, occurring in suitable habitats throughout Ireland. However the abundance and luxuriance of wild marjoram along road sides in The Burren is not repeated in many other localities nowadays; this herb has suffered from modern methods of road verge management. In the 1720s Dr Threlkeld was moved to exclaim that he had never seen marjoram grow so tall in England.

For centuries marjoram has been prized as a healing herb: 'it is good for the Breast and Liver, comforts the Head and Nerves.' The dried leaves were infused to make a tea, and oil distilled from marjoram, according to Caleb Threlkeld, 'helps the Tooth-ach'.[3]

Origanum vulgare (*Máirtín fiáin*) is a creeping perennial with deciduous shoots; it survives the winter as a network of underground rhizomes. The four-sided stems rise about a third of a metre high, and the flowers are borne in a lax, branched panicle at the tip of each shoot. The softly hairy leaves are oval, arranged in opposite

254

Origanum vulgare: marjoram

pairs along the stems, and rarely are they larger than a thumb-nail. The calyx formed from five equal sepals can be tinged with reddish-green, while some plants have dark burgundy sepals. The five petals are fused into a funnel-shaped, two-lipped corolla that is typical of some members of the Lamiaceae. Each individual blossom is little more than half a centimetre long, and each should have four straight stamens, two protruding prominently from the mouth and two much shorter. Occasional inflorescences have a small proportion of female flowers, with no stamens and corollas shorter than usual.

Wandering through the meadows in August I am always amazed that one of the most conspicuous plants is selfheal (*Prunella vulgaris*), a herb that in another place could be a weed. So vigorous and so colourful, Burren selfheals can be mistaken for exotic orchids. *Prunella vulgaris* belongs to the same family as wild marjoram–Lamiaceae–and has that family's diagnostic four-cornered stem and opposite pairs of leaves. The flowers are in a tiered spike, and in general each tier of the spike has six flowers; the inflorescences of the most robust plants are composed of five or six tiers. The corolla is deep purple-blue, the upper lip hooded, and each separate blossom is cupped in a two-lipped, dark red calyx. Unlike *Origanum*, the stamens in *Prunella* do not protrude but are contained within the flower, the anthers held underneath the upper lip of the corolla.

To selfheal is attributed the virtue of healing wounds and curing sore throats. Dr Threlkeld was restrained: 'Serviceable for Wounds and Ulcers is restringent; used in *Fevers*, and for Gargles.'[4] In Donegal the plants is known as heart's ease, while the Irish names include *duan ceannchosach–duan* is a kidney, and *ceannchosach* might literally be translated as spongy ankle, whatever that may signify.

Prunella vulgaris does not grow in drifts like wild marjoram, and where it is especially abundant–at Poll Salach, for example, between the road and the ocean–the individuals are often concealed by the rank foliage of the lush summer grasses.

Flowers tall enough to rise above the other greenery and wave in the breeze can colour a landscape. None of The Burren's herbs does this more spectacularly, to my mind, than devil's-bit scabious (*Succisa pratensis*)–as long as plenty of rain has fallen, the green roads shimmer in royal blue as the devil's bit blossoms in late summer.

I feel a particular affection for this scabious and its fellow members of the teasel family, Dipsacaceae, as that was the group of plants Dr Thomas Coulter of Dundalk studied before he travelled to Mexico and California. He spent sixteen months, from May 1822 until September 1823, working in Geneva at the herbarium of Augustin-Pyramus de Candolle seeking to understand and classify scabious and its relatives. He reassigned species to more appropriate genera, and thus his name is often appended to the plants' correct Latin names–for example *Knautia arvensis* (L.) Coulter signifies that it was the Dundalk botanist who recognized that Linnaeus' species *Scabiosa arvensis* really belonged in *Knautia*, not *Scabiosa*, and he published that opinion.

Thomas Coulter surely was familiar with devil's bit scabious in the mountainy pasture around Dundalk; it is common throughout Ireland, inhabiting meadowlands on both acid and alkaline soils yet nowhere does it grow in such profusion as in The Burren.

Succisa pratensis is a perennial herb with a short, truncated taproot–botanists describe such a root as premorse, that is 'as if bitten off'. Devil's bit scabious hibernates as a rosette of dark green, slightly hairy leaves. The flowering stems start to elongate in the midsummer and by August they can be half a metre tall–in a particularly dry season, like that of 1990, the stems remain quite short. The main stalks are tinged with dark purple, but the hemispherical head of young buds is green. As the buds develop a crimson hue caps the head, and then in late summer the flowers begin to open from the rim inwards to the centre. Each floret has a tubular corolla with four lobes, and four stamens with light blue filaments carrying red anthers.

Inflorescences are unisexual or hermaphrodite.[5] In hermaphrodite heads, long filaments hold the anthers high above the corolla. In the unisexual heads–the flowers will be female–the anthers are small, white and hardly visible above the rim of the corolla. Devil's bit flowers generally are royal blue, but there are rare exceptions. I have seen pale pink and even a few pure white ones–in the latter, the red anthers are especially striking.

Morsus diaboli is the mediaeval name for this beautiful plant–literally translated it is 'bite of the devil', and of course alludes to the rootstock's bitten-off appearance; according to legend, Satan, jealous of possible benefits the species might yield to the human race, bit away some of its root.[6] *Urach bhallach* is the Irish synonym, and like many Gaelic names, the translation into English is apparently nonsensical for it means spotted greenery.

Devil's bit is reputed to make you sweat–it is a sudorific herb. Herbalists, including the famous Nicholas Culpepper, asserted that scabious could be used also against plague, worms, wind, fever, and the bites of venomous beasts, etcetera. Caleb Threlkeld was not one to pass over religious allusions lightly: 'This is a great sudorifick' he declaimed,

> the Name *Devils-bit* made that Scribbler *Colepepper* Drol upon the ignorant *Fryars*, who say the Root was once longer, until the Devil bit away the rest of it for spite, for he needed it not to make him sweat, who is always tormented with fear of the Day of Judgement.'[7]

Presumably Threlkeld used devil's-bit in the remedies he prescribed to his patients, and he did affirm that the herb was 'good to dissolve congealed Blood, and therefore serviceable against the ill Effects of Falls and Bruises...'

Knautia arvensis, field scabious differs from devil's bit scabious in a number of crucial characters, and these were recognized by Thomas Coulter as meriting its removal from the genus *Scabiosa*. For example, in *Knautia* the calyx has eight or more teeth, whereas the calyx of *Scabiosa* consistently has just five; in *Knautia* the receptacle is hemispherical and hairy, but in *Scabiosa* it is elongated and devoid

Succisa pratensis
devil's-bit scabious

Prunella vulgaris
selfheal

Knautia arvensis
field scabious

of hairs. The most obvious difference between *Knautia arvensis* and *Succisa pratensis* is in flower colour and size–the field scabious has delicate lavender-blue heads which are about twice the diameter of those of the devil's bit. Moreover, the flower heads of field scabious are fluffier, less compact, due in part to the longer, irregular petal-lobes of the outer florets–in devil's bit the individual florets are all equally lobed and the same size and so they form a neat, compact inflorescence.

Field scabious is a perennial herb with a descending tap-root that is not 'bitten off'. The winter rosette is composed of simple leaves although a few may be divided. The flowering stems can be a metre tall and the stem leaves, arranged in opposite pairs, are usually deeply divided with opposite, linear, lateral lobes and an elliptical terminal lobe.

Among the vernacular names for field scabious is gipsy rose; the Irish name is *cab an ghasáin*, and it is also known as cardies. As for the name scabious, there are unpleasant connotations because the word has the same root as scabies–*scabiosa herba* is an old phrase-name, the herb for curing scabies, scab, itch, and according to Threlkeld 'it takes black and blew Markes out of the skin'. And, if you are one of the Irish abroad, remember that scabious is a remedy against 'the bitings of serpents'. Incidentally *Knautia* commemorates a German botanist, Christoph Knaut.

Dipsacaceae–teasels, scabious and their relatives–resemble the daisies and other members of Asteraceae (or Compositae) in possessing composite heads (capituli) of small flowers. Teasels and their congeners can quickly be recognized by the prominently exserted stamens and anthers; in Asteraceae (the daisy family) the anthers are on short filaments and are furthermore joined by their sides forming a collar around the style. Among The Burren's flora, there are several herbs, called knapweeds, looking like scabious, but belonging to the daisy family and the similarity in floral form is underlined by a confusing overlap in vernacular names. In some parts of Ireland knapweeds are called bachelor's buttons, a name also used, and more frequently so, for devil's bit and field scabious. No wonder botanists do their best to avoid using common names!

By coining the Latin name *Centaurea scabiosa* Carl Linnaeus was clearly seeking to draw attention to the superficial similarities between this *Centaurea* species and *Scabiosa*, while rejecting the mistaken views of earlier botanists who thought it was just a large scabious and used the name *Scabiosa major*.

The colour of the blossoms of greater knapweed is sumptuous purple; an occasional plant has flowers that seem to have more red in the petals, making the tone even richer. A variant with lavender-pink blossoms that I know from Poulnalour is quite eccentric and very uncommon. *Centaurea scabiosa* is a stately perennial, growing at least a metre tall in the rich Burren loam. The leaves are deeply lobed with opposite segments which may sometimes also be pinnatifid; they are rich green, and often glossy. The flower-heads, composed of two different types of floret, are about four centimetres in diameter. In the centre of each capitulum is a cluster of hermaphrodite, tubular florets from which emerge styles surrounded by dark anther collars; the petals making up the corolla tube are narrow and remain fused for most of their length. Larger, sterile florets with longer and broader petals make up the outer ring; there is no emerging style and the petals separate for about half their length. The stiff, almost woody bracts encrusting each capitulum have pale bristles around the margins, so the flower-buds seem paler than those of common knapweed.

The filaments of the stamens are sensitive to touch, contracting by several millimetres. When an insect touches a stamen, the filament bends, pulling down the collar of anthers which rubs against hairs on the style, jut below the stigma branches, so that some of the pollen is brushed on to the insect. Once the insect departs, the filaments relax slowly and the collar returns to its original position, and the process can be repeated. The stigma is not receptive at this stage; slowly the style elongates through the collar, and the lobes of the stigma separate so that the flower can be pollinated.[8]

Greater knapweed is not widespread in Ireland; it is absent from northern counties but occurs in scattered localities in the east and south. The principal concentration of populations is on the limestone soils of Galway and Clare–The Burren is the stronghold of *Centaurea scabiosa*. In Britain greater knapweed is most abundant on the chalk downs of south-eastern England.

The heads of common knapweed are not as large as those of the greater knapweed, and the colour of the florets tends to purple more than to crimson. In general, *Centaurea nigra* does not have an outer ring of sterile flowers with long petals; all the florets are fertile and hermaphrodite. Hardhead is an apt name for this species and alludes to the tightly bracts-encased buds which look like pine cones and feel woody; the margins of the upper portion of each bract is coarsely fringed with black teeth. *Centaurea nigra* is a shorter herb than greater knapweed; the ribbed stems rise about half a metre tall from a rosette of soft, hairy leaves that usually are entire.

Centaurea scabiosa
greater knapweed

Centaurea nigra
knapweed

Leucanthemum vulgare
ox-eye daisy

Achillea millefolium
yarrow

Common knapweed is widespread in Ireland, Britain and Europe, on acid and alkaline soils. Both *Centaurea scabiosa* and *Centaurea nigra* are variable species, and botanists in Europe often divide them into clusters of microspecies.

Mínscoth (suggesting a fine blossom) and *mínscoth mór* are the Irish synonyms for common and greater knapweeds respectively, but in some sources *mullach dubh*, meaning black top, is also used. As I mentioned earlier, bachelor's buttons is a name once used in Ireland, and if the traditions are upheld, a young girl should gather a bunch of knapweeds (or one of the other bachelor's buttons) in bud, give each one the name of one of her sweethearts, and when the bachelor's buttons blossom the one that blooms finest represents her future husband.

The daisy family contributes many colours to the summer tapestry of The Burren. On the coastal rocks are lavender sea asters (*Aster tripolium*). White-and-yellow sea mayweed (*Tripleurospermum maritimum*) marks the storm line on the sandy shores at Bishop's Quarter. The spindly stems of sneezewort (*Achillea ptarmica*) topped by white flowers lurk in the damper patches near some eastern loughs. And there are hawkweeds, dandelions and wall lettuce (*Mycelis muralis*) everywhere.

One of the great displays in The Burren is massed ox-eye daisies, *Leucanthemum vulgare*; in Irish, appropriately, ox-eye is called *nóinín mór*, the big daisy. They begin to bloom in late May. Along the coast road, a little west of Ballyvaghan, clouds of ox-eyes almost smother the stone walls. Elsewhere they mingle with knapweeds and ladies bedstraw, yarrow and harebells in exuberant, natural herbaceous borders that no gardener can emulate.

Leucanthemum has flower-heads that conform to the pattern for the family. There is an outer series white ray florets that are female; the strap-like, solitary 'petal' is actually composed of five, linear petals fused together. The disc florets are hermaphrodite with a bright yellow tubular corolla, again formed from five fused petals. In this genus ray and disc florets are capable of setting seed–each yields a single, pale grey, markedly ribbed achene (a one-seeded fruit). Unlike the achenes of dandelions and thistles, the ox-eye daisy achene does not have a parachute and so the species is not distributed by wind.

Yarrow, *Achillea millefolium*, is also a member of Asteraceae, but the structure of its flower-head is different. Instead of a single inflorescence on a solitary stalk, there are numerous individual small heads aggregated in a flat corymb. As in daisies, the outer florets in each little head are female with a single broad ray–usually there are five ray-florets in a head. The inner florets are tubular, hermaphrodite and white, or creamy. Yarrow flowers are white or pink or rose-coloured–the colour range is similar to that in cat's-paw, with white the predominant tone.

The aromatic foliage of yarrow is unmistakeable; the leaves are about ten centimetres long, lance shaped, and very finely divided. Yarrow leaves have been used medicinally for centuries–they contain alkaloids including achillein, and their characteristic fragrance is produced by volatile oils. From time immemorial, yarrow has been regarded as a magical plant, used in amulets to ward off evil spirits, and there are numerous incantations involving it. Fabulous properties were imputed to yarrow, yet some of its reputation may not be so far-fetched; modern research suggests that the array of complex chemicals in yarrow includes some with known anti-inflammatory properties. Yarrow was a woundwort particularly useful in healing injuries caused by iron–swords and spears–and to alleviate piles and stop bleeding.[9]

In Ireland yarrow is one of the herbs of St John's Day, 24 June, a most significant festival in the Irish folk-calendar, in essence, although not exactly, Midsummer Day. The eve is still marked in parts of Ireland by the lighting of bonfires and in former time herbs were gathered before sunrise when the dew was still on them. The herbs of St John were orpine, ivy, vervain, yarrow, mugwort, Danewort, great plantain, corn marigold, and St John's wort itself.[10] There is no shortage of most of these in the barony of Burren: ivy is everywhere and vervain, a wispy, tall herb with tiny lavender flowers, can be found about Corcomroe; St John's worts are common herbs of road sides and pastureland as is the great plantain. Corn marigold and mugwort, both members of the daisy family, are plants of waste ground, and seem now almost restricted to the Aran Islands. Danewort is not a native plant yet there are patches on the roadside not far from Béal an Chloga and also in Cahergrillaun townland among other places–its Latin name is *Sambucus ebulus* and it is a relative of elder (*Sambucus nigra*), but instead of being a woody shrub, Danewort is a tall, erect herb with flat panicles of white purple-anthered flowers.

Like St John's wort (*Hypericum* spp.) yarrow was cut by moonlight with a black-handled knife[11] for use either as an ingredient of medicines or as a love-herb. Girls used it, placing it beneath their pillows at night, to provoke dreams of husbands; as they gathered the herb they had to recite this incantation.

Good morrow, good yarrow, good morrow to thee
Send me this night my true love to see
The clothes that he'll wear, the colour of his hair
And if he'll wed me.[12]

Dr Threlkeld, if he knew about this, makes no mention of love songs, only that yarrow 'is cooling, drying and binding; and extolled by some in benign *Gonorrhaea's*'. He recorded its Irish name, *athair thalún* ('Ahair Talhum')–creeper of the ground–which John Cameron suggested was a corruption of *earr thalmhainn*[13]–that which clothes the earth, a name that would not be inappropriate, in the context of The Burren, for harebell.

Among all my summer memories of walking in The Burren, one of the most enduring is of an afternoon at the beginning of August 1987. There were fluffy clouds in the sky but they were fleeting. As I rambled over the mountain I spotted a solitary tuft of harebells sprouting from a dark scailp. There were no other flowers in sight. The colour of the delicate bells was the colour of the bright sky; the green stems were an irrelevance. On the plateau of Cappanawalla, the scorched, grey limestone spread to a horizon delineated by a stone wall, one of those gossamer walls that let the wind through–but there was not even a breath of wind that day. The world within my view was serene, and its colours were grey and white and harebell blue.

Even looking into the nodding, five-lobed bell that simple palette of colours is not outraged. The ovary at the base is white, and the style a darker shade of blue. The five stamens have greatly enlarged, bulbous bases and elongated anthers. Before the bells open, pollen is shed onto the style, and the stamens wither so that pollen is presented on the style to any visiting wasps, bees or hoverflies that come searching for the nectar. At this time, and for several days following, the harebell's three stigmas are not receptive. Nectar is trapped deep in the bell beneath the bulbous bases of the filaments so the insects have to work hard for their food–as they do so, pollen is dusted on to their backs. After a few days the stigmas become mature and they separate slowly and curl back so that when a pollen-laden bee enters the flower, it dusts grains onto a stigma. If pollination does not happen the coiling style branches will eventually curl back so far that they touch the style and self-pollination takes place. *Campanula rotundifolia* thus does not rely entirely on insects to ensure its reproduction.

August roadsides are hazy blue, a lovely, caerulean carillon of harebells. Seed is ripe from September and is shed from the capsules through small pores. The seeds lie dormant over winter, germinating in spring; by May there are clusters of seedling harebells everywhere. A good crop of seedlings each year is important because *Campanula rotundifolia* is a short-lived perennial. The basal leaves have heart-shaped blades–not round as the Latin name suggests–on long stalks, while the leaves on the flowering stems are linear and sessile.

It is not wise to pick harebells; like thorn trees, these flowers are protected by the 'Little People' by goblins, fairies and witches.[14] Scotch bluebell and harebell may be the preferred vernacular names nowadays, but *Campanula rotundifolia* is also witch-bells and witch-thimbles, and the devil's bell. *Brog na cubhaig*, a Gaelic phrase meaning cuckoo's shoe, is another of its names although this has been bestowed on corn-cockle (*Agrostemma githago*) and butterwort (*Pinguicula vulgaris*) also. *Méaracán gorm* (blue thimble) and *méaracán púca* are two Irish synonyms; the first is its accepted one nowadays, and the second can be translated as goblin's thimble. Why the harebell was malevolent, a goblin plant, is not explained by surviving lore. It would not be a bad thing to propagate the idea that harebell-gatherers will come to no good, even though there is no scarcity of harebells during a Burren August.

Nor is there a shortage of lady's bedstraw: Reginald Farrer included it among 'the whole department of a lady's plenishing', with ladies' tresses and lady's fingers. *Galium verum* carpets the green roads from wall to wall, and froths along the verges of tracks; on the hills it dances in the breeze with harebells and heathers. Lady's bedstraw and *Asperula cynanchica* (squinancywort) are constant associates on calcareous dunes at Fanore and Bishop's Quarter.

Lady's bedstraw is a member of the family Rubiaceae which also encompasses madder (*Rubia*), and *Asperula*. The genera have four-cornered stems, and similar floral structure, yet are easy to tell apart. Madder is a bulkier plant than lady's bedstraw and squinancywort, with broader stem, longer shoots and larger leaves; it has green flowers and black, juicy fruits. Squinancywort is a diminutive, rock-hugging herb usually with prostrate stems, and pink and white petals. Lady's bedstraw has fluffy spikes of minute yellow flowers, and needle-leaves arranged in whorls on stems that sprout from a creeping rootstock. Small insects act as pollinators; they are attracted by the sweet honey-like perfume that is particularly intense on still, humid evenings, and simply by crawling over the inflorescence they carry pollen grains from flower to flower on their feet.

Lady's bedstraw has several well-attested uses. For centuries it was employed as a rennet-plant for curdling milk so that cheese could be produced, but the use

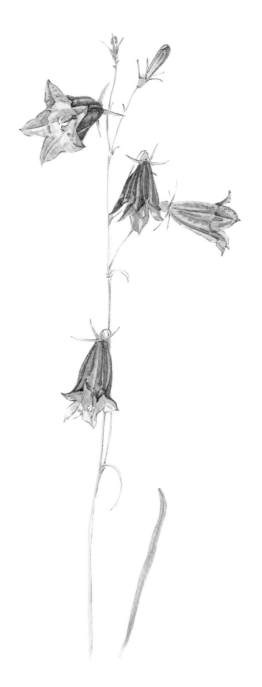

Campanula rotundifolia
harebell

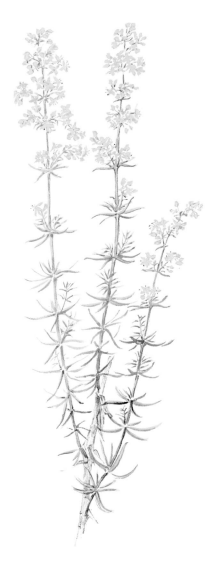

Galium verum
Lady's bedstraw

seems to have died out. Like madder, the fine rhizomes yield a red dye, and the dried foliage, with the fragrance of hay, was literally bed-straw.[15] The Irish name means scent of the skin, *boladh chnis*, but what that refers to, who knows?

There are seven species of *Galium* in The Burren, but only *Galium verum* has yellow flowers. Frederick Foot recorded lady's bedstraw as 'everywhere', and he was the first to find northern bedstraw (*Galium boreale*), a white-blossomed species that frequents turlough margins and flushes.[16]

There is a herb-meadow at the foot of Cinn Aille that surely has been grazed perhaps for centuries. Towards the end of summer, the grasses are almost smothered by flowers–blue devil's-bit scabious and white grass of Parnassus are the most memorable, although yarrow, knapweeds and lady's mantle are also plentiful.

Grass of Parnassus, *fionnscoth*, the fair blossom, is not a grass (in botanical terms, *Parnassia* does not belong to Poaceae or Monocotyledones): 'Called a Grass from fatning of Cattle, as is supposed, for otherwise it has no Affinity with that Tribe', wrote Caleb Threlkeld.[17] *Parnassia* occupies, according to some botanists, a family of its own, Parnassiaceae, and is allied to the saxifrages; like vetch, bedstraw, primrose and saxifrage, grass of Parnassus is a dicotyledon. The misnomer with its undertones of heroic Greece was an ancient misidentification by the general company of apothecary-botanists, made permanent by the Flemish botanist Mathias de L'Obel (who is commemorated in *Lobelia*). The early botanists believed this white-blossomed herb was the same as one their Classical predecessors said came from Mount Parnassus, home of Apollo and The Muses, but *Parnassia palustris*, while it is native in Greece as well as most of western and northern Europe, is not an inhabitant of that sacred mountain. The Latin name remains attached to the wrong plant, and cannot be altered.

Grass of Parnassus is a perennial herb, dying down in winter, and in full flower in August. The stalked leaves, with heart-shaped blades, yellow-green or sea-green, form a neat rosette. The beautiful flowers are borne on solitary, five-winged stems that are clasped above the base by a single, stalkless, heart-shaped leaf. At the tip of each stalk is a single, upward-looking bloom, a delicate saucer of five overlapping white petals lined with darkly translucent veins. Lying on the petals and alternating with them are fringes of white with glisters of gold at their tips; these are staminodes–modified, infertile stamens–and each has about thirteen gold-tipped filaments. The exact nature of the golden tips is not clear–they are often described as glands, but are better termed pseudo-nectaries because they do not secrete nectar and may be deceptive lures.[18] In *Parnassia* five fertile stamens with yellow anthers and white filaments, are arranged opposite each petal. In the centre is a solitary ovary which may be pale green or tinted delicately with pink–after pollination this forms the fruit and then is honey-coloured.

Grass of Parnassus is a variable plant; several subspecies are described as well as a number of ecologically distinct variants including one from dune slacks with shorter flowering stems yet larger blossoms–the dune subspecies is not reported from The Burren where, in any case, pristine dune slacks are few and far between. Dr Threlkeld knew *Parnassia* from wet places at Inchicore, west of Dublin, and I knew it in Fermanagh too, as a plant of lough shores and damp flushes. In The Burren, grass of Parnassus behaves in the same, predictable manner, inhabiting the damper places of The Burren such as turlough margins, for it does tend to like a constant supply of water.

Two true grasses–member of Poaceae (or Graminae)–stand out in the rockscape of Burren. Blue grass (*Sesleria albicans*) has characteristic stumpy flower-heads. Quaking grass also has distinctive spikes but they are loosely branched and at the tip of each of the arms is a small heart-shaped purse of flowers. So slender are the branchlets that even in the softest breeze they quiver, or as John Gerard noted, 'it is not possible with the most stedfast hand to hold it from shaking'[19]–hence the English name, quakers or quaking grass. *Gramen tremulum phalaris pratensis* was the old polynomial, the trembling grass of the meadows. Doddering dickies sums it all up nicely.

Briza media is a perennial grass, and it is ubiquitous where there is a fair depth of soil and grazing is light. The leaves are hairless, slender and blunt, up to about fifteen centimetres long and less than one half a centimetre wide. Flower spikes begin to sprout from the leaf-tuft in late May, and by June they have fluffed out and the spikelets can begin to dance on windy days. Each flattened spikelet is composed of a set of six to a dozen overlapped florets; when fresh they are shiny and purple tinted. At flowering time, the three fragile stamens elongate and protrude from the head of florets so that the pollen is released into the air; later the two, hairy styles emerge to catch pollen grains wafted from some neighbouring doddering dickie.

By August, quaking grass has ripened seed and taken on the colour of hay, light gold; the panicles still shiver in the breeze. These dainty relics of summer persist through autumn until flattened by winter storms.

Parnassia palustris
grass of Parnassus

Briza media
quaking grass

273

For all its elegance, *Briza media* is not an important species in natural pasture. For ages farmers have known that they cannot feed many cows on a field of quaking grass. In his exemplary *An essay on the indigenous grasses of Ireland*, John White, undergardener in the Glasnevin Botanic Gardens recorded that quaking grass was

> Common on sides of hills, in pastures, and in meadows. This grass is of no great worth, either as a pasture, or for meadows. It is not very prolific in stems, neither are they very high: the leaves are but short, nor do they hold their verdure long: and, in short, it has very little to recommend it except the beauty of its panicle. Cows, sheep and goats eat it.[20]

The native name for *Briza media* is *féar gortach*, hungry grass. Is it the true hungry grass?

The hungry grass is a very unlucky plant especially to those unfortunates who tread on it. It is a fantasy, a mirage of a plant; we cannot assign a name to it.

> It cannot be distinguished from other kinds of grass; it grows on the spot where some poor wretch died of starvation in the bad times, and when you step on it you too suffer the pangs of famine. Experienced men often carried a bread crust in their pockets as a precaution, for the smallest morsel of food banished the hunger pain.[21]

Wind-tossed whitethorn by wall: Glenisheen townland

AMONG THE STONES ABOVE THE ASH

It is a whisper among the hazel bushes;
It is a long, low, whispering voice that fills
With a sad music the bending and swaying rushes;
It is a heart-beat deep in the quiet hills.

Seamus O'Sullivan: 'The Twilight People'

The retreat of glaciers and the return of warm-water currents to the north-western reaches of the Atlantic Ocean brought to a close an 'ice age' that had lasted about sixty thousand years. Although often thought of as a single, uniform glacial epoch, the climate actually fluctuated with relatively warmer periods interspersed by very severe ones. Most of Ireland was covered by ice at some time; any small areas which were perpetually ice-free endured permafrost and only the hardiest plants survived, lichens, perhaps some mosses, a scattering of annual herbs and maybe several ground-hugging perennials that could flower and set seeds during the short, frigid summer. Trees, shrubs and larger perennials were absent. Thus few, indeed perhaps none of the flowering plants native today in Ireland were growing even near the coast throughout the last 'ice age'.

275

As the ice-bound conditions ameliorated gradually, more plants were able to colonize those moraines and rocky screes being uncovered as the glaciers vanished. The hardiest species migrated northwards in the wake of the melting–similar events take place at the present day in, for example, western Norway where mountain glaciers are retreating and advancing on a lesser scale. Thus, twelve thousand years ago, the heaps of gravel and clay dumped by glaciers at Fanore (where the Caher River disgorges nowadays), about Béal an Chloga, and below Glasgeivnagh Hill, were open habitats for pioneer 'Arctic' plants–mountain avens, dwarf birch, creeping juniper and crowberry, alpine willows, purple saxifrage–to invade and colonize. Such perennial herbs and prostrate shrubs still had to survive frosty conditions, even in The Burren; more robust shrubs and tall trees could not have thriven in the early post-glacial millennia.[1]

Warming proceeded. The massive ice sheets melted, returning water to the sea so that the level of the world's oceans rose more than one hundred metres. The Atlantic Ocean reclaimed the western continental shelf, inundated the land between Scotland and Ulster, and between Wales and Leinster, reforming the Irish Sea and isolating Ireland from Britain and the European mainland again. The rising ocean waters stopped the invasion of Ireland by plants and animals from southern Europe, but not before some trees, shrubs and herbs had established populations within Irish territory. To invade Ireland after the Irish Sea interposed between Ireland and Britain, all land-dwelling animals and plants had to negotiate that 'water jump'–few succeeded, and so the Irish flora and fauna is impoverished compared with that of Britain.[2]

Woodlands are the natural climax of the progression through scrubby patches of birch and alder from the Arctic herbfields that established on moraines and drumlins immediately following the glacial retreat. When the climate was congenial for shrubs and trees to colonize The Burren, juniper and birch were the first to appear, and soon Scots pine and hazel came into the region, quickly followed by aspen, alder, oak, willow and wych elm.[3]

How do we know that this sequence? All flowering plants (from oaks to daisies) and gymnosperms (juniper and Scots pine, for example) produce pollen grains–they are the male reproductive cells. Each microscopic pollen grain has an imperishable, ornamented, waxy, outer casing so tough that in most environmental conditions it is indestructible. By examining a grain with a microscope its distinctive form and size allow botanists to identify the parent species.

Pollen grains engulfed in layers of peat are especially well preserved, and when extracted layer by horizontal layer, the sequence of different pollen types, and their proportional frequencies, can be used to reconstruct a history of the vegetation in the surrounding region. Every undisturbed bog in Ireland is a gigantic sandwich of pollen, an archive of the vegetation, a 'book' that can be read by botanists, one layer representing a 'page' in the history of our indigenous flora and of human interference with the post-glacial wilderness.

Pollen grains are tiny and many are dispersed by wind–this is especially true of native tree species including yew, Scots pine, ash, birch and hazel. Because pollen can be blown considerable distances from parent plants, the pollen sequence from a peat bog must be interpreted with great care, but studies of present-day vegetation types and their characteristic 'pollen rain' allow botanists to reconstruct general and regional patterns and changes in, for example, the woodland flora. Although there are no deep peat bogs within the karst area of The Burren, the vegetation history of The Burren can be reconstructed by analysis of pollen profiles from bogs in the vicinity, and by studying other undisturbed sediment sequences such as those in the Carron polje, and the loughs about Mullach Mór.[4] The meagre pollen record for north-western Clare suggests that throughout the mildest part of the post-glacial period, The Burren was abundantly wooded, with open pine forest and hazel scrub and, for a time, yew woodland; elm and oak were also plentiful at least in lowland, eastern parts. Open areas also existed for the pollen sequences include herbs and grasses; exposed cliffs and mountain tops, and areas near the coast probably never supported forests but were the strongholds of the beautiful dwarf shrubs and herbs that abound today.

Throughout the glacial epoch and for a couple of thousand years after the ice vanished, Ireland was uninhabited. Man made landfall at least nine thousand years ago; in the north of Ireland at Mount Sandel, a few kilometres south of Coleraine, there is a settlement dating from c. 9000 to c. 8500 years ago (c. 7010 to c. 6490 BC). The first settlers survived by foraging for edible plants, fishing and trapping wild animals including pig and hare.[5] The impact of these earliest human settlers on the natural environment was negligible. However about six millennia ago domesticated cattle, sheep and goats were imported and crop-grains (and their attendant weeds) were introduced. With the advent of agriculture, the felling of native woodlands commenced in earnest.

Man's activities during six millennia of farming The Burren have led to the extinction of one native species of tree. Scots pine (*Pinus sylvestris*) was eradicated about the beginning of the Christian era, approximately fifteen hundred years ago, and this species is probably not represented anywhere in Ireland today by truly native trees because our ancestors cut down the forests with alacrity.

Had Mesolithic tribes continued to subsist as hunter-gatherers like the Mount Sandel folk, and had Neolithic farmers not felled trees to clear land for herds and crops, this island would be cloaked today, except in the wettest and most exposed places, by stately woodlands of oak and ash with an understorey of holly and hazel. Crucially, there is excellent evidence to suggest that The Burren as we know it, a rocky plateau largely devoid of soil, would be a very different place; instead of a bare limestone wilderness, forests of Scots pine or woodlands of yew–similar to fragments that persist near Killarney by the shore of Lough Leane in County Kerry–with hazel scrub would cloak the barony's hills.

Populations of other trees, including elm and yew, have fluctuated dramatically since Mesolithic times, perhaps because of climatic changes and disease rather than man's activities. Elm was present in The Burren's woodlands before cereal farming began, but about 5100 years ago it dwindled rapidly, according to the pollen record. The sudden decline of the elm was formerly attributed to clearance of woodlands by Neolithic farmers, but there is now evidence (from Connemara, for example) that the fading-out started before the massive prehistoric forest clearances, suggesting that disease may have been the cause. Remarkably yew (*Taxus baccata*) became a significant tree in The Burren about the same time as elm declined, and soon apparently was abundant–yew's increase is clearly shown in the pollen sequence and at its maximum, one in every five grains trapped in sediments came from yew.[6] However yew declined too; during the last two millennia its pollen has been preserved only in minute quantities indicating that no longer was yew plentiful within the region. Today, wych elm (*Ulmus glabra*) is also rare but widespread in north-western Clare, occurring only as scattered trees, never in stands that could be termed woodlands. Oaks are even scarcer being absent from the western uplands of The Burren; trees of sessile oak (*Quercus petraea*) grow in the lowlands between Corrofin and Mullach Mór along with English oak (*Quercus robur*) which is also found about Coole Lough although it may not be native there. Aspen (*Populus tremula*) is more abundant–there are groves on the hillocks around the western side of Lough Gealáin, and you can hear the trees long before you see them, as their long-stalked leaves chatter dementedly in the breeze.

Present-day 'natural' woodlands in The Burren are secondary regrowth and are dominated by hazel and ash, not by Scots pine and yew, nor by elm and oak.

Hazel is ubiquitous, even growing out of the scailps as stunted, wind-pruned shrubs in quite exposed sites. Where there is shelter, the hazels grow taller; in the most secluded hollows and in the lea of hills there are small patches of woodland composed almost entirely of hazel trees with branches rising as much as eight metres. Ash is less frequent–in some localities it does dominate the woodlands, overshadowing the hazel, although such woods are almost always situated in the shelter of hills and cliffs.

But there cannot be woodlands in The Burren, can there? Did not Edmund Ludlow write that this is

> ...a country where there is not water enough to drown a man, wood enough
> to hang one, nor earth enough to bury him...

and has not everyone since then repeated that tedious triad as incontrovertible truth? There is plenty of water in The Burren, enough to drown the incautious, and earth deep enough for the interment of innumerable generations, and there are woods and trees although relatively few individuals strong enough, I will admit, for gallows. Enfolded in Mac Duach's wood, soothed by a carillon of birds and the plash of a spring, there is no doubting the irrelevance of that 'lugubrious epigram'[7] to parts of The Burren–I do not give a jot for his cantankerous raving. The Burren woodlands are among the most wonderful aspects of this strange land. There are trees in many places, on the northern slopes beyond the castle of Gleninagh, in the secret amphitheatre, built by water, of Poll an Bhalláin, snuggling into the swirls of the terraces of Mullach Mór and–in miniature–deep in the pots on the flank of Sliabh Eilbhe.

The most magical is the greenwood which hangs like a curtain from the 'frowning' cliff that is called Cinn Aille, draping the scree with hazels, helleborines, ferns and mosses. Scattered amongst the nut trees are sallys, ash and rowan. A tiny oratory of St Colman MacDuach, once a snug retreat but long-since abandoned, is also silent. Its dressed stones are following that ineluctable trail of all The Burren's limestone back to their source, dissolving in the rain and tumbling to the ground to become part of the natural rock-garden. Long ago prayers were told in this hazel wood, and Mass intoned to the accompaniment of the babble of clear water. The pious chant is over. Silence is all that is heard; the cliffs amplify that silence as once they amplified *Agnus Dei, dona nobis pacem.*

In the shadow of Cinn Aille, enveloped by moss and moist air, I can appreciate that the hermit monks of early Christian Ireland were well attuned to the wilderness that they chose to retreat in, and that carefully they chose for their sanctuaries the best sites with an ever-flowing stream, a wood of nut-trees and rowan berries, and, a few steps away, some drumlins of rich soil for pasture, for grazing a milch-cow and fattening cattle, for a garden of leeks and fragrant herbs. In the dappled light, in the warm silence, above the little ruined church, I am invisible among the orchids, and think that perhaps here was the place where the poet made Marbhán sing his beautiful paean to the wild woods.

> *A Marbain, a dithrubaig*
> *cid na cotlai for colcaid?*
> *Ba meinciu duit feiss i-mmaig*
> *cenn do raig for lar ochtgiag.*

> Hermit Marbain, why do you not sleep upon a bed?
> More often would you sleep out of doors,
> with your head, where the tonsure ends
> upon the ground of a fir-grove

> *Ata uarboth dam i caill*
> *nis-fitir acht mo Fhiada*
> *Uinnius di-siu, coll an-all*
> *bile ratha, nosn-iada.*

> I have a hut in a wood
> None knows it but my Lord:
> An ash-tree this side, a hazel beyond
> A great fern makes the door.[8]

The sober truth is otherwise: even Cinn Aille is unlikely to have had woodland cascading down the screes two hundred years ago. Before the Great Famine, 1845-1847, Ireland was more densely populated than today and, like every other barony, Burren supported a much larger population than at present. The chance of trees and shrubs surviving was slim, given the pressure not just from grazing by cattle, sheep and feral goats but also from the peasant farmers who surely cut all standing brushwood for fuel—so scarce was firewood in the barony that both mountain avens and bracken were 'much used as fuel by the poor peasantry'.[9] There is other written and photographic evidence that suggests The Burren was even more sparsely wooded than today, and that scrub patches and rough hedges were wanting. Perhaps most significantly, neither Thaddeus O'Mahony nor Frederick Foot make any reference to hazel copses or substantial areas of woodland,

and when Foot noted ash he stated only that it was 'very abundant in the dwarf form'. Thomas Corry visited Cinn Aille, and while he described seeing dropwort and hawkweed, he makes no mention of woods. Dr Jerome Fahey noted that 'only a few of the hazel copses of [The Burren's] valleys remain' and he described the oratory's setting too:

> The cliff which shelters the ruined oratory of St Colman is the loftiest in the Burren Mountains. Rising in crescent form against the north, it encloses within its sheltering embrace the ruins... Its situation, even at the present day [1893], is one of singular loneliness... Though forest trees flourish there no longer, and the rugged limestone ledges, which rise like gigantic terraces one above the other, are everywhere visible, yet it is rarely that one sees a more striking view than that which is commanded by the plateau in which St Colman's oratory is situated.[10]

Early photographs of Burren landmarks, dating between 1880s and 1920s, portray landscapes that were essentially tree-less. Robert Welch's famous series includes one of Ballyvaghan with low bushes of shrubby cinquefoil stretching into the distance towards the parish church—I have already mentioned this view (p. 96) and the fact that tall hazel scrub covers the area nowadays. William Lawrence's photograph of Oughtmama shows ruined chapels and pristine stone walls—today those walls are shrouded by bushes and the little churches almost hidden by rank scrub. Regeneration of scrub can be attributed to changes in society—people no longer need to cut firewood because they have peat briquettes, bottled gas and electricity and to changes in agricultural practices, particularly reduced grazing pressures following the introduction of silage and artificial foodstuffs. Shrubs and trees have more chance nowadays to grow tall, and scrub can advance over Burren pavements.

Woodlands are not simply habitations for trees. Between the canopy of leaves and the surface of the ground, there are innumerable niches in which a multitude of plants and animals thrive. Deciduous woodlands, such as those of hazel and ash, are especially rich in herbs, ferns and mosses, and have two distinct, seasonal phases—a leafless winter one when sunlight streams past the bare twigs and branches to the woodland floor, and a summer one when the soil becomes dry and a lot less light reaches the ground inside the wood because most is captured by the leafy canopy. The seasons are reflected by the ground-flora—the flowering herbs tend to blossom early in spring, set seeds quickly and disappear before light-levels plummet and the trees take up most of the moisture from the soil.

Meconopsis cambrica
Welsh poppy

Lonicera periclymenum: honeysuckle

Wood sorrel (*Oxalis acetosella*), lords-and-ladies (*Arum maculatum*), barren strawberry, wood anemone (*Anemone nemorosa*), lesser celandine (*Ranunculus ficaria*) and ramson (*Allium ursinum*) are obvious during March and April in hazel spinneys–there is no scarcity of them in the greenwoods of Tobar MacDuach, Poll Salach and Poll an Bhalláin. The dramatic arrow-shaped, darkly mottled leaves of *Arum* are never seen in summer because they have withered and only spikes of scarlet fruits betray the presence of lords-and-ladies. Barren strawberry and wood sorrel leaves do linger and hidden flowers are produced in summer whereas, like lord-and-ladies, the celandines, ramsons and wood anemones disappear rapidly. So, the summer months are mossy; ferns are in full leaf, and there are late orchids in some of the hazel woodlands.

I had been intrigued by a name on the map.[11] An opportunity chanced and I wandered into foxy hazel scrub on the flanks of Aillwee Mountain hoping my walk would lay to rest the mystery of that word–there are other puzzling marks and cryptograms but none quite so irresistible as this one. New fields and tracks that did not appear on any chart disturbed my path, and a fox cub wandered across a meadow full of drowsy buttercups and bees, and I sat to watch it play. I dandered on and in the bright midday reached my destination to see sunbeams flaunt a cluster of brilliant poppies.

Many gardeners curse *Meconopsis cambrica* (Welsh poppy, *poipín Breatnach*) for its fecundity and, occasionally, for its promiscuity too. But those delightful, silky flowers, lemon suns dancing among the moss-gaitered stems of the hazel on Aillwee Mountain could not but be admired. Four large, overlapping petals, slightly pleated and crumpled from their unfolding, form the simple flower; in its centre is a ribbed, solitary ovary surrounded by a multitude of stamens as yellow as the petals. Most of the leaves are clustered at the base of the flower-stems; each one is stalked with a lobed blade and lobes that are also divided.

Meconopsis is related closely to *Papaver*; the genera differ in the colour of the latex that oozes from broken stems, and in the form of the fruit and the arrangement of the stigmas. In 'true' poppies (species of *Papaver*) the latex is usually white, whereas *Meconopsis cambrica* and its fellows produce yellow latex. The stigma in *Papaver* is a disc on top of the ovary; in *Meconopsis* a distinct style separates the ovary and the stigma.

Welsh poppies are often not truly wild; many are garden escapees. In The Burren, the species is known from only two localities, discovered during the past two decades, where the plants perhaps are indigenous. Tim Robinson saw the population on Aillwee Mountain in 1975, and some time later discovered another near Kilnaboy. The nearest native colony, reported for well over one century, thrives on Muckanaght, one of the western peaks of the Twelve Bens in Connemara. Whereas *Meconopsis cambrica* is an uncommon, secretive plant in The Burren, other woodland understorey species are neither rare nor elusive, and many inhabit pavement scailps as well as hazel copses. This is one of The Burren's botanical contradictions–why do honeysuckle, tutsan, wood sage and wood anemone, grow on the exposed, rock-strewn expanses of Black Head and Aillwee Mountain? Elsewhere in Ireland they shun open, wind-swept habitats, preferring woodlands, shaded and calm.

Honeysuckle (*Lonicera periclymenum*) is ubiquitous in Ireland; almost every hedgerow has cascades and The Burren's hedges are no exceptions. For me the finest honeysuckle plants are those that decorate the most exposed pavements, sending nosegays of trumpet-flowers from scailps to perfume the breezes. In Ballyryan, around Oughtdarra, and about Formoyle, the pavement honeysuckles have soft apricot blooms not heavily tinged with red.

The flexible, long stems of honeysuckle are easily recognized and gave rise to the Irish name *féithleann*. The leaves are widely-spaced, paired, oval and pale grey beneath. The flowers are clustered, about a dozen in a group, at the tips of lateral shoots. Each trumpet comprises five petals, fused into a tube when in bud, and after opening, four petals remain fused to form an upper lip while the remaining petal curls to form the lower one. From the flaring mouth emerge five stamens and a slender style tipped by a disc-like stigma. The length of the trumpets varies–at their best at least four centimetres long, but a few years ago at Murrough I found a green-blossomed honeysuckle with short, deformed flowers.

Honeysuckle is marvellously adapted for pollination and a superb keeper of time. The buds are vertical to begin with, and between 6 o'clock and 7 o'clock in the evening the anthers, still enclosed in the buds, burst open to release pollen; some while later the bud itself opens, the lower lip separating to let the anthers poke out. The flower now changes its position to horizontal, when the upper lip splits slightly to release the style which curves downwards. The perfume exuded by the trumpet is most powerful at this time of the evening, attracting hover-flies which collect the pollen, and hawk moths that sip the nectar but also to be dusted with pollen. If a moth goes to another flower, yesterday's bloom, it will transfer pollen to the stigma of the other flower. The fragrance fades by the morning, and the flower colour also is transformed as the days pass; most honeysuckle blossoms are white inside when first open, but change to yellow after pollination.

Lonicera belongs to the same family as guelder rose (*Viburnum*) and elder (*Sambucus*), Caprifoliaceae; most of these genera have fleshy, juicy fruits. When ripe in October, honeysuckle berries are translucent and scarlet like those of guelder rose; they are of little or no value as food, except for birds. Indeed if it was not for the beauty and fragrance of the blooms, *Lonicera periclymenum* would be ignored as a tedious nuisance because of its strangling, entangling shoots: honeysuckle, wrote Geoffrey Grigson, 'hugs more like a killing snake than a friend, often squeezing saplings into a spiral.'[12] The stems as they climb revolve at the tip, 'in its winding it follows the sun from east to west',[13] twisting clockwise around any upstanding

Corylus avellana: hazel catkins

thing, whether a garden pergola or a branchy bush–the stems of honeysuckle always twine in the same direction. And there is no shortage of hazel boughs in The Burren for entwining.

Hazel thrives almost anywhere in The Burren from sea-level to the mountain tops, sprouting in scailps and colonizing the screes. It is a characteristic plant of limestone pavements and will frequent mildly acidic habitats too but not as a dominant species. Individuals are not long-lived; the antique hazels in the wood beneath Cinn Aille, enveloping Tobar MacDuach, look as if they might once have been coppiced, but yet the standing trunks are probably less than a century old.

Everyone is familiar with the catkins ('lamb's tails') that dangle in the breezes of February and March, shedding a haze of golden pollen grains. A catkin is a congregation of minute male flowers, each crowded individual with little grace, but together producing the tassle. The female flowers are more than inconspicuous; they sprout on the same shoots and are betrayed by pairs of bright red styles. Breezes

Corylus avellana: hazel nuts

pollinate hazel, wafting pollen from male catkins to the female flowers. The styles trap a few grains and fertilization can then proceed; the ovary swells and by autumn the brown nuts cupped in ragged-lobed leafy involucres are ready to drop to the woodland floor.

Hazel leaves do not unfurl until the catkins have withered and dropped to the ground; each leaf has a heart-shaped base and is softly hairy. In summer the foliage dapples the sunlight in the wood, and catches the drizzle.

> A soft day, thank God:
> The hills wear a shroud of silver cloud;
> The web of the spider is a glittering net;
> The woodland path is wet,
> And the soaking earth smells sweet
> Under my two bare feet,
>   And the rain drips,
> Drips, drips, drips from the leaves.[14]

No matter what the weather outside, the heart of a hazel spinney is always moist, mellow and mossy. In autumn the leaves change colour to cinnamon and butter, and are shed, gliding down to earth, to melt back into the rich loam that covers the woodland floor.

In 1990 there was an abundant crop of nuts. The red squirrels must have had a feast! In my mind's eye, I like to picture a Burren squirrel gnawing a neat hole in hazel nut and extracting the kernel, enjoying its crisp texture. Carefully the squirrel puts that empty shell on the pile accumulating under an overhanging rock, and gathers another to gnaw. The heap of emptied nuts grows each autumn, the lowest shells slowly darkening and rotting; the pile has been there for several years, and each season new husks are added. I have never seen the squirrel who uses the grotto, only the neatly opened shells.

Coll is the Irish synonym for hazel; the native species is *Corylus avellana*. In olden days hazel was a pagan tree, a worshipful, magical plant. On May Day, you were wise to bring hazel twigs indoors to protect the household from evil spirits and fairies. Carrying a hazel nut in your pocket was considered efficacious against lumbago and rheumatism, and hazel buds eaten in porridge with dandelions, chickweed and wood sorrel cured coughs, colds and sore throats.

Coll was *airig fedo* (a noble of the wood) in ancient Irish law-codes:[15] cut a branch without due cause and you forfeited a year-old heifer, or a milch-cow if you cut a tree at its base. There are six other noble trees: oak, ash, yew, holly, pine and apple, each of great value to primitive communities. Hazel yielded pliable, strong rods for wattles to build houses and make fences, fodder for animals and a charcoal that was one of the ingredients of gun-powder. Dr Threlkeld was not enamoured with hazel because of its devilish uses:

> That a divining Rod of this Wood should be used to find out Metalls, is owing to the Impostures of *Satan*, whose Design is to abuse the Creatures with vain Amusements under the old Colour of Knowledge more than is fit for Men.[16]

On a mundane level, the nuts are nutritious but Threlkeld warned that they caused 'Wheasing and Pursiness, and do fatten'. The hazels of The Burren must have produced thousands of bushels of nuts since Neolithic tribes settled there; they were a free and valuable food of men and beasts, an additional reason for the law-makers to protect it.

The living branches of *Corylus avellana*, like those of many other trees, provide niches for less advanced plants and animals to colonize. The bark of a hazel twig is a mosaic of silver and golden grey, outlined in black and perhaps stippled too, patterning caused by lichens which live in the bark, without harming the hazel. Furthermore the Burren's hazel trees have a rich epiphytic flora–epiphytes are plants that grow on other plants, using their hosts only as a habitat, without causing any damage–they are not parasites. Dr C. H. Dickinson and Dr T. K. Thorp, of Trinity College, Dublin and the University of Glasgow respectively, studied the epiphytes of a patch of hazel scrub at the base of Mullach Mór and found that *Frullania dilatata* was the most abundant liverwort and the common mosses were *Neckera complanata* and *Ulota crispa*.[17] These form cushions or feathery foliage close-pressed to the trunks. On the 'bare' sections of the stems they counted fifteen different lichens, some of these being the epicormic or corticolous–bark dwelling–species causing the mosaics.

The complexity of the living world is exemplified by these bark lichens–what seems to be a sterile, yet living twig of hazel is a complicated 'city' inhabited by microscopic plants and even those plants, the lichens, are not as simple as they seem. Each lichen is an amalgam of two quite different plants, an alga and a fungus living in harmony, in a mutually beneficial, symbiotic relationship. While Jonathan Swift's doggerel was meant to attack fellow poets, his allusion to a many-layered system of interdependence is apt–

> So, naturalists observe, a flea
> Hath smaller fleas that on him prey;
> And these have smaller fleas to bite 'em
> And so proceed *ad infinitum.*
> Thus every poet in his kind,
> is bit by him that comes behind.[18]

As a species within the complex, interacting pattern of vegetation in limestone areas, hazel is essentially a pioneer plant. Shrubs become established in scailps and grow to form sheltering thickets above the pavement; thus hazel scrub initiates a progression, taking many decades, that ends–when Nature is allowed to take an uninterrupted course in true woodland-replacing the thickets. If ever man and his grazing beasts are entirely removed from The Burren, and plants are allowed to grow unchecked, hazel scrub will cover the now-bare pavement, except perhaps on the most exposed hillside and cliffs. In areas where the soil is deep, this tall hazel scrub will mature into woodland dominated by ash; hazel itself eventually is ousted.

Fraxinus excelsior: ash

🌿 *Fraxinus excelsior,* ash, is one of the climax trees of woodlands on lime-rich soils; the other is oak (*Quercus petraea*) but, as I have noted, oaks are almost entirely absent from north-west Clare.

In winter ash trees are dramatic. When the subtler light of winter strikes one, the bark gleams softly. There is a solitary, wind-swept, crooked ash on the pavement in Cappasheen townland, east of the New Line which has an austere, gallows-like station against the rounded hill–it is perhaps the most photographed tree in Ireland! A sheen of pale gold washes it too.

The Cappasheen tree is out-of-place and out-of-character for most ash trees grow either tall in sheltered woodlands, or as dwarfed, pruned shrubs wedged in scailps. At close range, the black winter-buds regularly arranged in opposite pairs along the twigs contrast starkly with the pale grey bark; a solitary bud, like the 'onion' dome of a Russian church, crowns each stem. Ash is one of the last trees to break into leaf. The buds burst in April releasing catkins of flowers without petals, reduced to a pair of stamens topped by claret anthers, and inconspicuous styles; the pollen is pale yellow and is shed into the breeze for pollination is effected

Taxus baccata: yew

by the wind. Flowering takes place before the leaves expand; slowly above the fuzzy ruff of developing fruits, a fresh green coronet of foliage burgeons. Ash leaves are distinctive, compound, composed of ten or a dozen leaflets in pairs along the central rachis tipped by a solitary one. If you ever find an ash leaf without that terminal leaflet, just an even number, you have a leaf as lucky as the 'four-leaved' clover. With an 'even-ash' in your hand, before the day is out, you will meet your lover.

Fuinseog is the Irish name for ash which was the fifth noble tree of the woods, *airig fedo*; the same penalties applied for illicit cutting as with hazel. Ash is still one of the most highly prized timbers; hurleys are fashioned from ash because the wood is elastic and strong, tough enough to clash with leather in the excitement of the game. The wood is fine-grained and smooth when skilfully planed. In bygone ages, royal thrones were fashioned from ash, and so were spears:

> life-blood on a spear-shaft
> darkens the grain of ash.

291

The wood was burned to keep away the devil, and there is an ancient belief, stemming from Greek mythology, that the leaves hold snakes at bay[18]–a faculty of no use at all, at all in Ireland!

The fruits–'keys'–of *Fraxinus excelsior* are as distinctive as the foliage; they are winged achenes (single-seeded fruits) capable of rotating as they fall and of drifting in the wind. Blown far and wide by breezes, ash can become a weed but not in The Burren. The keys develop through the summer and are ripe when the leaves turn creamy-brown, disintegrate and fall, leaving the smooth, pearl-barked trees to hibernate.

A forest of evergreen, sombre yew can develop where shallow soils overly limestone, but nowhere in The Burren is there such a woodland. In County Kerry, on the shores of the Killarney loughs, a mature yew forest has survived, a mossy place, gloomy, solemn and quiet as a cathedral. The Muckross yew wood provides a glimpse at what might have been had men not wielded stone and iron axes in the barony of Burren. The night-dark, over-wintering foliage allows only a fraction of the sunlight recorded in a deciduous woodland to penetrate to the floor of a yew wood. The evergreen shoots act as a blanket enclosing a still, humid atmosphere in which mosses, and little else, flourish. A yew wood is silent, soft, sombre, and has none of the wonderful spring flower-carpet that is so delightful in the spinneys of hazel and ash on the limestones of Clare.

We are all familiar with yew as a sentinel, funereal tree in churchyards, an association that belongs to immemorial time. In the marvellous nature verses of Suibne Geilt (Mad Sweeney), a fictional petty king, 'wood-lover and tree-hugger', yew is singled out in precisely this context:

> The yew tree in each churchyard
> wraps night in its dark hood.[20]

Taxus baccata is a true native plant, although the vast majority of trees growing in Ireland today have been planted and many of these are the upright cultivar sometimes called the Florencecourt yew (*Taxus baccata* cv. Fastigiata) that was discovered before 1750 on the flank of Cuilcagh Mountain in County Fermanagh.[21] The association of yew and Christian burial-grounds undoubtedly has its origin in pagan cults that held evergreen trees sacred. In time the earthy gods and their symbolic trees became Christianized–yew became a funerary tree, but also the source of highly-valued timber for croziers, shrines and tablets upon which ogham was written. Long ago slabs of yew marked graves at Corcomroe Abbey.[22]

In The Burren, yew trees are especially conspicuous, silhouettes in extraordinary shapes. Some have been plastered by the wind against cliffs and then on their landward side they are trimmed by goats as neatly as any gardener intent on topiary. They haunt the terrace-cliffs of Mullach Mór. On Sliabh na gCapall yews emerge from scailps immaculately trimmed. By Lough Gealáin there are almost invisible trees that have been mown into bizarre, deep green pillows snugly filling solution hollows in the pavement. The thick stems of the pillows are wedged between the walls of scailps; they are natural 'bonsai', dwarfed because their root-runs are restricted and goats have been the most assiduous topiarists. The foliage of *Taxus baccata* is poisonous to most animals, including human beings, but not to goats whose distasteful, rancid stench lingers beside the Mullach Mór trees.

Yew is not a flowering plant, but a gymnosperm, related distantly to pines, spruces and larches, trees that are, in common parlance, 'conifers'. In *Taxus*, male pollen-producing strobili–tiny, catkin-like structures–are produced on separate plants to the female strobili. Yews do not produce woody cones; their single-seeded fruits are composed of a juicy, bright red cup (aril) holding a single seed like a egg in its egg-cup–while the seed is poisonous and should never be eaten, the fleshy aril is harmless. Given the frequent mentions of yew fruits in ancient verses, arils surely were relished by hermits and people as sweetmeats.

> Fresh spring wells and falls of water–
> delicious to drink–break forth in plenty,
> with yew-tree berries, and cherry and privet.[23]

Iubhar (yew) was the fourth of the noble trees of Irish forests. There is a particularly intriguing concentration of stunted yews in Muckinish West townland, on the low ground which is by tradition the site of the Wood of Siudaine where Conor O'Brien, King of Thomond, was slain by his cousin in a battle during 1267/8. Conor's grandfather had founded the abbey at Corcomroe which is a short walk away over the fields; Conor (Conchobar na Siudhaineach) was buried there and his tomb is reputed to be that in the presbytery covered with a naively sculpted sleeping effigy of a robed king.

Kings of Thomond may have ridden to battle in a chariot with shafts of holly (*cuileann*), for mediaeval texts attest that that was one of the uses of its timber. There is also evidence that the foliage was cut for cattle fodder in severe winters. Bird-lime was made from the bark, and from the leaves some apothecaries devised medicines for treating colic. And from time immemorial holly was

Ilex aquifolium: holly

acclaimed as a talisman giving protection against goblins and evil spirits–in Ireland holly bushes were believed to be gentle plants, beloved by the fairies, and nowadays, of course, it is quintessentially a Christmas plant. The pagan evergreen of mid-winter has a symbolism; the spine-margined leaves signify a crown of thorns and the red berries are drops of blood.

Holly, the third noble tree (*airig fedo*), is most conspicuous in the middle of winter. About Ballyvaghan there are innumerable bushes growing among hazels; the hollies are doubly distinctive, dark and evergreen, as well as tall and conical yet that shape has nothing to do with grazing and wind for these are sheltered,

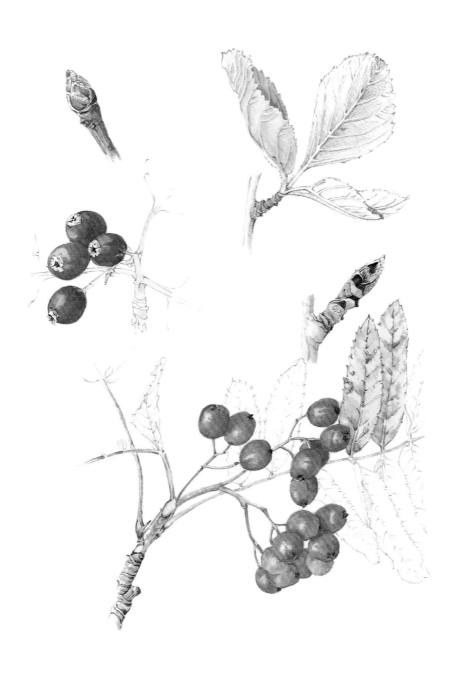

Sorbus hibernica: Irish whitebeam
Sorbus aucuparia: rowan

ungrazed shrubs. Like yew, holly is occasionally found emerging from scailps, nibbled to rock-level by goats or pinched back by winds. One of the most remarkable trees that I know grows from a bluff near Mullach Mór–the trunk surges horizontally from a cleft and then turns skyward while the roots seem to be trying to force the limestone strata apart.

Male and female flowers are produced on separate bushes. A male holly never has red berries, but is covered in spring by small clusters of yellow-anthered flowers. The female blossoms are similar but instead of a pair of stamens, there is in the centre a single green ovary capped by a style and stigma. Each flower–whether male or female–has four white petals which are often tinted claret or pink in bud.

Burren hollies have leaves of extraordinary beauty, marvellous, rippling dark green leaves that I fancy are finer than the leaves of hollies elsewhere in Ireland. There is no air pollution in The Burren, no dust and grime to tarnish their lustre. The leaf margins are edged with a pale band of translucent gold and are remarkably sinuous, their rapier-sharp thorns alternately pointing in opposite directions. Set a leaf on a flat rock and it stands on tiptoe like some gothick beast with its defensive scimitars raised.

Ilex aquifolium does not form dense thickets by itself. Shrubs or small trees–single stemmed bushes–are scattered through regenerated hazel scrub, and there are many in the informal hedgerows. There are few hollies in the more mature hazel and ash woodlands, and it is also absent where there is heavy grazing.

The other tree species indigenous in The Burren grow only as scattered clusters dispersed through hedgerows and scrub-patches in the eastern lowlands, or as isolated, lonely individuals in underwoods and on the pavements of the limestone hills. None is abundant enough to dominate woods or copses; there are no rowan forests, spindle spinneys or whitebeam woods.

Mountain ash, *caorthann*, was one of the 'commoners' of the wood (*athig fedo*), a companion to alder, birch, willow and hawthorn. Rowan, quicken and *Sorbus aucuparia* are other synonyms for a beautiful tree with a green filagree of leaves in summer, frothy, creamy flowers during late spring and a fire of scarlet berries from late August until the greedy birds have devoured them a few short weeks later. This species was amongst the most sacred to the pre-Christian peoples of Europe: did the Irish learn its virtues from the Norse invaders, as Dr A. T. Lucas suggested?[25] Rowan kept the dead from rising, helped to speed the hound, and protected milk and the dairy.[26]

The name 'mountain ash' alludes to the superficial resemblance of rowan with ash (*Fraxinus excelsior*). The similarities evaporate when the leaves are compared closely, for rowan leaflets are more numerous, smaller, and have finely serrated margins; ash leaflets have plain margins and the leaves are generally coarser. There are so many other differences that no-one should confuse the two species; for example the pointed winter buds of *Sorbus aucuparia* are protected by black, fringed scales, and they are in opposite pairs.

Sorbus aucuparia is a member of an inextricable (taxonomically speaking) genus distributed throughout temperate regions of Europe and Asia; in European gardens some of the species from the Himalayas and China with white and golden fruits have ousted the native red-berried rowan and whitebeams. Like *Rubus* (blackberries, brambles), *Sorbus* comprises a few well-defined groupings within which are countless minor, weakly separated, but often geographically restricted variants that can be termed microspecies. Many microspecies, including native ones, produce viable seeds without pollination, an asexual process termed apomixis. One consequence of apomixis is that seedlings and parent trees are identical. Given that the differences between microspecies can be invisible (for example, the number of chromosomes in a cell) or almost so—perhaps a matter of careful calculation of a range of intergrading features—there is ample scope for confusion and for disputes about the identity of particular plants. Thus, while there is no chance of rowan being mistaken for anything else, whitebeams are intractable; Irish whitebeam (*Sorbus hibernica*), a microspecies unique to Ireland, is not easy to identify because it closely resembles common whitebeam (*Sorbus aria*).[27]

Broadcast across pavements and in hedgerows there are numerous compact trees of whitebeam. In spring the green, pointed buds burst and release a neat cluster of leaves so closely felted with hairs that the silver sheen is almost as pure a white as that of the petals of a magnolia. The leaves expand as the days lengthen; when mature they are broadly oval with parallel secondary veins, undivided but toothed around the margins.

To distinguish common whitebeam (*Sorbus aria*) from Irish whitebeam (*Sorbus hibernica*) you must carefully examine the silver-backed leaves in summer and the speckled red fruits in autumn; even then botanists, even long-time whitebeam students, can be so perplexed that they give up without putting a definite name on a tree. Irish whitebeam was characterized by E. F. Warburg as having leaves with small, uniform marginal teeth and a greyish-white undersurface, and scarlet

Viburnum opulus: guelder rose

berries that are globular (not barrel-shaped) and speckled mainly near the stalk.[28] Common whitebeam leaves are irregularly toothed and white underneath even in mid-summer, and the fruits are barrel-shaped and speckled all over.

Intrepid wanderers, with a penchant for the niceties of microspecies, can decide the identity of the whitebeam trees and bushes they encounter–good luck.

In May whitebeams bear umbels of cream-white flowers like those of hawthorn and blackthorn, but larger; *Sorbus* (whitebeams and rowan) belongs to the same family–Rosaceae (rose family)–as apple, hawthorn and blackthorn and thus the pattern of their flowers is similar. Five petals are a mark of Rosaceae. Stamens are three to five times as numerous as the petals.

Whitebeams are sporadic throughout the hills and eastern lowlands. A fine tree stands proud on the slope above Newtown Castle, and I have seen others inland from Poll Salach, at Cinn Aille, and in hedgerows on the New Line. They are most conspicuous in early summer when the whiteness of the unfurling leaves is truly startling; by autumn the winds have shredded the foliage into shabby

Euonymus europaeus: spindle

tatters which, all the same, achieve some splendid golds and browns. The dark red fruits hide among the larger leaves, so they are never as obvious as those of the rowans.

Autumn is the finest season for the woodlands. The grey walls of Poll an Bhallain, warmed by the soft sunlight of September, ring to the cry of a raven and

> …the wind, the forest wind, in its falling
> Sets the withered leaves fluttering to and fro.[29]

Poll an Bhallain is a dimple in the rockscape, a natural amphitheatre created when an enormous cavern was so undermined by water that its roof collapsed and it gaped at the sky. Gales growl overhead. In the shelter of the rock-walls, there is a ruff of woodland and among the ash and hazel are many rowans–seen from the rim in autumnal fruit, they are gleaming rubies set in rock-grey coronet.

Heather and harebells with devil's bit and milkwort encircle the amphitheatre. New colours have transmuted the hazel-greens of summer; at the first touch of frost, bracken fronds become golden brown and the leaves of bloody cranesbill turn blood-red. The rowans hold their proud bunches of scarlet berries for blackbirds and thrushes to devour, but the leaves have no need to linger, so they disintegrate and shuffle softly from the silver twigs. Birds strip the fruits of the guelder roses quickly. Equinoctial gales strip the ash keys. Keys and leaflets race each other through the air in wayward spirals. The heart-shaped leaves of hazels noisily and lazily flutter down until they reach the woodland floor where for a winter they will lie and then melt away to enrich the earth. Young leaves and ripe fruits of the coming year depend on this recycling of redundant herbage.

The guelder rose is that 'rose by any other name…', *Viburnum opulus*, yet not a rose but a relative of elder and honeysuckle, and one of the loveliest of our native shrubs. Guelder roses are abundant throughout The Burren, decorating hedgerows and pavement, lurking among hazel scrub and in the potholes. Obscure in winter, when little more than dun-coloured twigs, the bushes are most handsome with flowers in June then fade into winter with a blaze of berries and leaves.

The leaves are like those of a sycamore, five-lobed arranged in opposite pairs. The pancake-heads of creamy white blossoms are clusters of small five-petalled flowers. Two types and sizes of flowers make up each cluster: those around the outside are the largest, the whitest, and sterile, and as they age often acquire flushes or freckles of red: the inner creamy-white flowers scarcely have any petals showing, yet they are fertile, capable of being pollinated and setting fruit. 'Get them close and they smell like crisply fried, well-peppered trout, if you can imagine that trouty, peppery smell with a touch of sweetness.'[30] In autumn, guelder roses are spectacular. The leaves turn wine-red–claret to burgundy depending on sharpness of the season and on the plant itself. On shoots that bore flowers during the summer past, there are bunches of translucent, scarlet berries like large red currants. They look appetizing but they are not—eaten raw they make you sick. The fruit can be cooked and made into jelly, and has been used as a substitute for cranberries.

Names! At least we agree that *Viburnum opulus* is the one and only botanical name. 'Guelder rose' is another matter, for as Geoffrey Grigson pointed out, this properly is the name for a garden plant, the 'rose' from Geldern, a town in Germany near the frontier with Holland. That Guelder rose only has sterile flowers in a rounder cluster like a snowball, 'goodly flowers of a white colour, sprinckled or dashed heere and there with a light and thinne carnation colour.'[31] The time-accustomed English name for the wild, fertile shrub is water-elder, and that was the name Caleb Threlkeld knew. The native Irish name is *caor-chon*, dog berry, possibly because of the foetid aroma of over-ripe berries. In the north of Ireland traveller's-joy was its name , although elsewhere that is reserved for *Clematis vitalba*.

For most of the year *Euonymus europaeus* (spindle, *feoras*) is an unremarkable shrub, the kind of plant passed by without a glance. Even in flower, spindle is thoroughly inconspicuous; the four-petalled blossom is pale green, hidden among the same green greenery of quadrangular stems and pairs of opposite, ovate leaves.

Spindle and guelder rose are both native in The Burren, and like *Viburnum opulus*, there are shrubs and even small trees of spindle dispersed across the pavements, concealed in hedgerows and anonymous in the hazel spinneys. Yet for one season, spindle does commandeer attention even more than the guelder rose. Dr Patrick Browne, writing in the late eighteenth century, may be quoted in spindle's honour.

> This shrub makes a most beautiful appearance in ye months of Novr & December. Then ye leafs are all of & ye capsules which are a fine crimson colour open & expose ye seeds wrapt up in a scarlet pulp, wh gives ye whole ye appearance of flowers.[32]

The insignificant green flowers cluster in the axils of the leaves; each one has four stamens alternating with the petals, and a four-celled ovary. Small insects pollinate spindle during May and June. The fruits develop through the summer, the ovary swelling into a strange four-lobed capsule that will ripen to deep coral-pink by October. The lobes split along the outer seams and reveal one or two brilliant orange seeds–correctly the orange coat is an aril completely enclosing a seed. If the autumn winds are not too vigorous, the withering blood-red leaves provide a dark backdrop that makes the coral and orange fruits all the more sumptuous.

In bygone days, spindle branches were used to make spindles, tooth-picks and skewers (hence the name prick-timber tree, prickwood, or pricktree); the hard, white wood is favoured for viola bows and the keys of virginals. A powder of dried berries is reputed to kill lice. It is not wise to eat the fruits of *Euonymus europaeus*, they purge violently. John Gerard, the London herbalist, in his great herbal, quoted the ancient Greek philosopher and 'father of botany', Eresios Theophrastos:

Malus sylvestris: crab apple

> This shrub is hurtfull to all things, as *Theophrastus* writeth, and namely to Goats: hee saith the fruit hereof killeth; so doth the leaves and fruit destroy Goats especially, unlesse they scoure as wel upwards as downwards…[33]

There are few plants that will kill a goat—not even yew, as we have seen, but there are modern reports which seem to uphold some of the Greek philosopher's observations; sheep and goats are mildly affected if they eat spindle.

There is an old apple tree in the wood that shelters in the first swirl of Mullach Mór. In autumn small creamy apples, flushed pink, litter the ground underneath. In bygone days these would have been gathered for nothing was wasted in the countryside. Nowadays they are left as food for slugs and worms and the small mammals of the woodland, and whatever remains after they have feasted rots with the decaying leaves and enriches the woodland soil.

Like hazel and ash, the wild apple was a noble tree to our ancestors; the penalties for damaging one were the same. According to *Bretha Comaithchesa* (Laws of Neighbourhood), *crann fia-úil* (apple) was valued for its fruit as a food, and for the yellow dye that came from its bark.[34] Wild or crab apple is not a common tree; in many localities the wildings are trees that have sprouted from discarded

Crataegus monogyna: hawthorn

apple-cores, throw-backs from sweet apples of the orchard and not true *Malus sylvestris*. One such plant, with wickedly tart fruits, grows on the road into Gleninagh near the meeting of five roads beyond Newtown—its apples are many times larger than the fruits on the trees at Mullach Mór. The Mullach Mór apple trees, the pattern for the painting, grow far from roads and houses and have the small fruits expected of the true wild plant.

Malus sylvestris is native in western Europe from Scandinavia to Portugal, and through southern Europe into western Asia. The species can be distinguished, according to modern sources, from the domesticated apple by fruits less than three centimetres in diameter, by small leaves (hairless below when mature), by thorny branches, and by hairless sepals, pedicels and receptacle. The presence of hairs on the undersurface of mature leaves, on receptacle, sepals and pedicels, is an indication that the apple tree is a domesticated one (*Malus sylvestris* subsp. *mitis*); the fruits, of course, are large and (in some cultivars) sweet.

Two other prominent Burren shrubs are members of the rose family and both are well-entrenched in Irish folk-lore: hawthorn (*Crataegus monogyna*) and blackthorn (*Prunus spinosa*).

303

Throughout Ireland solitary, wizened hawthorn bushes are often seen in some woe-begotten place because zealous folk have decided that they are fairy thorns. We are all heirs to an innate fear of the fairy thorn. Fairies meet beside thorn bushes, and sometimes live in them. If a fairy thorn is cut, it bleeds and screams; the 'Little People' are provoked into retaliation and take terrible revenge. In an era when too few trees are left standing, this is an admirable notion, and so mature hawthorns are usually not molested although every other green plant in their vicinity has been removed. By observing some simple rules, the human race and fairy-thorns can coexist. When walking in the countryside, you may rest beside a thorn bush. But don't hang your jacket or rucksack on it because you will disturb the washing already hung out by the fairies. So be warned; do not interfere in any way with *sceach gheal*, and even if you are sceptical about the existence of fairies, it is best not to tempt fate. Do not damage any wild tree, bush or herb.

The old gods of the greenwood have been translated into Christian saints; lonely hawthorns draped over wells and springs are often sacred in the Christian tradition of Ireland. According to Monsignor Fahey there were in the 1890s some ancient hawthorns at the 'beautiful fountain dedicated to St Colman' below Cinn Aille, 'and in early summer still fill the air with the fragrance of their blossoms.'[35] Dr Jerome Fahey did not say that these 'very old' thorns were rag bushes, but it is not unlikely that they were. Rags were tied to holy bushes as votive offerings, like Buddhist prayer-flags of the Himalayas. I do not know of any rag bushes in The Burren; there is a 'blessed bush' on Corkscrew Hill beside the marks of St Brigid's knees,[36] but I have not seen it and it may not be a thorn or a rag bush. We must assume that the pious rags did not interfere with the fairies' washing already hung out to dry on the whitethorns; the two faiths can and do coexist.

In The Burren isolated hawthorns are not usually alone because of the fairies; like other trees I have chronicled, *Crataegus monogyna* is a constituent of the native flora and happens to grow mainly as solitary specimens that sprouted where a bird 'raised its tail'. Some hawthorns have dramatic shapes–near Glenisheen wedge-tomb one bush stands in the shelter of a gossamer dry-stone wall, but its head is swept eastwards by the buffeting of the wind. Beside the pilgrim path to Tobar MacDuach there is another one to which I always pay respects, a dwarf of a hawthorn with young shoots little more than a few millimetres long, a strange, almost cactus-like leprechaun that must be ages old yet is only two hands tall.

Sceach gheal, literally the bright bush, was not so highly regarded in olden times as the wild apple; hawthorn was just a 'commoner' of the woods, probably because it did not yield many useful products. The dark red haws (*sceachóirí* in Irish) are not palatable although the sweetish, dry flesh from a freshly picked one can be nibbled. The fairies even guard the whitethorns when in fruit and there is an old belief that eating haws will give you jaundice—how does one account then for Dr Caleb Threlkeld's remark that 'The *Haws* are accounted Diuretick, good for the *Stone, Gravel* and *Pleurisy*.'?[37]

Hawthorn is deciduous. The sharp spines on the branches are condensed leafless branchlets. The leaves are unmistakeable, wedge-shaped at the base of the blade, with five prominent parallel-sided lobes; they begin to emerge about mid-April, or in a mild season perhaps earlier, and when very young are nice to eat—as a young schoolboy I can remember eating these as 'bread-and-cheese' although I could never, like Richard Mabey, taste the connection.[38] Later, usually about the first week of May, the flowers open, clusters of white, five-petalled blossoms—another common name for *Crataegus monogyna* is whitethorn—with pale flesh-tinted anthers. The blossom exudes that heavy. musky fragrance with sexual undertones, a wonderful aroma when wafted by soft breezes through the wide-open countryside; there is a prevailing belief that it is unlucky to bring hawthorn flowers indoors, and the heavy perfume can be unpleasant and cloying in a confined space. But recalling the fairies' taste for revenge, you should not even think of picking may-blossom to put in a vase.

May Day was the day for hawthorn although during the last few years, Irish folk would have been hard-pressed to find any in blossom. Washed by dew and woven into garlands with marsh marigolds and rowan, hawthorn was one of the flowers that protected all from bewitching. On a more mundane level, I read that the flowers make an intoxicating, wicked liqueur: pick them fresh, steep in water, add a spoonful or two of sugar, and leave to ferment for a few days, top up with brandy, and leave for a few months.[39] I must try it some day, and I'm sure the fairies would share it. In The Burren hawthorns with pale red flowers are not uncommon in some townlands. By late August and early September the green foliage has darkened, and the haws are ripe and glow in the autumnal sunshine with a wonderful lustre that is enhanced when Atlantic mists drizzle them with dew-drips.

Prunus spinosus: blackthorn

Blackthorn is cut, so it cannot be a fairy thorn, yet it too has much associated lore: to court ill-fortune, put blossom from *draighean* in your buttonhole or indoors in a vase; to court good-fortune take a shillelagh in your hand as you stride across the scailps.

Prunus spinosa begins to bloom before the leaves appear. White, starry blossoms blizzard hedgerows and neglected scrub in March and April, or earlier if the winter is unusually mild. Again, each flower has five white petals surrounding a brush of white and yellow stamens. The leaves are unexciting—lustreless ovals on short stalks, and frequently disfigured by galls. There are blackthorns with very narrow, elliptical leaf-blades and flexible shoots quite unlike the sharply spined robust branches that are liable to tear your clothes when you try to scramble through them. Narrow-leaved variants are most abundant around the turlough rims; they grow below the winter high-water mark and thus are submerged until about April, even May, and as a consequence blossom much later that the upright, dry-ground shrubs. I do not know if this turlough blackthorn remains low-growing and willowy when it is cultivated; one day I hope to find out.

Hedera helix
ivy

Blackthorn is prominent again in autumn; the leaves turn shades of butter and the sloes, tongue-wringingly bitter, are ripe, wonderfully black-blue with a silverwash bloom. When the first frost is past, they can be gathered carefully avoiding the stubby thorns. Steeped with sugar in gin, the raven sloes slowly give up their juices and within a couple of months you will pour from the jar a fragrant, rich burgundy nectar.

Autumn fruits merely herald new life because they contain the seeds of future plants. And the flowering of The Burren is never ending. Even in late autumn tiny flower-buds are burgeoning on the mudworts in the rock-pools. The rosettes of dense-flowered orchids appear among the dying leaves of blue grass, although you will have to call on your memory of the flowering spikes to find them. *Erophila verna* is forming buds for the new year. The croziers of sea spleenworts are uncurling in the seaside scailps. Ivy is in full flower.

Ivy (*eidhneán*) must be ranked as one of the finest and conspicuous of The Burren's wildflowers. It is ubiquitous. On the cusp of cliffs that shield Oughtdarra from the north wind, a curtain of ivy rises from the terrace, a solid green cloak. Nearer the breakers, on the flat pavement of Poll Salach, ivy has retreated into the scailps, where no wind can molest it. There are rock-clinging ivies over the Cave of the Wild Horses, and ivy has lent its native name to the cave of the great stalactite, Poll an Eidhneáin (Pol-an-Ionian).[40] The walls of the many roads seem stitched together by plaits of ivy woven between the stones into the gaps through which wind should sough.

In October mature ivies with their adult shoots in the sun are crowned by green panicles that swarm with wasps and small insects eager for the pollen and nectar which the blooms provide. Five stamens alternate with small, pale green petals and they fall away soon after pollination leaving the ovary to ripen. Ivy fruits are black berries, a favourite food for blackbirds.

Ivy is a true climbing plant, holding fast to branches, stones and cliffs by short adhesive roots that fringe the aerial stems. In shade it flops along the ground rooting less frequently, but sometimes a shoot will venture to begin clinging to a tree-trunk.

The colour of ivy leaves range from glossy dark green through claret and gold to, very occasionally, cream-veined like a sage cheese. Beside the path to *Seacht Srotha na Taosca* where seven streams surge from Glasgeivnagh Hill and cascade through ferns and woodrushes before vanishing again, I found the variegated ivy hat is pictured here. As winter sets in, ivy leaves deepen to the dark green that ould be so sombre except for the pale grey rocks. When the gales nip by and ouch the foliage, the rims of the leaves and the veins may take up colours iscarded by spindle and burnet rose, claret and burgundy. In spring the young reen-leaved shoots gradually overwhelm the old leaves, and the curtains of ivy nimic the meadows–walls once almost black become cheerful and bright, and he redundant leaves sometimes add to the display by turning golden-yellow before ropping from the stems.

I should digress again, briefly, into taxonomy because the naming of an ivy ; not as uncomplicated as might be supposed, and one Latin name, *Hedera helix*, ; not adequate for ivies in Ireland. Recent studies have confirmed that two ivies, iffering in characters, several of which cannot be seen by the naked eye, nor ven by someone wielding a hand-lens, grow wild here. One of the ivies has arge, uniform, broadly lobed leaves, and the scent of the cut stems is distinctly weet and resinous–quite pleasant. The other ivy has a very disagreeable odour nd two distinctly different leaf types are produced. The former is the Atlantic vy (or Irish ivy), *Hedera hibernica*; the latter is the common ivy, *Hedera helix*. Microscopic, multi-rayed hairs (trichomes) form a fuzzy scurf on the undersurfaces f the leaves and young shoots in both species; under a hand lens, the hairs of Atlantic ivy can be seen as flat like star-fish closely appressed to the leaf, while hose of common ivy stand up and are brush-like. The Atlantic ivy has ninety-six hromosomes; common ivy has only forty-eight. Thus Atlantic ivy, *Hedera ibernica*, is a tetraploid species, or if you prefer a western subspecies (*Hedera elix* subsp. *hibernica*).[41]

Atlantic ivy tends to grow in western parts of Ireland, Britain and south-vestern Europe where the climate is relatively milder, and so it is the ivy that otanists could expect in The Burren. But identification of ivies in the field is not easy, as the hairs can easily be abraded or lost, especially from common ivy. As the distinctions, although real, are almost invisible, I must leave you to decide or yourselves what the ivy is that you find.

In such a place as Burren, at the waning of a year, there is no need to speculate bout our ancestors' reverence for plants, for sallies as talismans against enchantment nd to bring luck on a journey, for evergreens–yew, holly and ivy–as winter iomes of the benign spirits of the earth. Ivy and holly were plants of great power, capable of protecting against evil; they are also cheerful, looming through the nizzle on soft days, or catching fractured sunlight during those limpid afternoons

Salix aurita: spelaeodendron, eared willow

when the pavements are liquid mirrors indistinguishable from the ocean.

I have come full circle to the end of the year and my journey along the bohreen and over the pavements of The Burren is complete. Once more rain washes across a deserted rockscape driven by gales in a cleansing fury. Turloughs are full to their brims and Bewick's swans graze the grass around. Winter does strip the vestiges of spring foliage and autumn fruits from the resilient skeletons of trees and shrubs, yet The Burren is not lifeless. There are flowers on the mudworts in the rock-pools at Poll Salach, and on the whitlow grass and herb Robert around Cathair Dhúin Irghuis. Some early hazel catkins quiver in the wind. Every rusty-back fern is plump and green. The plum-coloured withies of the sallies and the spelaeodendrons that conceal the underworld of The Burren about Cullaun, display the first hints of white catkins. Still there are flowers.

> They are among the stones above the ash
> Above the briar and thorn and the scarce grass;...

W. B. Yeats: 'The dreaming of the bones'

310

Trumpeting angel: Noughaval

ENVOI

A Stranger here
Strange things doth meet, strange Glory see.
Strange Treasures lodg'd in this fair World appear,
Strange all and New to me:
But that they mine should be who Nothing was,
That Strangest is of all; yet brought to pass.

Thomas Traherne: 'The Salutation'

The Burren *is* a strange place, rich and rare, barren and fertile; it provokes wonder and contempt. To me, The Burren is ineluctable.

An adjective commonly used in descriptions is 'lunar', implying aridity and eccentricity, but that is only a distant, superficial view, and an uncomprehending one that denies the abundant moisture and exuberant vegetation. Over six hundred different flowering plants and ferns, more than half of Ireland's native vascular flora, grow in The Burren as well as uncounted numbers of mosses, fungi and other lesser plants, and there are more sites of archaeological importance in the barony than in any region of similar size elsewhere in Ireland.

This incomparable landscape, and its vegetation and fauna have been altered by mankind during more than five millennia. By a twist of fate we inherited a beautiful, bewildering place, and we must treasure it so that, in turn, we bequeath no less rich and strange a land to our successors.

We are still tampering with The Burren. The most visible changes in recent years have been the removal of walls and eradication of small meadows, and their replacement by much larger fields containing an artificial pasture of sown grasses; undoubtedly such transformations bring benefits to farmers and allow more efficient farming, but grey pavements, walls and wildflowers are essential to The Burren.

The immediate future of The Burren's rockscape, turloughs, ancient remains, plants and animals is a matter of concern to many people. Some will argue that because The Burren is an artefact and not an unaltered wilderness, conservation of the 'lunar' hills, albeit endowed with a rich flora and fauna, is an illogical and irrational aspiration; they are a small minority. There may be others who will propose that a part (or perhaps all) of the area should be fenced off, declared out-of-bounds and left embalmed in unnatural isolation: those conservationists do not understand The Burren and the processes which moulded it; their zeal is misplaced.

In between are numerous folk who want to see that The Burren survives as a natural rock-garden enriched with caves and cathairs. We all have to recognize that it is both a much modified landscape in which people have to live and earn a living, and a unique mosaic of exceedingly rich habitats. Furthermore, everybody must be persuaded that native wildflowers and animals have to be encouraged, particularly by grazing of the pavements by free-ranging cattle, sheep and goats; if the benign pressure of grazing animals does not continue, hazel scrub will spread to choke the pavement and many smaller herbs will be ousted. A corollary is that farming should be encouraged, and farmers enabled to pursue traditional methods of husbandry, to maintain sensible stocking levels, and to continue to practise winterage; they should be paid to do so if conservation means they are less efficient and so cannot earn an adequate living. Any decline in farming, or careless alteration in agricultural practises will accelerate the expansion of hazel copses and woodlands–in other words, the grey hillscape with gentians will retreat under green forests and ferns.

Vital elements of The Burren's human landscape–tumbledown churches, stone walls and 'green roads'–must also be preserved, and intrusive new buildings and careless siting of such things as silage dumps must be forbidden. Landowners have to be persuaded not to enlarge fields by knocking down walls and bulldozing pavement, and not to 'improve' pasture by applying overdoses of fertilizers or by spreading glacial drift and re-seeding; again compensation should be paid.

Preservation of an ancient building or object is relatively easy, and precise restoration can be undertaken; the dolmen at Poulnabrone was dismantled, excavated and put back again, stone by stone. Conservation of the landscape and its complicated, finely-balanced ecosystem is not so simple, demanding hard work, substantial expenditure, and continuous vigilance; restoration of a degraded landscape is even more difficult and its success is utterly unpredictable.

Conservation cannot be achieved by passivity. I agree with Aldo Leopold, who wrote, in an essay entitled 'Land pathology', that

> Conservation is a protest against destructive land use. It seeks to preserve both the utility and the beauty of the landscape.[1]

When we accept that the present-day Burren is worth conserving, the status quo will be maintained only by active management with political backing at local, national and international levels. Furthermore, The Burren's survival requires consensus between the native people, politicians, and those who acknowledge its international scientific and historic significance.

The Burren and other hitherto 'undeveloped' regions in Ireland are now thought of as magnets to attract tourists, and the projected increase in the number of visitors could have more dramatic consequences for the landscape and wildlife than five millennia of farming. The Burren is situated astride one of the main tourist routes, and tourists should be encouraged to linger, look and learn. The profitable tourists are those who come to the area to stay for several days; most of them are discerning and expect to see a wild land, not an artificial theme-park–they want flowers, and peace and quiet, not hills demeaned by bill-boards, litter and interpretative centres. The importance of maintaining the unique quality of the wild places and the farmlands, resplendent with flowers, the whole extraordinary Burren landscape, its diversity and desolation, cannot be over-stressed. When places like The Burren are degraded, tourists stop coming, and there is yet another contradiction: visitors can destroy the tranquillity they seek, threaten wildlife, and alter beyond restoration the landscape that attracted them in the first place.

I would be foolish to ignore the consequences of this book, and I am aware that I may contribute to the tourist influx. I must plead that my purpose is to inform readers about The Burren, to describe the flora, and to persuade everyone that it deserves conservation, so that three and a half centuries hence pilgrims to Kilmacduagh will be able to see juniper creeping over the rocks, Spring gentians and mountain avens.

> A land there is, a little lap of earth,
> Near neighbour to the dawn and the south wind,
> The first to feel the sweet new-risen sun,
> Nor hurt at all by his primaeval fire.
> It knoweth but the clemency of heaven,
> And in one lap holds the delights of earth.

Bernard Sylvestris of Tours: *Cosmographia*[2]

NOTES AND REFERENCES

1. In the study of herbs
1. Trevor 1984: 158.
2. Jennings 1971.

2. A patrimony of stones
1. Stokes 1894: 321.
2. Robinson 1975.
3. Williams 1970; Whittow 1974.
4. Foot 1863; Br.Mus.(Nat.Hist.) 1983.
5. Farrington 1965; Finch & Walsh 1973.
6. Williams 1963; see Tratman 1969: 96-123.
7. Self 1979.
8. Self 1979: 94.
9. Self 1979: 19-20.
10. Robertson pers.comm.; for the 'original' version of 'Song inspired by Doolin Cave' see Lloyd 1964: 4-5 (see also Tratman 1969: 21).

    There are five verses to this immortal song and it was first 'performed' on 5 August 1953, the day after the University of Bristol Spelaeological Society team had confirmed that Doolin Cave, which was discovered on 3 August by Geoff Fuller, Stan Wood and Straun Robertson, passed *under* the Aille River, a 'then well nigh incredible fact'.
11. Robertson pers.comm.: spelaeodendron is not *Salix caprea* (cf. Self 1979: 19-20).

3. Who can have trod in the grass?
1. Yeats 1919.
2. O'Mahony 1858.
3. Nelson 1979.
4. Walsh 1978.
5. Firth 1894.
6. Firth 1894: I, 292.
7. Mac Neill 1990.
8. Lhuyd 1707; Nelson 1979.
9. Lhuyd 1712.
10. Lucas 1740.
11. Rutty ms.
12. see Nelson 1991.
13. Kelly 1990.
14. Mackay 1806: 182 (e.g. *Lycopodium selago*–'On moist grounds near Gleninagh, bottom of Burren mountains, in great abundance').
15. Lyne and Mitchell 1985.
16. O Cillín 1977: 43.
17. Carter 1846.
18. Whitla 1851.
19. O'Mahony 1858.
20. Moffat 1898.
21. Moffat 1898: 51-52.
22. Foot 1862: 143.
23. Foot ms.
24. Foot 1862.
25. Healy 1988.
26. Stewart 1879.
27. Corry 1880.
28. Murphy 1987; Foot 1863.
29. see e.g. Stone 1906.
30. Praeger 1895.
31. specimen in DBN.
32. Praeger 1909: 51-54; Praeger 1934: n. 346-351
33. Praeger 1950: 112.
34. Webb 1962; Ivimey-Cook & Proctor 1966; Maloch 1976.
35. Threlkeld 1726.

4. Strange, effected Pavements
1. Foot 1863: 8.
2. e.g.Jennings 1971; Clayton 1966.
3. Foot 1863; Langridge 1971.
4. Quin & Freeman 1947.
5. Foot 1863: 18.
6. Mackay 180
7. Foot 1862: 151.
8. Foot 1862: 151.
9. Nelson 1991.
10. Rutty 1772 (see Hill 1991)
11. Hutchinson 1968; Proctor and Yeo 1973.
12. If these parts of Clare are included in The Burren, this becomes the second Burren species protected by law (the other is *Viola hirta*).
13. Druce 1909: 210.
14. Threlkeld 1726.
15. Wade 1808.
16. Weir 1986.
17. Grigson 1955.
18. Foot 1862: 149.
19. Mitchell 1975.
20. Threlkeld 1726.
21. How 1650: 64; Nelson 1979.
22. Stelfox 1955.
23. Yeo 1985.
24. Grigson 1955: 105-107.

5. Her winter weeds outworn

1. Exact climatological data for The Burren is not available as there has been no permanent meteorological station in the region for any substantial period - a small facility is at Ballyvaghan, and there are scattered rainfall stations, but the nearest major climatological station is Shannon Airport, about 50 km south-south-east of Ballyvaghan.
2. Praeger 1909: 6.
3. A measure of drying power is mean potential evapotranspiration which in winter is over 125 mm, and in summer is between 400 and 425 mm
4. Heslop-Harrison 1960.
5. Dickinson, Pearson and Webb 1964.
6. Grigson 1955.
7. Foot 1862: 148.
8. Clark 1969.
9. Levinge 1893.
10. Dixon, 1982.
11. Bond 1988; Heath and Emmet 1989.
12. Classey 1950; Classey 1951; Robinson 1950
13. Cockayne 1954.
14. Grigson 1955.
15. Threlkeld 1726.
16. Valentine 1979.
17. Grigson 1955
18. Threlkeld 1726; Doolan 1991: 164.

6. On the green roads

1. Kelly 1990.
2. Lyne and Mitchell 1985.
3. Farrer 1919: I, 391
4. Threlkeld 1726: 125-126.
5. Foot 1862: 149.
6. Grigson 1955.
7. Braun-Blanquet 1952.
8. Cameron 1883; Grigson 1955.
9. Grigson 1955.
10. Webb and Gornall 1989.
11. Threlkeld 1726: 117-119.
12. Rutty ms.
13. Threlkeld 1726: 118-119.

7. Turloughs–the half-drowned Burren

1. Dinneen 1927.
2. Lucas 1740.
3. Foot 1862.
4. Praeger 1909.
5. O'Mahony 1858.

6. Foot 1864: 150.
7. Elkington 1969; Elkington 1984; Elkington and Woodell 1963.
8. Campbell and Lenz 1990.
9. Praeger 1932; Webb and Scannell 1983.
10. Roden 1991.
11. Richards 1981.
12. Richards 1972.
13. Coxon 1987.
14. Williams 1970.
15. Praeger 1932.
16. Corry 1880: 191, 203; Druce 1909: 210
17. More 1855; Corry 1880: 203; Levinge 1892; Druce 1909.
18. Praeger 1934.
19. Ivimey-Cook and Proctor 1966.
20. King 1685.
21. Kelly 1990: 81-82.
    '...terra lacus or a lake rising out of the earth, but some gentlemen of learning derive it from the Celtick word of pretty much the same sound and signification...'
22. Browne ms.
23. Lyne and Mitchell 1985.

8. Patrick B. O'Kelly

1. This chapter is an edited version of my article (*The Kew Magazine* 7 (1990)); the vignette of hart's tongue fern was originally reproduced in the same place. Unacknowledged quotations are from that paper and O'Kelly's catalogues.
2. Piper 1986: plate 4.
3. Kent and Allen 1984; specimens labelled 'Dr O'Kelly' are in the National Museum of Wales, Cardiff.
4. Preston 1989.
5. Scannell 1988.
6. Anonymous, 'Clare plants', 1893.
7. Praeger 1949.
8. I am most grateful to Theresa Andreucetti for her invaluable assistance with research on P. B. O'Kelly.

9. The receipt of fern-seed

1. Foot 1863.
2. Druery 1884.
3. Lowe 1908; Nelson 1990; Nelson (in press).
4. Anonymous 1893.
5. Anonymous 1890.
6. Phillips in Anonymous 1890.
7. Lhuyd 1712.
8. Walford 1812.

9. O'Mahony 1858.

10. Keogh 1735.

11. Wade 1804.

12. Threlkeld 1726: 20.

13. Wilmanns and Brun-Hool 1983; Darlington 1981; Camus, Jermy and Thomas 1991.

14. Page 1982.

15. Anonymous 1890.

16. Lowe 1908: 70.

17. Carter 1846.

18. Foot 1863.

19. Foot 1863; Lowe 1908: 42.

20. see facsimile Nelson 1987.

21. O'Mahony 1858.

22. Foot 1862.

23. Foot 1862.

24. Kinahan 1860.

25. Foot 1862; Kinahan 1860.

26. Foot 1863.

27. Page 1976.

28. Page 1989; Rumsey, Sheffield and Haufler 1991.

29. Corry 1880.

10. Tussocks of unbroken glory

1. Farrer 1919.

2. How 1650.

3. Threlkeld 1726.

4. Wade 1804.

5. Mackay 1806.

6. Mackay 1825.

7. Farrer 1919.

8. Corry 1880: 201.

9. Elkington 1963.

10. Corry 1880: 201.

11. Farrer 1919. There are no published reports of the paler variants in The Burren, except when plants exhibited at horticultural shows are stated to have been grown from Burren seed - e.g. *Bulletin of the Alpine Garden Society* 37 (1967), 357 ['white flushed with blue']; 39 (1970), 356 ['Clare']: 43 (1975), 297 ['ice-blue']

12. Elkington 1972.

13. Proctor 1957.

14. Proctor 1956.

15. Foot 1862.

16. O'Mahony 1858.

17. Elkington 1971.

18. How 1650.

19. Lhuyd 1712; Nelson 1979; Mitchell 1971.

20. Webb and Scannell 1983: 63.

21. Porsild 1959.

22. Praeger 1934: n.106

23. Crabtree 1982.

24. Trevor 1984.

25. O'Mahony 1858.

26. Yeo 1985.

27. Corry 1880.

28. Corry 1880.

29. Webb 1950; Webb and Gornall 1989.

30. Webb 1950: 199-206.

31. e.g. Praeger 1909: plate 18.

32. Mackay 1836.

33. Keogh 1735.

34. Foot 1862.

35. in Doolan 1991: 164.

36. Keogh 1735: 'Palma Christi, or the Greater Spurge. Hib: Crugh Christugh or Christy, Lat. Cataputia major vel Ricinus... It grows plentifully in the Barony of Burrin...'

37. Moore 1854.

38. Foot 1862.

39. Foot ms.

40. Forbes 1989.

41. Scannell 1988.

42. O'Kelly [Oxford] ms: O'Kelly to Druce, 26 July 1909

43. O'Kelly [Oxford] ms: O'Kelly to Druce, 31 July 1909.

44. Foot 1862.

45. Foot 1862.

46. Lucas 1740; Nelson 1991.

47. Grigson 1955.

48. Threlkeld 1726.

49. Webb and Scannell 1983: 107.

11. A provocation of orchids

1. Power 1990.

2. Stalley 1975; Stalley 1987.

3. Nelson and Stalley 1989.

4. Nelson in Piper 1986.

5. Hayward 1964: 126-127.

6. Raymond Piper pers.comm.

7. Threlkeld 1726: 115.

8. Keogh 1735.

9. Power's translation (1990) is quoted at the head of the chapter. Another recent translation of note is by Kinsella (1986):

    A sterling aid in arranging pairs
    is the bite of an apple, or powdered herbs
    a little Balls-of-joy or Lumps-of-dung,
    the Shining Splicer, or Hammer-the-Hole,

Nannygoat's-Bait or Maiden's Dart.
Goldenlove - all lustful spells,
the burning up of leaves in secret,
and more of the like that shouldn't be learned.

10. Foot 1862: 154.

11. Webb and Scannell 1983.

12. Moffat 1898: 171

13. Moore 1864.

14. Moffat 1898: 169 ff.

15. Reichenbach 1865; the original correspondence from Moore to Reichenbach has not been traced but may be in Vienna.

16. Moore 1864; More 1865.

17. Praeger 1934: n.38.

18. Drude 1912.

19. Levinge 1892; More's comments are in Moffat 1898: 379-380.

20. Pugsley 1934.

21. More 1865 (also in Moffat 1898: 560-561).

22. Moore and More, *Cybele* 1866: 283.

23. Moore and More 'On the climate...' 1866.

24. More 1893 (also in Moffat 1898: 554).

25. Webb 1983.

26. see facsimile pp. 115-118.

27. O'Kelly 'A botanical ramble...' 1903.

28. Druce 1909.

29. O'Kelly [Oxford] ms.

30. Vermeulen 1947.

31. Webb and Scannell 1983.

32. O'Mahony 1858: 30.

33. O'Mahony 1858: 30.

34. Summerhayes 1951: 145; Proctor and Yeo 1973.

35. Summerhayes 1951: 224-225; Clapham, Tutin and Warburg 1962: 1030-1031.

36. O'Mahony 1858.

37. Clapham, Tutin and Warburg 1962: 1049.

38. Foot 1862: 155; Moore 1864.

39. Grigson 1955.

40. Gerard 1633: 402.

41. Summerhayes 1951: 44-45.

42. Foot 1862.

43. Webb and Scannell 1983.

44. Wells 1967.

45. Wells 1967.

46. Gerard 1633: 219.

47. Threlkeld 1726: 115.

12. Carnivores and parasites

1. Foot 1862: 153.

2. Whitla 1851.

3. O'Mahony 1858.

4. Press and Grave 1989.

5. Rumsey and Jury 1991.

6. Pugsley 1930; Webb and Scannell 1983: 156.

7. Corry 1880.

8. Webb and Scannell 1983: 161.

9. Praeger 1903.

10. Heslop-Harrison 1949.

11. Roden 1984.

12. Webb and Scannell 1983; Steiger 1987.

13. *Pinguicula grandiflora* forma *chionopetra* is not published as this work goes to press; formal publication will follow.

14. 'Veronica' 1886.

15. Scully 1916.

13. A wealth of heather

1. cited by W. H. Phillips (1901) and perhaps his own composition as I cannot trace it in other sources.

2. Drew 1990.

3. Webb 1947; Grime 1963; for review see Gimingham 1972: 109.

4. Clapham, Tutin and Warburg 1962: 362.

5. Cameron 1883; Grigson 1955.

6. Browne ms.

7. Clapham, Tutin and Warburg 1962: 204.

8. Webb and Scannell 1983: 42.

9. Ivimey-Cook and Proctor 1966:

10. Grigson 1955; Threlkeld (1726) had these names from counties Laois and Offaly for St John's wort - 'Allais Muire' (*allais Muire*: Mary's sweat), 'Beahnova' (*beathnua*), 'Taed Coluim Kille' (*téad Coluim Cille*, Columbcille's rope), 'Beahnua Bicinionn' (*beathnua baineann*) and 'Beahnua firionn' (*beathnua fireann*).

11. Foot 1862.

12. Lhuyd 1712.

13. Bell and Tallis 1973.

14. Threlkeld 1726: 53

15. Rutty 1772: 136.

16. Gimingham 1960.

17. Bannister 1965.

18. Phillips 1901 (see note 1 this chapter).

19. Summerfield, 1973; Summerfield, 1975.

14. Stony seaboard

1. Guiry in Webb and Scannell 1983: 287-291; Roden 1991.

2. Nelson 1978; Nelson 1986.

3. cf. O Cillín 1977: 16.

4. Threlkeld 1726: 55.

5. Praeger 1913.

6. Keogh 1735.

7. Ingrouille and Stace 1986.

8. Natural History Museum ms; my thanks to Dr D. E. Allen from bringing this to my attention.

9. Moffat 1898: 53

10. Moore and More 1866: 240-241.

11. Baker 1954.

12. Proctor and Yeo 1973.

15. Down the bohreens fuchsia-high

1. Nelson 1991.

2. Webb and Scannell 1983.

3. Webb 1962.

4. Webb and Scannell 1983: 123

5. Webb 1947.

6. Webb and Scannell 1983: 148.

7. Nelson 1984; Walsh and Nelson 1987: plate 9.

8. Walsh and Nelson 1987: plate 12.

9. It is sometimes stated (e.g. Stalley 1987: iv) that the 'ruined abbey' was Corcomroe; in fact Betjeman was alluding to St Sourney's Church, Drumacoo, and the St George family mausoleum. Sir John Betjeman confirmed this in a letter to Anita Leslie, 17 July 1980 (courtesy Gordon St G. Mark).

16. Behold the earth apparelled with plants

1. Gerard 1633; 4.

2. Corry 1880: 204.

3. Threlkeld 1726: 115.

4. Threlkeld 1726: 126.

5. Adams 1955.

6. Grigson 1955.

7. Threlkeld 1726: 103.

8. Hutchinson 1946; Proctor and Yeo 1973.

9. Corrigan 1984: 24.

10. Grigson 1955; Danaher 1972.

11. Laird 1904: 203.

12. Danaher 1972: 147-148.

13. Threlkeld 1726: 102; Cameron 1883.

14. Grigson 1955.

15. Grigson 1955.

16. Foot 1862.

17. Threlkeld 1726: 73.

18. Proctor and Yeo 1973.

19. Gerard 1633: 86.

20. White 1808. White reported that its Irish name was luascadhfhér medhon (*luascadhfhéar meán*), a straight translation of *Briza media*

21. Danaher, 1963: 165; Cameron, 1883: 90.

17. Among the stones above the ash

1. Watts 1962, 1977, 1984, and in Webb and Scannell 1983: xxxvi-xl.

2. Nelson 1979; Preece, Coxon and Robinson 1986.

3. Crabtree 1982.

4. Crabtree 1982; Watts 1984.

5. Mitchell 1978 and Harbison 1988 provide useful summaries.

6. Watts 1984, and in Webb and Scannell 1983.

7. Fahy 1893: 66.

8. Murphy 1956; Kinsella 1986.

9. O'Mahony 1858; Foot 1862.

10. Fahy 1893: 67.

11. Robinson 1977.

12. Grigson 1955.

13. Step 1905: II, 103.

14. Winifred Letts, 'A Soft Day'.

15. For this and subsequent notes on trees, see Kelly 1976.

16. Threlkeld 1726: 43.

17. Dickenson and Thorp 1968.

18. Jonathan Swift, 'On poetry'.

19. Grigson 1955.

20. Heaney 1982.

21. Nelson 1981.

22. Spellissy and O'Brien 1987: 27.

23. Kinsella 1986.

24. Robinson 1977; Fahy 1893.

25. Lucas 1963; Danaher 1972.

26. Grigson 1955.

27. Walsh, Ross and Nelson 1983: plate 1.

28. Warburg 1957.

29. Seamus O'Sullivan, 'The twilight people'.

30. Grigson 1955: 355.

31. Gerard 1633: 1469.

32. Browne ms.

33. Threlkeld 1726: 55.

34. Mahon, [1981]; Hill, 1990.

35. Fahy 1893: 66

36. Robinson 1977.

37. Threlkeld 1726: 116.

38. Mabey 1972.

39. Mabey 1972.

40. Tratman 1969; Self 1979.

41. McAllister and Rutherford 1989.

18. Envoi

1. see Oelschlaeger 1991: 228.

2. Helen Waddell 1933: 172.

BIBLIOGRAPHY

A. W. Adams, '*Succisa pratensis* Moench.', *Journal of Ecology* 43 (1955), 709-718 [Biological Flora of the British Isles].

[Anonymous], '[The fifth meeting of the Winter session... February 19th...]', *Proceedings of the Belfast Naturalists' Field Club* (1889-1890), 220-230.

[Anonymous], 'Fern exhibition at Chiswick, August 23 and 24, 1892', *Journal of the Royal Horticultural Society* 15 (1893), cxxvii-cxxix.

[Anonymous], 'Clare plants', *The Irish Naturalist* 2 (1893), 251.

[Anonymous], 'A correspondent calls our attention...', *Journal of Botany* 44 (1906), 40.

H. G. Baker, 'The *Limonium binervosum* complex in western and northern Ireland', *Proceedings of the Botanical Society of the British Isles* 1 (1954), 131-141.

R. Bannister, '*Erica cinerea* L.', *Journal of Ecology* 53 (1965), 527-542 [Biological Flora of the British Isles].

J. N. B. Bell and J. H. Tallis, '*Empetrum nigrum* L.', *Journal of Ecology* 61 (1973), 289-305 [Biological Flora of the British Isles].

J. Betjeman, 'Ireland with Emily', *New bats in old belfries*. 1945 [quoted from Earl of Birkenhead (editor), *John Betjeman's collected poems*. London, John Murray, 1958.]

K. G. M. Bond, 'Species profile [The Burren green]', *Newsletter of the Irish Biogeographical Society* 1 (new series) (1988), 3.

J. D. Bradley and E. C. Pelham-Clinton, 'The Lepidoptera of The Burren, Co. Clare, W. Ireland', *Entomologist's Gazette* 18 (1967), 115-153.

J. Braun-Blanquet, 'Pflanzensoziologische Ueberlegungen also Hilfsmittel zur Erkennung systematischen Einheiten am Beispiel von *Antennaria hibernica* dargelegt', *Vegetatio* 3 (1952), 298-300.

British Museum (Natural History), *British palaeozoic fossils*. Fourth edition. London, British Museum (Natural History), 1983.

J. Cameron, *Gaelic names of plants (Scottish and Irish) collected and arranged in scientific order...* Edinburgh & London, William Blackwood and Sons, 1883.

J. M. Camus, A. C. Jermy and B. A. Thomas, *A world of ferns*. London, Natural History Museum Publications, 1991.

C. Carter, 'Botanical ramble in Ireland', *Phytologist* 2 (1846), 512-514.

A. R. Clapham, T. G. Tutin and E. F. Warburg, *Flora of the British Isles*. Second edition. Cambridge, University Press, 1962.

S. C. Clark, 'Some effects of temperature and photoperiod on growth and floral development in three winter annuals', *New Phytologist* 68 (1969), 1137-1144.

[E. W. Classey], '*Luceria* (*Calamia*) *virens* L. in Britain', *Entomologist's Gazette* 1 (1950), 189.

E. W. Classey, 'Burren - 1950. General introduction', *Entomologist's Gazette* 2 (1951), 86-87.

K. M. Clayton, 'The origin of the landforms of the Malham area', *Field Studies* 2 (1966), 359-384.

E. A. Cockayne, 'The Irish subspecies of *Calamia virens* L., (Lep: Caradrinidae)', *Entomologist's Gazette* 5 (1954), 155-156.

D. Corrigan, 'The scientific basis of folk medicine: the Irish dimension', in R. Vickery (editor), *Plant-lore studies*. London, The Folklore Society, 1984, pp. 10-42

T. H. Corry, 'Notes of a botanical ramble in the county of Clare, Ireland', *Proceedings and reports of the Belfast Natural History and Philosophical Society 1879-1880*, 167-207.

C. E. Coxon, 'The spatial distribution of turloughs', *Irish Geography* 20 (1987), 11-23.

C. E. Coxon, 'An examination of the characteristics of turloughs, using multivariate statistical techniques', *Irish Geography* 20 (1987), 24-42.

K. Crabtree, 'Evidence for The Burren's forest cover', in S. Limbrey and M. Bell (editors), *Archaeological aspects of woodland ecology. British Archaeological Reports (international series)* 146 (1982), 105-113.

T. G. F. Curtis, H. N. McGough, P. J. Foss and A. McNally, 'The occurrence of *Limosella aquatica* L. in limestone solution hollows at Fisherstreet, Co. Clare (H9)', *Irish Naturalists Journal* 22 (1987), 248-249.

G. E. D., '[*Dryas octopetala*]', *Phytologist* 2 (1845), 64.

K. Danaher, 'The hungry grass', *Biatas* (June 1963), 164-167.

K. Danaher, *The year in Ireland. Irish calendar customs.* Cork, Mercier Press, 1972.

A. Darlington, *The ecology of walls.* London, Heinemann, 1981.

R. David, 'The Burren flora', *Irish Naturalists Journal* 13 (1960), 169.

C. G. Davidson and L. M. Lenz, 'Models of inheritance of flower colour and extra petals in *Potentilla fruticosa* L.', *Euphytica* 45 (1990), 237-246.

C. H. Dickinson, C. M. Pearson and D. A. Webb, 'Some micro-habitats of The Burren, their micro-environments and vegetation', *Proceedings of the Royal Irish Academy* 63 B 16 (1964).

C. H. Dickinson and T. K. Thorp, 'Epiphytic lichens on *Corylus avellana* in The Burren, County Clare', *Lichenologist* 4 (1968), 66-72.

H. Dierschke, 'Teucrio scorodoniae - Geranietum sanguinei, a new saum association of the Trifolio-Geranietea in Ireland', *Journal of Life Sciences Royal Dublin Society* 3 (1982), 175-179.

P. Dinneen, *Foclóir Gaedilge agus béarla. An Irish-English dictionary.* Dublin, Irish Text Society, 1927.

J. M. Dixon, '*Sesleria albicans* Kit. ex Schultes', *Journal of Ecology* 70 (1982), 667-684 [Biological Flora of the British Isles].

L. Doolan, 'Lore and cures and blessed wells', in J. W. O'Connell and A. Korff (editors), *The book of The Burren.* Kinvarra, Tír Eolas, 1991. pp. 155-171.

G. J. Doyle, 'Minuartio-Thlaspietum alpestris (Violetea calaminariae) in Ireland', *Journal of Life Sciences Royal Dublin Society* 3 (1982), 143-146.

G. J. Doyle, '*Lychnis flos-cuculi* L. and *Carex disticha* Hudson in The Burren hills', *Irish Naturalists Journal* 22 (1986), 74-77.

D. P. Drew, 'Accelerated soil erosion in a karst area: The Burren, western Ireland', *Journal of Hydrology* 61 (1983), 113-124.

D. P. Drew, 'The hydrology of the Burren, County Clare,' *Irish Geography* 23 (1990), 69-89.

G. C. Druce, 'Notes on Irish plants', *The Irish Naturalist* 18 (1909), 209-213.

O. Drude, 'The flora of Great Britain compared with that of Central Europe', *New Phytologist* 11 (1912), 236-255.

C. T. Druery, '*Scolopendrium vulgare* var. *cristatum* O'Kelly (Stansfield)', *The Gardeners' Chronicle* 21 (new series) (1884), 57.

T. T. Elkington, 'Cytotaxonomic variation in *Potentilla fruticosa* L.', *New Phytologist* 68 (1969), 151-160.

T. T. Elkington, '*Gentiana verna* L.', *Journal of Ecology* 51 (1963), 755-767 [Biological Flora of the British Isles].

T. T. Elkington, '*Dryas octopetala* L.', *Journal of Ecology* 59 (1971), 887-905 [Biological Flora of the British Isles].

T. T. Elkington, 'Variation in *Gentiana verna* L.', *New Phytologist* 71 (1972), 1203-1211.

T. T. Elkington, 'Cytogenetic variation in the British flora: origins and significance', *New Phytologist* 98 (1984), 101-118. (see also J. L. Harley and D. H. Lewis, 1984).

T. T. Elkington and S. R. J. Woodell, '*Potentilla fruticosa* L.', *Journal of Ecology* 51 (1963), 769-781 [Biological Flora of the British Isles].

J. Fahey, *The history and antiquities of the diocese of Kilmacduagh.* Dublin, M. H. Gill & Sons, 1893. [Facsimile edition, KG, 1986].

A. Farrington, 'The last glaciation in the Burren, Co. Clare', *Proceedings of the Royal Irish Academy* 64 B 3 (1965).

R. Farrer. *The English rock-garden.* London, Thomas Nelson & Sons, 1919 (2 volumes).

J. M. Feehan, *The secret places of The Burren.* Cork, Royal Carbery Books, 1987.

T. F. Finch and M. Walsh, 'Drumlins of County Clare', *Proceedings of the Royal Irish Academy* 73 B 23 (1973).

C. H. Firth (editor). *The memoirs of Edmund Ludlow.* Oxford, Clarendon Press, 1894 (2 volumes).

F. J. Foot, 'On the distribution of plants in Burren, County of Clare', *Transactions of the Royal Irish Academy* 24 (Science part III) (1862), 143-160.

[Foot read the paper on 28 April 1862; his title was 'On the botanical peculiarities of the Burren district, county of Clare'. Offprints, issued separately, are clearly dated 1862, but the third part of vol. 24, as issued with other papers, is dated 1864.]

F. J. Foot, 'On the ferns of west Clare, being a list of those growing west of a line drawn north and south through the town of Tulla', *Proceedings of the Natural History Society of Dublin* 3 (1863), 6-9. [also in *Natural History Review* 7 (1860), 36-40].

F. J. Foot, 'Natural history notes on the mammalia of the west coast of Clare', *Proceedings of the Natural History Society of Dublin* 3 (1863), 104-106.

F. J. Foot, 'Explanations to accompany Sheets 114, 122 and 123 of the maps of the Geological survey of Ireland, illustrating parts of the counties of Clare and Galway', *Memoirs of the Geological Survey*. Dublin, HMSO., 1863.

F. J. Foot, '[letter on *Cystopteris fragilis* and *Digitalis purpurea*]', *Proceedings of the Natural History Society of Dublin* 4 (1865), 2 [see also p. 108].

F. J. Foot and S. Haughton, 'Meteorological journal kept at Ennistimon and Ballyvaughan, County of Clare, during the year 1861... with note on the windrose of the County of Clare in 1861...', *Journal of the Royal Dublin Society* 3 (1862), 327-341.

A. C. Forbes, 'Some legendary and historical references to Irish woods, and their significance', *Proceedings of the Royal Irish Academy* 41 B 3 (1932).

R. S. Forbes, 'The population behaviour of pyramidal bugle *Ajuga pyramidalis* L. in the Burren, Co. Clare', *Irish Naturalists Journal* 23 (1989), 54-59.

G. Gardner, 'The reproductive capacity of *Fraxinus excelsior* in the Derbyshire limestone', *Journal of Ecology* 65 (1977), 107-118.

J. Gerard, *The herball or generall historie of plantes... very much enlarged... by Thomas Johnson...* Second edition. London, 1633. [facsimile, New York, Dover Publications, 1975].

C. H. Gimingham, '*Calluna* Salisb. a monotypic genus', *Journal of Ecology* 48 (1960), 455-483.

C. H. Gimingham, *Ecology of heathlands*. London, Chapman and Hall, 1972.

H. Godwin, 'The spreading of the British flora considered in relation to conditions of the Late-glacial period', *Journal of Ecology* 37 (1949), 140-147.

G. Grigson. *The Englishman's flora*. London, Phoenix House, 1966.

M. E. Griffiths and M. C. F. Proctor, '*Helianthemum canum* (L.) Baumg.', *Journal of Ecology* 44 (1956), 677-682 [Biological Flora of the British Isles].

J. P. Grime, 'Factors determining the occurrence of calcifuge species on shallow soils over calcareous substrata', *Journal of Ecology* 51 (1963), 375-390.

J. P. Grime, 'The ecology of species, families and communities of the contemporary British flora', *New Phytologist* 98 (1984), 15-33. (see also J. L. Harley and D. H. Lewis, 1984).

G. Haggett, 'An original account of rearing *Luceria virens* Linn.', *Entomologist's Gazette* 4 (1953), 314-321.

P. Harbison. *Pre-Christian Ireland from the first settlers to the early Celts*. London, Thames and Hudson, 1988.

J. L. Harley and D. H. Lewis (editors), *The flora and vegetation of* Britain, Origins and changes - the facts and their interpretation. London, The New Phytologist Trust, 1984 (reprinted from *New Phytologist* 98 (1984)).

H. C. Hart. *A list of plants found in the islands of Aran, Galway Bay*. Dublin, Hodges, Foster & Co., 1875.

R. Hayward, *Munster and the city of Cork*. London, Phoenix House, 1964. [illustrations by Raymond Piper]

J. Healy, 'Some people and townlands of Kilkeedy parish', *The Other Clare* 12 (1988), 38-43.

S. Heaney, 'An Aisling in The Burren', in *Station Island*. London, Faber and Faber, 1984. p. 47.

S. Heaney, 'The god in the tree', in S. Mac Réamoinn (editor) *The pleasures of Gaelic poetry*. London, Allen Lane, 1982. pp. 23-34 (see also translations).

J. Heath and A. M Emmet (editors), *The moths and butterflies of Great Britain and Ireland*, volume 10: Noctuidae (part II). Colchester, Harley Books, 1990. p. 248-249.

G. L. Herries Davies and N. Stephens. *Ireland.* London, Methuen, 1978. [The geomorphology of the British Isles series].

J. Heslop-Harrison, '*Pinguicula grandiflora* Lam. in N. Clare', *Irish Naturalists Journal* 9 (1949), 311.

J. Heslop-Harrison, 'A note on temperature and vapour pressure deficit under drought conditions in some microhabitats of The Burren limestone, Co. Clare', *Proceedings of the Royal Irish Academy* 61 B 6 (1960).

D. J. Hill (editor), *Indigenous vegetables useful in dying and painting; from the observations of authors, the practises of the ancient Irish, and some new experiments by John Rutty M.D.* Bristol, Department of Continuing Education, University of Bristol, 1990 [1991].

[W. How], *Phytologia Britannica.* Oxford, Pulleyn, 1650.

S. E. Howarth and J. T. Williams, '*Chrysanthemum leucanthemum* L.', *Journal of Ecology* 56 (1968), 585-595 [Biological Flora of the British Isles].

C. E. Hubbard, *Grasses, a guide to their structure, identification, uses, and distribution in the British Isles.* Revised edition. London, Penguin Books, 1968.

H. C. Huggins, 'Lepidoptera of the Burren in May and June 1956', *The Entomologist* 90 (1957), 139-142.

J. Hutchinson, *Common wild flowers.* Revised edition. West Drayton, Penguin Books, 1946.

T. C. Hutchinson, '*Teucrium scorodonia* L.', *Journal of Ecology* 56 (1968), 901-911 [Biological Flora of the British Isles].

M. J. Ingrouille and C. A. Stace, 'The *Limonium binervosum* aggregate (Plumbaginaceae) in the British Isles', *Botanical Journal of the Linnean Society* 92 (1986), 177-217.

R. B. Ivimey-Cook, 'The vegetation of solution cups in the limestone of the Burren, Co. Clare', *Journal of Ecology* 53 (1965), 437-445.

R. B. Ivimey-Cook and M. C. F. Proctor, 'The plant communities of The Burren, Co. Clare', *Proceedings of the Royal Irish Academy* 64 B 15 (1966).

R. B. Ivimey-Cook and M. C. F. Proctor, 'The application of association-analysis to phytosociology', *Journal of Ecology* 54 (1966), 179-192

J. N. Jennings. *Karst.* Canberra, Australian National University Press, 1971. [An introduction to systematic geomorphology, vol. 7].

K. Jessen, S. T. Andersen and A. Farrington, 'The interglacial deposit near Gort, County Galway, Ireland', *Proceedings of the Royal Irish Academy* 60 B 1 (1959).

J. B. Jukes, *The student's manual of geology.* Second edition. Edinburgh, Adam and Charles Black, 1862.

D. L. Kelly and E. N. Kirby, 'Irish native woodlands over limestone', *Journal of Life Sciences Royal Dublin Society* 3 (1982), 181-198.

F. Kelly, 'The old Irish tree-list', *Celtica* 11 (1976), 107-124.

J. Kelly (editor), *The letters of Lord Chief Baron Edward Willes to the Earl of Warwick 1757-62. An account of Ireland in the mid-eighteenth century.* Aberystwyth, Boethius Press, 1990.

D. H. Kent and D. E. Allen, *British and Irish herbaria.* London, Botanical Society of the British Isles, 1984.

J. Keogh, *Botanalogia universalis hibernica, or, a general Irish herbal...* Cork, George Harrison, 1735 [for a modern travesty of this work, see M. Scott, 1986.]

J. R. Kinahan, 'Undescribed variety of *Blechnum spicant*', *Phytologist* 4 (1853), 1033-1038.

J. R. Kinahan, 'On the classification and nomenclature of ferns', *Phytologist* 4 (1853), 1033-1038.

J. R. Kinahan, 'Three days among the bats in Clare', *Zoologist* 19 (1861), 7617-7624.

W. King, 'Of the bogs and lough of Ireland', *Philosophical Transactions of the Royal Society, London* 15 (1685), 948-960. [also in *A natural history of Ireland in three parts. by several hands...* Dublin, G. Grierson, 1726.]

T. Kinsella, *The new Oxford book of Irish verse.* Oxford, Oxford University Press, 1986.

H. Laird, 'A bohareen of Irish botany', *Journal of the Limerick Field Club* 2 (1904), 196-210.

J. G. D. Lamb, 'The occurrence of *Gentiana verna* L. on different soil types in Co. Clare', *Irish Naturalists Journal* 15 (1966), 187-191.

J. G. D. Lamb, 'Soil preferences of *Gentiana verna*', *Gardeners Chronicle* 162 (part 4. 26 July 1967), 7.

D. Langridge, 'Limestone pavement patterns on the island of Inishmore Co. Galway', *Irish Geography* 6 (1971), 282-293.

H. C. Levinge, '*Neotinea intacta* in County Clare', *Journal of Botany* 30 (1892), 194-195.

H. C. Levinge, '*Limosella aquatica* in Ireland', *Journal of Botany* 31 (1893): 309-310.

M. C. Lewis, 'Genecological differentiation of leaf morphology in *Geranium sanguineum* L.', *New Phytologist* 68 (1969), 481-503.

E. Lhuyd, *Archaeologia Britannica*. Oxford, The author, 1707. [facsimile issue edited by Anne O'Sullivan and William O'Sullivan: Shannon, Irish University Press, 1971.]

E. Lhuyd, 'Some farther observations relating to the antiquities and natural history of Ireland', *Philosophical Transactions* 27 (1712), 524-526.

W. Lotschert, 'Ecological comments on some Irish plants', *Journal of Life Sciences Royal Dublin Society* 3 (1982), 255-259.

E. J. Lowe, *British ferns and where found*. London, Swan Sonnenschein & Co., 1908.

A. T. Lucas, 'The sacred trees of Ireland', *Cork Historical and Archaeological Society Journal* 68 (1963), 16-54.

C. Lucas, 'A description of the cave of Kilcorny in the Barony of Burren in Ireland, contained in a Letter from Mr. Charles Lucas, Apothecary at Dublin, to Sir Hans Sloane...', *Philosophical Transactions of the Royal Society, London* 41 (1740): 360-364 [See also Tratman, 1969: 209-210. The original ms. letter (Sloane ms 4025, British Library, London) is fully transcribed in Nelson, 1991 qv.]

G. J. Lyne and M. E. Mitchell, 'A scientific tour through Munster: The travels of Joseph Woods, architect and botanist, in 1809', *North Munster Antiquarian Journal* 27 (1985 [1988]), 15-61. [original ms in University Library, Cambridge, Add. MS 4343.]

R. Mabey, *Food for free. A guide to the edible wild plants of Britain*. London, William Collins, 1972.

H. A. McAllister and A. Rutherford, '*Hedera helix* L. and *H. hibernica* (Kirchner) Bean (Araliaceae) in the British Isles', *Watsonia* 18 (1990), 7-15.

J. McGarry, *Place names in the writings of William Butler Yeats*. Gerrards Cross, Colin Smythe, 1976.

J. B. McGraw and J. Antnovics, 'Experimental ecology of *Dryas octopetala* ecotypes. I. Ecotypic differentiation and life-cycle stages of selection', *Journal of Ecology* 71 (1983), 879-897.

J. T. Mackay, 'A systematic catalogue of rare plants found in Ireland', *Transactions of the Dublin Society* 5 (1806), 121-184.

M. Mac Neill, *Máire Rua, Lady of Leamaneh*. Whitegate, Ballinakella Press, 1990.

B. Mahon, 'Traditional dyestuffs in Ireland', in A. Gailey and D. O hÓgáin (editors), *Gold under the furze. Studies in folk tradition presented to Caoimhín O Danachair*. Dublin, The Glendale Press, [1981]. pp. 115-128

A. J. C. Malloch, 'An annotated bibliography of The Burren', *Journal of Ecology* 64 (1976), 1093-1105.

J. Malato-Beliz, 'Some reflections on Mediterranean plants in Ireland', *Journal of Life Sciences Royal Dublin Society* 3 (1982), 277-282.

B. Merriman, 'Cuirt an Mhean-Oiche The Midnight Court' - see Power 1990.

S. Mills, *Nature in its place. The habitats of Ireland*. London, The Bodley Head, 1987.

F. Mitchell. *The Irish landscape*. London, Collins, 1976.

M. E. Mitchell, 'Irish botany in the seventeenth century', *Proceedings of the Royal Irish Academy* 75 B (1975), 275-284.

C. B. Moffat (editor), *Life and letters of Alexander Goodman More... with selections from his zoological and botanical writings*. Dublin, Hodges, Figgis, 1898.

K. Molloy and M. O'Connell, 'The nature of the vegetational changes about 5000 B.P. with particular reference to the elm decline: fresh evidence from Connemara, western Ireland', *New Phytologist* 106, (1987), 203-220.

D. Moore, 'Notes on some rare plants, including *Ajuga pyramidalis*, in Arran', *Phytologist* 5 (1854), 189-191.

D. Moore, '*Neotinea intacta*, Reichb., a recent addition to the British flora', *Journal of Botany* 2 (1864), 228-229.

D. Moore, '*Orchis pyramidalis flore pleno*', *Journal of Botany* 2 (1864), 319.

D. Moore and A. G. More, *Contributions towards a Cybele Hibernica*. Dublin, Hodges, Smith & Co., 1866.

D. Moore and A. G. More, 'On the climate, flora, and crops of Ireland', in *Proceedings of the Horticultural and Botanical Congress* (1866), 165-176,

A. G. More, 'Notes on the flora of the neighbourhood of Castle Taylor, in the County of Galway', *Proceedings of the Botanical Society of Edinburgh* 1855-1856, 26-30.

A. G. More, 'Note on the discovery of *Neotinea intacta*, Reich. in Ireland', *Transactions of the Botanical Society of Edinburgh* 8 (1865), 265-266.

A. G. More, 'A sketch of the botany of Ireland', *Journal of Botany* 31 (1893), 299-304 [a revised and corrected version of a 'sketch' published in *The south of Ireland guide*. Cork, Guy & Co., 1893.]

I. Murphy, 'The early years of the West Clare Railway', *The Other Clare* 11 (1987), 5-11.

E. C. Nelson, 'Tropical drift fruits and seeds on coasts in the British Isles and western Europe I: Irish beaches', *Watsonia* 12 (1978), 103-112.

E. C. Nelson, 'Records of the Irish flora published before 1726', *Irish Biogeographical Society Bulletin* 3 (1979), 51-74.

E. C. Nelson, 'Ireland's flora, its origins and composition', in E. C. Nelson and A. Brady (editors), *Irish gardening and horticulture*. Dublin, Royal Horticultural Society of Ireland, 1979. pp. 17-35.

E. C. Nelson, 'The nomenclature and history in cultivation of the Irish yew, *Taxus baccata* 'Fastigiata'', *Glasra* 5 (1981), 45-50.

E. C. Nelson, *An Irish flower garden*. Kilkenny, Boethius Press, 1984.

E. C. Nelson, 'The Burren, County Clare, Ireland', *The Kew Magazine* 2 (1985), 312-320

E. C. Nelson, 'Sea peas among tropical drift seeds', *BSBI News* 44 (1986), 16-17.

E. C. Nelson, *The first Irish flora Synopsis Stirpium Hibernicarum [of] Caleb Threlkeld*. Kilkenny, Boethius Press, 1987.

E. C. Nelson, '*Narthecium ossifragum* L. in The Burren, County Clare ', *Watsonia* 17 (1989), 359-360.

E. C. Nelson, ''A gem of the first water' - P. B. O'Kelly of The Burren', *The Kew Magazine* 7 (1990), 31-47.

E. C. Nelson, ''This garden to adorne with all variety'. The garden plants of Ireland in the centuries before 1700', *Moorea* 9 (1991), 37-54.

E. C. Nelson, 'Charles Lucas' letter (1736) to Sir Hans Sloane about the natural history of The Burren, County Clare', *Journal of the Irish Colleges of Physicians and Surgeons* (1991 - in press).

E. C. Nelson and R. A. Stalley, 'Medieval naturalism and the botanical carvings at Corcomroe Abbey (County Clare)', *Gesta* 28 (1989), 165-174,

S. P. O Cillín, *Travellers in County Clare 1459-1843*. Galway, S. P. O'Cillin and P. F. Brannick, 1977.

J. W. O'Connell and A. Korff (editors), *The book of The Burren*. Kinvarra, Tír Eolas, 1991.

M. Oelschlaeger, *The idea of wilderness from prehistory to the age of ecology*. New Haven, Yale University Press, 1991.

P. B. O'Kelly, 'A botanical ramble last June at Gortbweeheen Lake', *Journal of Limerick Field Club* 2 (1903), 190.

P. B. O'Kelly, 'A list of the rare plants found in a three hours ramble about the Lake of Inchiquin and River Fergus, in the neighbourhood of Corofin', *Journal of Limerick Field Club* 2 (1903), 191-192.

T. O'Mahony, 'Notes of a botanical excursion in Clare', *Proceedings of the Dublin Natural History Society* 1 (1858), 30-34.

C. E. H. Ostenfeld, 'Some remarks on the International Phytogeographic excursion in the British Isles', *New Phytologist* 11 (1912), 114-127.

C. N Page, 'The taxonomy and phytogeography of bracken', *Botanical Journal of the Linnean Society* 73 (1976), 1-34 (also published as F. H. Perring and B. G. Gardiner (editors), *The biology of bracken*. London, Academic Press, 1976.)

C. N. Page. *The ferns of Britain and Ireland*. Cambridge, Cambridge University Press, 1982.

C. N. Page, 'Three subspecies of bracken, *Pteridium aquilinum* (L.) Kuhn, in Britain', *Watsonia* 17 (1989), 429-434.

W. H. Paine, 'Alpine Ireland', *Irish gardening* 6 (1911), 97-100.

M. Parish and R. Piper, 'Irish pageant of flowers', *Ireland of the welcomes* 17 (July-August 1968), 21-31.

W. H. Phillips, 'A gossip about British ferns and their varieties, with notices of local finds; with illustrations', *Proceedings of the Belfast Naturalists Field Club 1889-1890*, 222-230.

W. H. Phillips, 'My hobby about ferns and its results. Personal reminiscences', *Proceedings of the Belfast Naturalists Field Club 1900-1901*(1901), 2-19. [also issued separately].

C. D. Pigott, '*Thymus* L.', *Journal of Ecology* 43 (1955), 365-387 (*T. drucei* Ronniger, pp. 369-379) [Biological Flora of the British Isles].

C. D. Pigott, 'Root distribution and soil heterogeneity [abstract], *Journal of Ecology* 50 (1962), 847-848.

C. D. Pigott and S. M. Walters, 'On the interpretation of the discontinuous distributions shown by certain British species of open habitats', *Journal of Ecology* 42 (1954), 95-116.

R. Piper, *Piper's flowers*. Belfast, Blackstaff Press, 1986. [see also Hayward, 1964; Parish & Piper, 1968.]

A. E. Porsild, '*Dryas babingtoniana*, nom. nov. An overlooked species of the British Isles and western Norway', *National Museum of Canada Bulletin* 160 (1959), 133-148.

P. C. Power (editor & translator), *Cuirt an Mhean-Oiche. The Midnight Court*. Cork & Dublin, The Mercier Press, 1990 (4th edition).

R. L. Praeger, 'Irish Field Club Union. Report on the conference and excursion held at Galway, July 11th to 17th, 1895. I. - General account', *The Irish Naturalist* 4 (1895), 225-235.

R. L. Praeger, '*Pinguicula grandiflora* in Clare', *The Irish Naturalist* 12 (1903), 269.

R. L. Praeger, 'Notes on the botany of central Clare', *The Irish Naturalist* 14 (1905), 188-193.

R. L. Praeger, 'On recent extensions of the range of some rare western plants', *The Irish Naturalist* 16 (1907), 241-243

R. L. Praeger, 'The British vegetation committee in the west of Ireland', *Naturalist* (1908), 412-416. [see also A. G. Tansley 1908].

R. L. Praeger, *A tourist's flora of the west of Ireland*. Dublin, Hodges, Figgis, & Co., 1909.

R. L. Praeger, 'On the buoyancy of the seeds of some Britannic plants', *Scientific proceedings of the Royal Dublin Society* 14 (new series) (1913), 13-62.

R. L. Praeger, 'The flora of the turloughs: a preliminary note', *Proceedings of the Royal Irish Academy* 41 B 4 (1932)

R. L. Praeger, *The botanist in Ireland*. Dublin, Hodges, Figgis, & Co., 1934.

R. L. Praeger, *Some Irish naturalists a biographical notebook*. Dundalk, Dundalgan Press, 1949.

R. L. Praeger, *Natural history of Ireland, a sketch of its flora and fauna*. London, Collins, 1950. [facsimile issue, Wakefield, EP Publishing, 1972].

R. L. Praeger and J. W. Carr, 'Irish Field Club Union. Report on the conference and excursion held at Galway, July 11th to 17th, 1895. III. - Botany. Phanerogams, Ferns, &c.', *The Irish Naturalist* 4 (1895), 248.

A. Pratt, *The flowering plants, grasses, sedges and ferns of Great Britain*. 6 volumes. London, Frederick Warne, [1855-1866].

R. C. Preece, P. Coxon, and J. E. Robinson, 'New biostratigraphic evidence of the post-glacial colonization of Ireland and for Mesolithic forest disturbance', *Journal of Biogeography* 13 (1986), 487-509.

M. Press and J. Graves, 'Punishment for suckers', *New Scientist* 127 (2 September 1989), 55-58.

C. D. Preston, '*Potamogeton* x *lanceolatus* Sm. in the British Isles', *Watsonia* 17 (1989), 309-317.

M. C. F. Proctor, '*Helianthemum* Mill.', *Journal of Ecology* 44 (1956), 675-692 (*H. canum* (L.) Baumg., pp. 677-682) [Biological Flora of the British Isles].

M. C. F. Proctor, 'Variation in *Helianthemum canum* (L.) Baumg. in Britain', *Watsonia* 4 (1957), 28-40

M. C. F. Proctor, 'Fens and turloughs: some results of a plant sociological approach [abstract]', *Journal of Ecology* 50 (1962), 847.

M. C. F. Proctor and P. F. Yeo, *The pollination of flowers*. London, Collins, 1973 [New Naturalist series]

H. W. Pugsley, 'A revision of the British *Euphrasiae*', *Journal of the Linnean Society, London (Botany)* 48 (1930): 467-544.

H. W. Pugsley, 'The Irish forms of *Neotinea intacta*', *Journal of Botany* 72 (1934), 54-55.

E. G. Quin and T. W. Freeman, 'Some Irish topographical terms', *Irish Geography* 1 (1947), 85-89, 151-155.

H. G. Reichenbach, '*Neotinea intacta*, Rchb.fil., the new Irish orchid', *Journal of Botany* 3 (1865), 1-5.

A. J. Richards, 'The *Taraxacum* flora of the British Isles', *Watsonia* 9 supplement (1972).

A. J. Richards, 'New species of *Taraxacum* from the British Isles', *Watsonia* 13 (1981), 185-193.

O. W. Richards, 'The fauna of an area of limestone pavement on the Burren, Co. Clare', *Proceedings of the Royal Irish Academy* 62 B 1 (1961).

A. Richardson, 'Lepidoptera from the Burren of Clare, W. Ireland', *Entomologist's Gazette*, 3 (1952), 73-74.

M. H. Rider, 'The Namurian in west County Clare', *Proceedings of the Royal Irish Academy* 74 B 9 (1974).

H. S. Robinson, '[Burren - 1950]. Narrative', *Entomologist's Gazette* 2 (1951), 89-94.

T. Robinson, *The Burren, a map of the uplands of North-West Clare, Eire.* Cill Ronain (Arainn, Co. na Gaillimhe), T. D. Robinson, 1977.

C. M. Roden, 'New stations for *Pinguicula grandiflora* Lam. and *Saxifraga* x *polita* (Haw.) Link in the west of Ireland', *Irish Naturalists Journal* 21 (1984), 369.

C. M. Roden, 'The Burren flora', in J. W. O'Connell and A. Korff (editors), *The book of The Burren.* Kinvarra, Tír Eolas, 1991. pp. 31-41.

E. S. Rohde. *The old English herbals.* New York, Dover Publications, 1971 (facsimile of 1922 London edition).

F. J. Rumsey and S. L. Jury, 'An account of *Orobanche* L. in Britain and Ireland', *Watsonia* 18 (1991), 257-295.

F. J. Rumsey, E. Sheffield and C. H. Haufler, 'A re-assessment of *Pteridium aquilinum* (L.) Kuhn in Britain', *Watsonia* 18 (1991), 297-301.

J. Rutty, *An essay towards a natural history of the county of Dublin.* Dublin, The author, 1772. [see also Hill 1991].

E. J. Salisbury, 'The reproduction and germination of *Limosella aquatica*', *Annals of botany* 31 (1967), 147-162.

M. J. P. Scannell, ' "Algal paper" of *Oedogonium* sp., its occurrence in The Burren, Co. Clare', *Irish Naturalists Journal* 17 (1972), 147-152.

M. J. P. Scannell, 'An early nursery catalogue of Patrick Bernard O'Kelly', *Society for the History of Natural History Newsletter* 33 (1988), 10-12.

M. J. P. Scannell, '*Ajuga* x *hampeana* Braun & Vatke in The Burren: P. B. O'Kelly vindicated', *Irish Naturalists Journal* 22 (1988), 488-490.

M. J. P. Scannell and D. M. Synnott, *Census catalogue of the flora of Ireland.* Second edition. Dublin, Stationery Office, 1987.

M. Scott (editor), *An Irish herbal. The Botanalogie Universalis Hibernica.* Wellingborough, Aquarian Press, 1986. [An inadequate attempt to update Keogh's *Botanalogia...*, 1735, qv.]

R. W. Scully, *Flora of county Kerry.* Dublin, Hodges, Figgis and Co., 1916.

C. Self (editor), *Caves of County Clare.* Bristol, University of Bristol Spelaeological Society, [1979].

[S. Spellissy and J. O'Brien], *Clare. County of contrasts.* [Ennis], S. Spellissy and J. O'Brien, 1987.

R. Stalley, 'Corcomroe Abbey, some observations on its architectural history', *Journal of the Royal Society of Antiquaries of Ireland* 105 (1975), 21-46.

R. Stalley, *The Cistercian monasteries of Ireland.* London & New Haven, Yale University Press, 1987.

O. Stapf, 'A cartographic study of the Southern Element in the British flora', *Proceedings of the Linnean Society of London,* session 129 (1916), 81-92.

J. F. Steiger, 'Pale-flowered varieties of *Pinguicula grandiflora*', *Carnivorous Plant Newsletter* 16 (1987), 104-105.

[A. W. Stelfox], 'The white form of *Orchis fuchsii* and *Orchis O'Kellyi*', *The Irish Naturalist* 33 (1924), 143-144.

A. W. Stelfox, '*Geranium robertianum* L. var. *celticus* Ostenfeld', *Irish Naturalists Journal* 16 (1969), 210.

E. Step, *The flowering plants, grasses, sedges and ferns of Great Britain ... by Anne Pratt.* New edition. London, Frederick Warne, 1905.

T. Stephenson and T. A. Stephenson, 'The forms of *Orchis maculata*', *Journal of Botany* 59 (1921), 121-128.

S. A. Stewart, 'A trip from Galway to Dingle', *Annual Reports and Proceedings of the Belfast Naturalists' Field Club* 1 (new series) (1879), 352-353.

W. Stokes, 'The prose tales in the Rennes Dindshenchas', *Revue Celtique* 15 (1894), 272-336.

J. H. Stone, *Connemara and the neighbouring spots of beauty and interest...* London, Health Resort Publishing Co., 1906.

W. Strabo, *Hortulus.* (Translated by R. Payne, commentary by W. Blunt). Pittsburgh, The Hunt Botanical Library, 1966.

R. J. Summerfield, 'Factors affecting the germination and seedling establishment of *Narthecium ossifragum* in mire ecosystems', *Journal of Ecology* 61 (1973), 387-398.

R. J. Summerfield, '*Narthecium ossifragum* (L.) Huds.,' *Journal of Ecology* 62 (1975), 325-339 [Biological Flora of the British Isles].

V. S. Summerhayes, *Wild orchids of Britain.* London, Collins, 1951. [New Naturalist series]

M. M. Sweeting, 'The enclosed depression of Carron, County Clare', *Irish Geography* 2 (1957), 218-224.

D. M. Synnott, 'Folk lore, legend and Irish plants', in E. C. Nelson and A. Brady (editors), *Irish gardening and horticulture.* Dublin, Royal Horticultural Society of Ireland, 1979. pp. 33-43.

D. M. Synnott and H. Bird. *Ferns of Ireland.* [Dublin], Folens, [not dated, c.1980]. [Irish Environmental Library series no. 68].

C. Threlkeld, *Synopsis stirpium Hibernicarum.* Dublin, The author, 1726 [facsimile issue, Kilkenny, Boethius Press, 1987. see Nelson 1987]

E. K. Tratman (editor), *The caves of north-west Clare, Ireland.* Newton Abbot, David & Charles, [1969].

W. Trevor, *A writer's Ireland. Landscape in literature.* London, Thames & Hudson, 1984.

D. H. Valentine, 'Experimental work on the British flora', *Watsonia* 12 (1979), 201-207.

P. Vermeulen, *Studies on dactylorchids.* Utrecht, Schotanus and Jens, 1947. (see esp. pp. 148-149 on *Orchis okellyi*).

Veronica [alias F. W. Burbidge], 'The Irish flora', *The Garden* 30 (1886): 239.

W. Wade, *Plantae rariores in Hibernica inventae...* Dublin, [Dublin Society], 1804.

Helen Waddell, *Peter Abelard a novel.* London, Constable, 1933.

[T. Walford], *The scientific tourist through Ireland by an Irish gentleman.* London, Booth, 1818.

L. Walsh, *Richard Heaton of Ballyskenagh 1601-1666. First Irish botanist.* Roscrea, Parkmore Press, 1978.

W. F. Walsh and E. C. Nelson, *An Irish florilegium II. The wild and garden plants of Ireland.* London, Thames and Hudson, 1987.

W. F. Walsh, R. I. Ross and E. C. Nelson, *An Irish florilegium. The wild and garden plants of Ireland.* London, Thames and Hudson, 1983.

E. F. Warburg, 'Some new names in the British flora', *Watsonia* 4 (1957), 55 [*Sorbus hibernica*].

W. A. Watts, 'Late-glacial pollen zones in western Ireland', *Irish Geography* 4 (1963), 367-376.

W. A. Watts, 'The Burren in Late-glacial and Post-glacial times [abstract]', *Journal of Ecology* 50 (1962), 847.

W. A. Watts, 'The late Devensian vegetation of Ireland', *Philosophical Transactions of the Royal Society, London* B 280 (1977), 273-293.

W. A. Watts, 'The Holocene vegetation of the Burren, western Ireland', in E. Y. Haworth and J. W. G. Lund (editors) *Lake sediments and environmental history.* Leicester, Leicester University Press, 1984. pp. 359-376.

D. A. Webb, 'The vegetation of Carrowkeel, a limestone hill in north-west Ireland', *Journal of Ecology* 35 (1947), 105-129

D. A. Webb, 'Two new western plant records', *Irish Naturalists Journal* 9 (1947), 100.

D. A. Webb, '*Saxifraga* L. (Section Dactyloides Tausch)', *Journal of Ecology* 38 (1950), 185-213 (*S. rosacea*, pp. 199-206) [Biological Flora of the British Isles].

D. A. Webb, 'The Burren and its problems [abstract]', *Journal of Ecology* 50 (1962), 846-847.

D. A. Webb, 'Noteworthy plants of The Burren: a catalogue raisonné', *Proceedings of the Royal Irish Academy* 62 B 9 (1962).

D. A. Webb, 'Plant records from Connemara and the Burren', *Irish* Naturalists Journal 20 (1982), 466-471.

D. A. Webb, 'The flora of Ireland in its European context', *Journal of Life Sciences Royal Dublin Society* 4 (1983), 143-160.

D. A. Webb and R. J. Gornall, *Saxifrages of Europe with notes on African, American and some Asiatic species.* London, Christopher Helm, 1989.

D. A. Webb and M. J. P. Scannell, *Flora of Connemara and the Burren.* Cambridge, Royal Dublin Society & Cambridge University Press, 1983.

D. A. Webb and M. J. P. Scannell, 'Flora of Connemara and the Burren: some corrections and additions', *Irish Naturalists Journal* 21 (1984), 286-288.

H. W. L. Weir, *Historical Genealogical Architectural notes on some houses of Clare.* Whitegate, Ballinakella Press, 1986.

T. C. E. Wells, 'Changes in a population of *Spiranthes spiralis* (L.) Chevall. at Knocking Hoe National Nature Reserve, Bedfordshire, 1962-65', *Journal of Ecology* 55 (1967), 83-99.

T. J. Westropp, 'The forests of the counties of the lower Shannon valley', *Proceedings of the Royal Irish Academy* 27 C 13 (1909).

W. H. S. Westropp, 'Sketch of the physical geology of north Clare', *Journal of the Royal Geological Society of Ireland* 13 (1872), 75-79

J. White, *An essay on the indigenous grasses of Ireland.* Dublin, [Dublin Society], 1808.

J. White, 'A history of Irish vegetation studies', *Journal of Life Sciences Royal Dublin Society* 3 (1982), 15-42.

J. White and G. Doyle, 'The vegetation of Ireland, a catalogue raisonné', *Journal of Life Sciences Royal Dublin Society* 3 (1982), 289-368.

F. Whitla, '[on *Orobanche rubra*]', *Phytologist* 4 (1851), 168.

J. B. Whittow, *Geology and scenery in Ireland.* Harmondsworth, Penguin Books, 1974.

J. Wilde, '*Limosella aquatica* L. - additional recent records', *Irish Naturalists Journal* 22 (1987), 365.

P. W. Williams, 'An initial estimate of the speed of limestone solution in County Clare', *Irish Geography* 4 (1963), 432-441.

P. W. Williams, 'Limestone morphology in Ireland' in N. Stephens and R. E. Glassock, *Irish geographical studies in honour of E. Estyn Evans.* Belfast, Department of Geography, The Queen's University, 1970. pp. 105-124.

O. Wilmanns and J. Brun-Hool, 'Plant communities of human settlements in Ireland. I. Vegetation of walls', *Journal of Life Sciences Royal Dublin Society* 3 (1982), 79-90.

W. B. Yeats, 'The dreaming of the bones', in *Two plays for dancers.* Dundrum, County Dublin, The Cuala Press, 1919 (Facsimile issue, Shannon, Irish University Press, 1970)

P. F. Yeo, *Hardy geraniums.* London, Croom Helm, 1985.

Manuscript sources

Browne ms. - Patrick Browne's Fasciculus (Linnean Society, London)

Foot ms. - Frederick Foot's field maps for County Clare and Galway (Geological Survey of Ireland, Dublin)

Natural History Museum ms. - 'Statice County Clare cult: in Glasnevin Garden 24 Aug: 1853' in G. E. Smith collection, Department of Botany (Natural History Museum, London)

O'Kelly [Oxford] ms. - letters to G. C. Druce (Fielding-Druce Herbarium, University of Oxford).

Rutty ms. - annotated copy of Threlkeld 1726 (Royal Irish Academy, Dublin).

ALPHABETICAL LIST OF PLANT PORTRAITS
WITH PROVENANCE

Phyllitis scolopendrium (hart's tongue fern)	Glencolumbkille viii.1987.	126
Pinguicula grandiflora (Kerry butterwort)	Newtown v.1988.	213
Pinguicula lusitanica (pale butterwort)	Dobhach Bhrainín, vi.1990.	209
Pinguicula vulgaris (butterwort)	Black Head, v.1988.	208
	(eight-petalled flower) Mullach Mór vi.1988.	
Polygala vulgaris (milkwort)	Black Head vi.1987.	82
Polypodium australe (polypody fern)	Formoyle Bridge i.1989.	138
Potentilla anserina (silverweed)	Carron vi.1988.	94
Potentilla fruticosa (shrubby cinquefoil)	Ballyvaghan viii.1987.	95
	(double flowered) Lough Gealáin vii.1987.	
Potentilla sterilis (barren strawberry)	Lough Gealáin iii.1988.	66
Primula veris (cowslip)	(plant) Formoyle iv.1987.	75
	(details of hybrid & cowslip) Keelhilla v.1990.	
Primula vulgaris (primrose)	Keelhilla iii.1988.	74
Prunella vulgaris (selfheal)	Poll Salach viii.1987.	259
Prunus spinosus (blackthorn)	(fruits) New Line x.1987.	306
	(flowers) Mulach Mór iii.1988.	
	(petals minute) Tobar MacDuach iii.1990.	
Rhinanthus minor (yellow rattle)	Poll Salach viii.1987.	205
Rosa pimpinellifolia (burnet rose)	(flower) Poll Salach v.1988.	53
	(hip) Rockforest viii.1987	
Rubia peregrina (madder)	Black Head vi.1987.	49
	(fruits) viii.1987	
Rubus saxatilis (stone bramble)	Caherbullog viii.1987.	56
	(foliage) Lough Gealáin vi.1988.	
Salix aurita (spelaeodendron, eared willow)	Cullaun iv.1990.	310
	(foliage) vi.1990.	
Saxifraga rosacea (Irish saxifrage)	Black Head vi.1987.	160
Saxifraga tridactylites (rue-leaved saxifrage)	Black Head vi.1987.	91
	(fruiting plant) Ballyvaghan viii.1987.	
Sesleria albicans (blue grass)	Tobar MacDuach iii.1988.	71
Solidago virgaurea (goldenrod)	Gort Road viii.1987.	168
Sorbus aucuparia (rowan, mountain ash)	(bud) Carron iv.1989.	295
	(fruits & leaves) Pollavollaun x.1989.	
Sorbus hibernica (Irish whitebeam)	(fruits) Gort Road x.1987.	295
	(young leaves) Newtown Castle v.1988.	
Spiranthes spiralis (Autumn Lady's tresses)	Poll Salach viii.1988.	197
Succisa pratensis (devil's bit scabious)	Poll Salach viii.1987.	258
	(pink) Formoyle ix.1990.	
Taraxacum palustre (turlough dandelion)	Lough Gealáin vi.1987.	99
Taxus baccata (yew)	Lough Gealáin. i.1990.	291
	[landscape: Lough Gealáin from Mullach Mór]	
Teucrium scorodonia (wood sage)	Gort Road viii.1987.	52
Thymus praecox (wild thyme)	New Line vii.1989.	201
Viburnum opulus (guelder rose)	Caherbullog viii.1987.	298
Vicia cracca (tufted vetch)	Ballyvaghan viii.1987.	254
Viola persicifolia (turlough violet)	Lough Gealáin vi.1987.	98
Viola riviniana (common dog-violet)	Formoyle vi.1987.	87

ACKNOWLEDGEMENTS

I have taken more than six years to complete this book, and during that time many people have assisted, not just with with research but also with hospitality in The Burren. I am most grateful to everyone who helped, and should single out my ever-patient botanical colleagues, Dr Paddy Coker, Paul Carter and Donal Synnott for their guidance, the Hewitts–Les, Jen and John–for their immense diligence in printing and design, Dr Straun Robertson for elucidating spelaeodendron, Catherine Gorman (formerly research assistant in the National Botanic Gardens, Glasnevin) whose cheerful help with innumerable small tasks made writing less burdensome; and, among others, I especially wish to acknowledge Dr Jean Archer, Serena Marner, Raymond Piper, Susyn Andrews, Jennifer and Paddy Woods, Peter Woods, Valerie Ingram, Moira and Peter Haden, Tim Robinson, Dr Roger Stalley, Dr David Drew, Dr Roy Alexander, Dr David E. Allen, Mary Sampson, Paul Hackney, Dr Éamon Ó hÓgáin, Mary Moroney, and Theresa Andreucetti. Anna Baggallay agreed, late in this book's gestation, to draw the maps and did so with calm efficiency in another hemisphere.

Wendy Walsh's paintings illuminate this book, and she often joined me in The Burren to wander pavements and look for plants, and again I have the pleasure of thanking her for making *The Burren: a companion to the wildflowers of an Irish limestone wilderness* such a joyful work.

The Conservancy of The Burren was established in 1990 to publish this volume and to ensure, according to our wish, that profits from sales should in perpetuity be devoted to the preservation of The Burren, its habitats and way of life. Helen Rackard and Michael Roberts helped make The Conservancy a reality.

I could not have completed this 'companion to the wildflowers' without the unstinted support of Catherine and Brendan O'Donoghue; they welcomed both Wendy and me into their home at any and every season and provided board, lodgings and working space. It is a pleasure to publish here my thanks to them for making the task of creating this book so much easier.

At the initiative of the members of the E.S.B. Gardening Society, we approached the Electricity Supply Board and received most generous patronage. The Board becomes custodian of the original watercolours by Wendy Walsh.

The author acknowledges the following individuals for their permission to publish copyright material: Michael Longley for 'In Ailwee Cave'; Mrs Richard Hayward for an extact from the late Richard Hayward's *Munster and the city of Cork*; Prof. Seamus Heaney (and Faber & Faber Ltd) for an extract from 'An Aisling in The Burren'; William Trevor for an extract from *A Writer's Ireland*; Dr Patrick Power for permission his translation of Brian Merriman's 'Cúirt an Mhean-Oíche'; John Murray (Sir John Betjeman's Estate and John Murray Publ.) for verses from 'Ireland with Emily'; Thomas Kinsella for his translation of Brian Merriman's 'Cuirt an Mhean-Oiche'; The Director, Hunt Institute for Botanical Documentation, Pittsburgh, for an extract from the English translation, by Raef Payne, of Walahfrid Strabo's 'Hortulus'.

INDEXES

INDEXES TO PLANTS
Figures in italic indicate illustrations

a. Irish names (only the major reference is cited–see index of botanical names below for all entries)

b. English names (only the major reference is cited–see index of botanical names below for all entries)

INDEX TO PEOPLE

INDEX TO PLACES
AND MISCELLANEOUS SUBJECTS

CONSERVANCY OF THE BURREN is a limited company, incorporated in Dublin (May 1990; reg. no. 159212). It aims to promote the conservation of The Burren and to inform people about its natural environment and history. Profits from the sale of this book, and royalties, will be devoted to the aims of the Conservancy. The directors are assisted in the management of the Conservancy by an invited board of trustees.

For further information please contact the author (c/o National Botanic Gardens, Glasnevin, Dublin 9) or Conservancy of the Burren (c/o An Bothain, Pier Road, Ballyvaghan, Co. Clare).

PLANTLIFE is a conservation group dedicated to the protection of plants and their habitats throughout Britain, Ireland and abroad. It campaigns to save endangered plants, and works to protect plant-rich places. Plantlife promotes the enjoyment and celebration of plants in art, literature and the countryside.

For further details please contact Plantlife, The Natural History Museum, Cromwell Road, London SW7 5BD.

DR CHARLES NELSON is taxonomist in the National Botanic Gardens, Glasnevin, Dublin; he has a special interest in the history of botany in Ireland, and has spent six years carrying out research for this book in libraries and botanical institutes, and in the field. Dr Nelson is author of more than 100 research papers, of works about Irish garden plants including *An Irish Flower Garden*, and is joint author of several others (for example, with the late Dr Eileen McCracken, of *The Brightest Jewel, a history of the National Botanic Gardens, Glasnevin, Dublin*). In 1991 he published *Shamrock, the botany and history of an Irish myth*.

MRS WENDY WALSH is acknowledged to be an outstanding botanical artist of international stature. She works entirely in watercolour, and has been commissioned to design stamps for postal authorities in Ireland and Kiribati (Gilbert Islands). Her plant portraits have been published in *The Kew Magazine*, and among her books are *An Irish Florilegium* and *An Irish Florilegium II*, and *A prospect of Irish flowers*. She is currently working on illustrations for a book about the trees of Ireland.